GRAPHING CALCULATOR MANUAL

JUDITH A. PENNA

WITH THE ASSISTANCE OF
Daphne A. Bell
Motlow State Community College

PRECALCULUS
GRAPHS & MODELS,
A UNIT CIRCLE APPROACH

ALGEBRA AND TRIGONOMETRY
GRAPHS & MODELS,
A UNIT CIRCLE APPROACH

Marvin L. Bittinger
Indiana University—Purdue University at Indianapolis

Judith A. Beecher
Indiana University—Purdue University at Indianapolis

David J. Ellenbogen
Community College of Vermont

Judith A. Penna
Indiana University—Purdue University at Indianapolis

Addison
Wesley

Boston San Francisco New York
London Toronto Sydney Tokyo Singapore Madrid
Mexico City Munich Paris Cape Town Hong Kong Montreal

Reproduced by Addison Wesley Longman from camera-ready copy supplied by the author.

Copyright © 2001 Addison Wesley Longman

ISBN   0-201-70942-2

1 2 3 4 5 6 7 8 9 10 VG 04 03 02 01 00

Contents

The TI-82, TI-83, and TI-83+ Graphics Calculators 1

The TI-85 Graphics Calculator 79

The TI-86 Graphics Calculator 149

The TI-89 Graphics Calculator 225

The TI-82, TI-83, and TI-83+
Graphics Calculators

Introduction to Graphs and the Graphing Calculator

GETTING STARTED

Press ON to turn on the TI-82, TI-83, or TI-83+ graphing calculator. (ON is the key at the bottom left-hand corner of the keypad.) You should see a blinking rectangle, or cursor, on the screen. If you do not see the cursor, try adjusting the display contrast. To do this, first press 2nd . (2nd is the yellow key in the left column of the keypad.) Then press and hold △ to increase the contrast or ▽ to decrease the contrast. If the contrast needs to be adjusted further after the first adjustment, press 2nd again then then hold △ or ▽ to increase or decrease the contrast, respectively.

To turn the grapher off, press 2nd OFF . (OFF is the second operation associated with the ON key.) The grapher will turn itself off automatically after about five minutes without any activity.

Press MODE to display the MODE settings. Initially you should select the settings on the left side of the display. The TI-83 and TI-83+ screen is shown on the left below and the TI-82 is shown on the right.

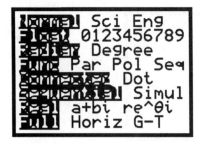 

To change a setting on the Mode screen use ▽ or △ to move the cursor to the line of that setting. Then use ▷ or ◁ to move the blinking cursor to the desired setting and press ENTER . Press CLEAR or 2nd QUIT to leave the MODE screen. (QUIT is the second operation associated with the MODE key.) In general, second operations are written in yellow above the keys on the keypad of the TI-83 and TI-83+ and in blue on the TI-82. Pressing CLEAR or 2nd QUIT will take you to the home screen where computations are performed.

The TI-82, TI-83, and TI-83+ graphing calculators are very similar in many respects. For that reason, most of the keystrokes and instructions presented in this section of the graphing calculator manual will apply to all three graphers. Where they differ, keystrokes and instructions for each will be given. TI-83/83+ screens will be shown in this manual unless noted otherwise.

It will be helpful to read the Getting Started section of the Texas Instruments Guidebook that was packaged with your graphing calculator before proceeding.

SETTING THE VIEWING WINDOW

The viewing window is the portion of the coordinate plane that appears on the grapher's screen. It is defined by the minimum and maximum values of x and y: Xmin, Xmax, Ymin, and Ymax. The notation [Xmin, Xmax, Ymin, Ymax] is used to represent these window settings or dimensions. For example, [−12, 12, −8, 8] denotes a window that displays the portion of the x-axis from -12 to 12 and the portion of the y-axis from -8 to 8. In addition, the distance between tick marks on the axes is defined by the settings Xscl and Yscl. In this manual Xscl and Yscl will be assumed to be 1 unless noted otherwise. The TI-83 and TI-83+ also have an Xres setting which sets the pixel resolution. We usually select Xres = 1. The window corresponding to the settings $[-20, 30, -12, 20]$, Xscl = 5, Yscl = 2, Xres = 1, is shown below.

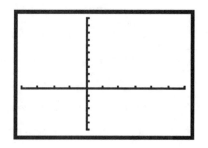

Press the WINDOW key on the top row of the keypad to display the current window settings on your grapher. The standard settings are shown below.

```
WINDOW
 Xmin=-10
 Xmax=10
 Xscl=1
 Ymin=-10
 Ymax=10
 Yscl=1
 Xres=1
```

To change a setting, position the cursor beside the setting you wish to change and enter the new value. For example, on the TI-83 and TI-83+, to change from the standard settings to $[-20, 30, -12, 20]$, Xscl = 5, Yscl = 2, on the WINDOW screen press (−) 2 0 ENTER 3 0 ENTER 5 ENTER (−) 1 2 ENTER 2 0 ENTER 2 ENTER . Note that the (−) key in the bottom row of the keypad must be used to enter a negative number. The blue − key in the right column of the keypad is used for the subtraction operation. The ▽ key may be used instead of ENTER after typing each window setting. On the TI-82 ▽ must be pressed first to position the cursor beside Xmin =. To see the window shown on the previous page, press the GRAPH key on the top row of the keypad.

QUICK TIP: To return quickly to the standard window setting $[-10, 10, -10, 10]$, Xscl = 1, Yscl = 1, press ZOOM 6.

PLOTTING POINTS

We can plot points on a grapher by entering their coordinates in a list and choosing an appropriate viewing window.

Example 2, page 3 (Page numbers refer to pages in the text.) Use a grapher to graph the points $(-3, 5)$, $(4, 3)$, $(3, 4)$, $(-4, -2)$, $(3, -4)$, $(0, 4)$, $(-3, 0)$, and $(0, 0)$.

We choose a viewing window that will display all of the points, noting that the x-coordinates range from -4 to 4 and the

y-coordinates range from -4 to 5. Thus, one good choice for a viewing window is the standard window $[-10, 10, -10, 10]$.

We will enter the coordinates of the ordered pairs on the STAT list editor screen. To clear any existing lists press $\boxed{\text{STAT}}$ 4 $\boxed{\text{2nd}}$ $\boxed{\text{L}_1}$ $\boxed{,}$ $\boxed{\text{2nd}}$ $\boxed{\text{L}_2}$ $\boxed{,}$ $\boxed{\text{2nd}}$ $\boxed{\text{L}_3}$ $\boxed{,}$ $\boxed{\text{2nd}}$ $\boxed{\text{L}_4}$ $\boxed{,}$ $\boxed{\text{2nd}}$ $\boxed{\text{L}_5}$ $\boxed{,}$ $\boxed{\text{2nd}}$ $\boxed{\text{L}_6}$ $\boxed{\text{ENTER}}$. (L_1 through L_6 are the second operations associated with the numeric keys 1 through 6.) The lists can also be cleared by first accessing the STAT list editor screen by pressing $\boxed{\text{STAT}}$ $\boxed{\text{ENTER}}$ or $\boxed{\text{STAT}}$ 1. These keystrokes display the STAT EDIT menu and then select the Edit option from that menu. Then, for each list that contains entries, use the arrow keys to move the cursor to highlight the name of the list at the top of the column and press $\boxed{\text{CLEAR}}$ $\boxed{\triangledown}$ or $\boxed{\text{CLEAR}}$ $\boxed{\text{ENTER}}$.

Once the lists are cleared, we can enter the coordinates of the points. We will enter the first coordinates (x-coordinates) in L_1 and the second coordinates (y-coordinates) in L_2. Position the cursor at the top of column L_1, below the L_1 heading. To enter -3 press $\boxed{(-)}$ 3 $\boxed{\text{ENTER}}$. Recall that the $\boxed{(-)}$ key in the bottom row of the keypad must be used to enter a negative number whereas the blue $\boxed{-}$ key is used for the subtraction operation. Continue typing the x-values 4, 3, -4, 3, 0, -3, and 0 in order, each followed by $\boxed{\text{ENTER}}$. The entries can be followed by $\boxed{\triangledown}$ rather than $\boxed{\text{ENTER}}$ if desired. Press $\boxed{\triangleright}$ to move to the top of column L_2. Type the y-values 5, 3, 4, -2, -4, 4, 0, and 0 in succession, each followed by $\boxed{\text{ENTER}}$ or $\boxed{\triangledown}$. Note that the coordinates of each point must be in the same position in both lists.

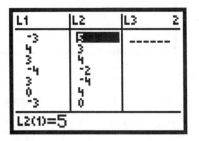

To plot the points, we turn on the STAT PLOT feature. To access the STAT PLOT screen, press $\boxed{\text{2nd}}$ $\boxed{\text{STAT PLOT}}$. (STAT PLOT is the second operation associated with the $\boxed{\text{Y} =}$ key in the upper left-hand corner of the keypad.) The TI-83 and TI-83+ STAT PLOT screen is shown on the left below and the TI-82 is shown on the right.

We will use Plot 1. Access it by highlighting 1 and pressing $\boxed{\text{ENTER}}$ or simply by pressing 1. Now position the cursor over On and press $\boxed{\text{ENTER}}$ to turn on Plot 1. The entries Type, Xlist, and Ylist should be as shown below. The last item, Mark, allows us to choose a box, a cross, or a dot for each point. Here we have selected a box. To select Type and Mark, position the cursor over the appropriate selection and press $\boxed{\text{ENTER}}$. Xlist and Ylist are also chosen in this manner on the TI-82. Use the L_1 and L_2 keys (associated with the 1 and 2 numeric keys) to select Xlist and Ylist on the TI-83 or the TI-83+. The entries should be as shown on the left below the TI-83 and TI-83+ and on the right for the TI-82.

On the TI-83 and the TI-83+ the plot can also be turned on from the equation-editor, or "Y =", screen. Press $\boxed{\text{Y} =}$, the key at the top left-hand corner of the keypad, to go to this screen. Then, assuming Plot 1 has not yet been turned on, position the cursor over Plot 1 and press $\boxed{\text{ENTER}}$. Plot 1 will now be highlighted.

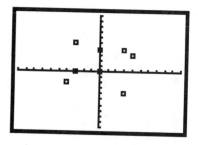

Note that there should be no equations entered on the "Y =" screen. If there are entries present clear them now. To clear an entry for Y_1, for example, position the cursor beside" $Y_1 =$" and press $\boxed{\text{CLEAR}}$. Do this for each existing entry. If this is not done, the equations that are currently entered will be graphed along with the data points that are entered.

To see the plotted points, press $\boxed{\text{GRAPH}}$.

QUICK TIP: Instead of entering the window dimensions directly, we can press $\boxed{\text{ZOOM}}$ 9 after entering the coordinates of the points in lists, turning on Plot 1, and selecting Type, Xlist, Ylist, and Mark. This activates the ZoomStat operation which automatically defines a viewing window that displays all the points and also displays the graph.

To turn off the plot, first press $\boxed{\text{2nd}}$ $\boxed{\text{STAT PLOT}}$ $\boxed{\text{ENTER}}$ or $\boxed{\text{2nd}}$ $\boxed{\text{STAT PLOT}}$ 1 to return to the Plot Set-up screen for Plot 1. Then select Off by positioning the cursor over Off and pressing $\boxed{\text{ENTER}}$. The plot can also be turned off on the TI-83 and TI-83+ by pressing $\boxed{\text{Y} =}$, positioning the cursor over Plot 1 at the top of the screen, and then pressing

ENTER . Plot 1 is now no longer highlighted.

SOLUTIONS OF EQUATIONS

Example 3, page 4 Determine whether each ordered pair is a solution of $2x + 3y = 18$.

        a) $(-5, 7)$ **b)** $(3, 4)$

We can substitute each pair in the expression $2x + 3y$. If the resulting value is 18, the pair is a solution of the equation $2x + 3y = 18$. If not, the pair is not a solution. To perform the substitutions, first press 2nd QUIT or 2nd CLEAR to go to the home screen. To substitute -5 for x and 7 for y in $2x + 3y$, press 2 ((−) 5) + 3 × 7 ENTER . The result is 11, so $(-5, 7)$ is not a solution of the equation. To substitute 3 for x and 4 for y, press 2 × 3 + 3 × 4 ENTER . The result is 18, so $(3, 4)$ is a solution.

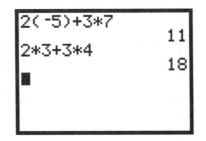

EDITING ENTRIES

You can recall and edit an entry if necessary. If, for instance, in entering the last expression in Example 3 above you pressed − instead of + , first press 2nd ENTRY to return to the last entry. (ENTRY is the second operation associated with the ENTER key.) Then use the ◁ key to move the cursor to − and press + to overwrite it. If you forgot to type the first 3, move the cursor to the + ; then press 2nd INS 3 to insert the 3 before the + . (INS is the second operation associated with the DEL key.) You can continue to insert symbols immediately after the first insertion without pressing 2nd INS again. If you typed 21 instead of 2, move the cursor to 1 and press DEL . This will delete the 1. If you notice that an entry needs to be edited before you press ENTER to perform the computation, the editing can be done directly without recalling the entry.

The keystrokes 2nd ENTRY can be used repeatedly to recall entries preceding the last one. Pressing 2nd ENTRY twice, for example, will recall the next to last entry. Using these keystrokes a third time recalls the third to last entry and so on. The number of entries that can be recalled depends on the amount of storage they occupy in the calculator's memory.

THE TABLE FEATURE

A table of x-and y-values representing ordered pairs that are solutions of an equation can be displayed. We must first enter the equation on the equation-editor screen before a table can be displayed.

Example 5, page 6 Create a table of ordered pairs that are solutions of the equation $y = \frac{1}{2}x + 1$.

First press $\boxed{\text{Y} =}$ to access the equation-editor screen. Then clear any equations that are present. (See Example 2 on page 4 of this manual for the procedure to follow.) Also turn off any plots that are turned on. (See Example 3 on page 7 of this manual for the procedure to follow.) Next enter the equation by positioning the cursor beside "$Y_1 =$" and pressing $\boxed{(}$ 1 $\boxed{\div}$ 2 $\boxed{)}$ $\boxed{\text{X, T, }\Theta, n}$ $\boxed{+}$ 1. On the TI-82 the $\boxed{\text{X, T, }\Theta}$ key produces the variable x. Whenever the $\boxed{\text{X, T, }\Theta, n}$ key is used in this manual, TI-82 users should press $\boxed{\text{X, T, }\Theta}$. Although the parentheses are not necessary on the TI-83 and TI-83+, the equation is more easily read when they are used. Parentheses must be used on the TI-82. If they are not, the expression $1/2x + 1$ will be interpreted as $\frac{1}{2x} + 1$.

```
Plot1  Plot2  Plot3
\Y1■(1/2)X+1■
\Y2=
\Y3=
\Y4=
\Y5=
\Y6=
\Y7=
```

Once the equation in entered, press $\boxed{\text{2nd}}$ $\boxed{\text{TblSet}}$ to display the table set-up screen. (TblSet is the second function associated with the $\boxed{\text{WINDOW}}$ key.) You can choose to supply the x-values yourself or you can set the grapher to supply them. To have the grapher supply the x-values, set "Indpnt" to "Auto" by positioning the cursor over "Auto" and pressing $\boxed{\text{ENTER}}$. "Depend" should also be set to "Auto."

When "Indpnt" is set to "Auto," the grapher will supply values for x, beginning with the value specified as TblStart and continuing by adding the value of ΔTbl to the preceding value for x. We will display a table of values that starts with $x = -3$ and adds 1 to the preceding x-value. Press $\boxed{(-)}$ 3 $\boxed{\triangledown}$ 1 or $\boxed{(-)}$ 3 $\boxed{\text{ENTER}}$ 1 to select a minimum x-value of -3 and an increment of 1. To display the table press $\boxed{\text{2nd}}$ $\boxed{\text{TABLE}}$. (TABLE is the second operation associated with the $\boxed{\text{GRAPH}}$ key.)

```
TABLE SETUP
 TblStart=-3
 ▵Tbl=1
Indpnt: Auto  Ask
Depend: Auto  Ask
```

```
  X  │ Y1  │
─────┼─────┤
 -3  │ -.5 │
 -2  │  0  │
 -1  │  .5 │
  0  │  1  │
  1  │ 1.5 │
  2  │  2  │
  3  │ 2.5 │
─────┴─────┘
X=-3
```

GRAPHING EQUATIONS

After entering an equation and setting a viewing window, you can view the graph of the equation.

Example 6, page 7 Graph using a grapher: $y = \frac{1}{2}x + 1$.

Enter the equation on the equation-editor screen as described in Example 5 above. The standard $[-10, 10, -10, 10]$ window is a good choice for this graph. Either enter these dimensions in the WINDOW screen and then press $\boxed{\text{GRAPH}}$ to see the graph or simply press $\boxed{\text{ZOOM}}$ 6 to select the standard window and see the graph.

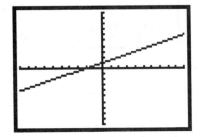

FINDING POINTS OF INTERSECTION

We can use the Intersect feature from the CALC menu to find the point(s) of intersection of two graphs. A menu is a list of options that appears when a key is pressed. Sometimes $\boxed{\text{2nd}}$ must be pressed first, followed by another key, to access a menu. Thus, multiple options, and sometimes multiple menus, may be accessed by pressing one or two keys.

Example 9, page 9 Use a grapher to find the point of intersection of the graphs of $x - y = -5$ and $y = 4x + 10$.

We begin by entering the equations on the equation-editor screen. Since equations must be entered in the form "$y =$", we solve the first equation for y, obtaining $y = x + 5$. Then press $\boxed{\text{Y} =}$ to go to the equation-editor screen. Clear any existing entries. Enter $y_1 = x + 5$ by positioning the cursor beside "$Y_1 =$" and pressing $\boxed{\text{X, T, } \Theta, n}$ $\boxed{+}$ 5. Next position the cursor beside "$Y_2 =$" and enter $y_2 = 4x + 10$ by pressing 4 $\boxed{\text{X, T, } \Theta, n}$ $\boxed{+}$ 1 0. Now graph the equations. We begin by using the standard window and see that it is a good choice because it shows the point of intersection of the graphs.

We we will use the Intersect feature from the CALC menu to find the coordinates of that point. To select this feature press $\boxed{\text{2nd}}$ $\boxed{\text{CALC}}$ 5. (CALC is the second operation associated with the $\boxed{\text{TRACE}}$ key.) The query "First curve?" appears at the bottom of the screen. The blinking cursor is positioned on the graph of y_1. This is indicated on the TI-83 and TI-83+ by the notation $Y_1 = X + 5$ in the upper left-hand corner of the screen. On the TI-82 a 1 appears in the upper right-hand corner of the screen. Press $\boxed{\text{ENTER}}$ to indicate that this is the first curve involved in the intersection. Next the query "Second curve?" appears at the bottom of the screen. The blinking cursor is now positioned on the graph of y_2 and the notation $Y_2 = 4x + 10$ should appear in the top left-hand corner of the screen on the TI-83 and TI-83+. On the TI-82 a 2 appears in the upper right-hand corner of the screen. Press $\boxed{\text{ENTER}}$ to indicate that this is the second curve. We identify the curves for the grapher since we could have as many as ten graphs on the screen at once. After we identify the second curve, the query "Guess?" appears at the bottom of the screen. Use the right and left arrow keys to move the blinking cursor close to the point of intersection of the graphs. This provides the grapher with a guess as to the coordinates of this point. We do this since some pairs of curves can have more than one point of intersection. When the cursor is positioned, press $\boxed{\text{ENTER}}$ a third time. Now the coordinates of the point of intersection appear at the bottom of the screen.

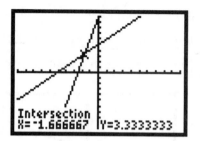

We see that the graphs intersect at the point $(-1.666667, 3.3333333)$. This is a decimal approximation for the point of intersection. If the coordinates are rational numbers, their exact values can be found using the "▷ Frac" feature from the MATH menu.

To do this first press $\boxed{\text{2nd}}$ $\boxed{\text{QUIT}}$ to go to the home screen. The x- and y-coordinates of the point of intersection are stored in the calculator as X and Y, respectively. To convert the decimal approximation for X to a rational number, press $\boxed{\text{X, T, }\Theta, n}$ $\boxed{\text{MATH}}$ $\boxed{1}$ $\boxed{\text{ENTER}}$. These keystrokes tell the grapher to use X, and then they access the MATH submenu of the MATH menu, copy item 1 "▷ Frac" to the home screen, and display the conversion. To convert Y to a rational number press $\boxed{\text{ALPHA}}$ $\boxed{\text{Y}}$ $\boxed{\text{MATH}}$ $\boxed{1}$ $\boxed{\text{ENTER}}$. (Y is the alphabetic operation associated with the 1 numeric key.) We see that the point of intersection is $\left(-\dfrac{5}{3}, \dfrac{10}{3}\right)$.

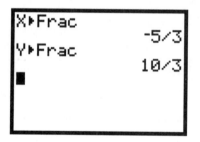

Chapter R
Basic Concepts of Algebra

ABSOLUTE VALUE

Section R.1, Example 3 Find the distance between -2 and 3.

The distance between -2 and 3 is $|-2-3|$, or $|3-(-2)|$. Absolute value notation is denoted "abs" on the grapher. On the TI-83 and TI-83+, it is item 1 on the MATH NUM menu.

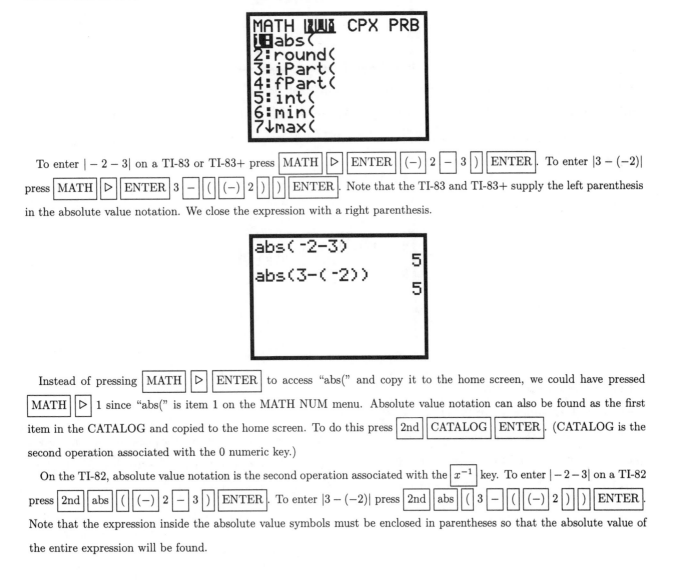

To enter $|-2-3|$ on a TI-83 or TI-83+ press $\boxed{\text{MATH}}$ $\boxed{\triangleright}$ $\boxed{\text{ENTER}}$ $\boxed{(-)}$ $\boxed{2}$ $\boxed{-}$ $\boxed{3}$ $\boxed{)}$ $\boxed{\text{ENTER}}$. To enter $|3-(-2)|$ press $\boxed{\text{MATH}}$ $\boxed{\triangleright}$ $\boxed{\text{ENTER}}$ $\boxed{3}$ $\boxed{-}$ $\boxed{(}$ $\boxed{(-)}$ $\boxed{2}$ $\boxed{)}$ $\boxed{)}$ $\boxed{\text{ENTER}}$. Note that the TI-83 and TI-83+ supply the left parenthesis in the absolute value notation. We close the expression with a right parenthesis.

Instead of pressing $\boxed{\text{MATH}}$ $\boxed{\triangleright}$ $\boxed{\text{ENTER}}$ to access "abs(" and copy it to the home screen, we could have pressed $\boxed{\text{MATH}}$ $\boxed{\triangleright}$ $\boxed{1}$ since "abs(" is item 1 on the MATH NUM menu. Absolute value notation can also be found as the first item in the CATALOG and copied to the home screen. To do this press $\boxed{\text{2nd}}$ $\boxed{\text{CATALOG}}$ $\boxed{\text{ENTER}}$. (CATALOG is the second operation associated with the 0 numeric key.)

On the TI-82, absolute value notation is the second operation associated with the $\boxed{x^{-1}}$ key. To enter $|-2-3|$ on a TI-82 press $\boxed{\text{2nd}}$ $\boxed{\text{abs}}$ $\boxed{(}$ $\boxed{(-)}$ $\boxed{2}$ $\boxed{-}$ $\boxed{3}$ $\boxed{)}$ $\boxed{\text{ENTER}}$. To enter $|3-(-2)|$ press $\boxed{\text{2nd}}$ $\boxed{\text{abs}}$ $\boxed{(}$ $\boxed{3}$ $\boxed{-}$ $\boxed{(}$ $\boxed{(-)}$ $\boxed{2}$ $\boxed{)}$ $\boxed{)}$ $\boxed{\text{ENTER}}$. Note that the expression inside the absolute value symbols must be enclosed in parentheses so that the absolute value of the entire expression will be found.

SCIENTIFIC NOTATION

To enter a number in scientific notation, first type the decimal portion of the number; then press 2nd EE (EE is the second operation associated with the · key.); finally type the exponent, which can be at most two digits. For example, to enter 1.789×10^{-11} in scientific notation, press 1 · 7 8 9 2nd EE (−) 1 1 ENTER. To enter 6.084×10^{23} in scientific notation, press 6 · 0 8 4 2nd EE 2 3 ENTER. The decimal portion of each number appears before a small E while the exponent follows the E.

```
1.789E-11
          1.789E-11
6.084E23
          6.084E23
```

The grapher can be used to perform computations in scientific notation.

Section R.2, Example 7 *Distance to a Star.* Alpha Centauri is about 4.3 light-years from Earth. One light-year is the distance that light travels in one year and is about 5.88×10^{12} miles. How many miles is it from Earth to Alpha Centauri? Express your answer in scientific notation.

To solve this problem we find the product $4.3 \times (5.88 \times 10^{12})$. Press 4 · 3 × 5 · 8 8 2nd EE 1 2 ENTER. The result is 2.5284×10^{13} miles.

```
4.3*5.88E12
          2.5284E13
■
```

ORDER OF OPERATIONS

Section R.2, Example 8 (b) Calculate: $\dfrac{10 \div (8 - 6) + 9 \cdot 4}{2^5 + 3^2}$.

In order to divide the entire numerator by the entire denominator, we must enclose both the numerator and the denominator in parentheses. That is, we enter $(10 \div (8 - 6) + 9 \cdot 4) \div (2^5 + 3^2)$. Press (1 0 ÷ (8 − 6) + 9 × 4) ÷ (2 ∧ 5 + 3 x^2) ENTER. Note that 3^2 can be entered either as 3 x^2 or as 3 ∧ 2.

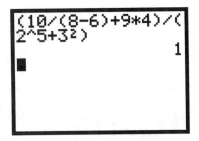

THE PATH GRAPH STYLE

Seven graph styles can be selected on the equation-editor screen of the TI-83 and the TI-83+. The path graph style can be used, along with the line style, to determine whether graphs coincide. This can be used to provide a partial check of certain algebraic procedures. The TI-82 does not have the capability to display a path graph style.

Section R.4, Example 2 Factor: $x^3 + 3x^2 - 5x - 15$.

Factoring by grouping, we find that $x^3 + 3x^2 - 5x - 15 = (x+3)(x^2-5)$. We can check this using two different graph styles on a grapher. First press $\boxed{\text{MODE}}$ to determine whether Sequential mode is selected. If it is not, position the blinking cursor over Sequential and then press $\boxed{\text{ENTER}}$.

Next, on the Y = screen, enter $y_1 = x^3 + 3x^2 - 5x - 15$ and $y_2 = (x+3)(x^2-5)$. We will select the line graph style for y_1 and the path style for y_2. To select these graph styles use $\boxed{\triangleleft}$ to position the cursor over the icon to the left of the equation and press $\boxed{\text{ENTER}}$ repeatedly until the desired style icon appears as shown below.

The grapher will graph y_1 first as a solid line. Then y_2 will be graphed as the circular cursor traces the leading edge of the graph, allowing us to determine visually whether the graphs coincide. In this case, the graphs appear to coincide, so the factorization is probably correct.

SELECTING DOT MODE

When graphing an equation in which a variable appears in a denominator, DOT mode should be used. To select DOT mode press $\boxed{\text{MODE}}$ and use $\boxed{\triangledown}$ and $\boxed{\triangleright}$ to position the blinking cursor over "Dot." Then press $\boxed{\text{ENTER}}$.

On the TI-83 and TI-83+ we can also select DOT mode by selecting the "dot" GraphStyle on the equation-editor screen. Position the cursor over the GraphStyle icon to the left of the equation to be graphed in DOT mode and press $\boxed{\text{ENTER}}$ repeatedly until the dotted icon appears. If the "line" icon was previously selected, $\boxed{\text{ENTER}}$ must be pressed six times to select the "dot" style.

RADICAL NOTATION

We can use the square-root, cube-root, and xth-root features to simplify radical expressions.

Section R.6, Example 1 Simplify each of the following.

a) $\sqrt{36}$ **b)** $-\sqrt{36}$ **c)** $\sqrt[5]{\dfrac{32}{243}}$ **d)** $\sqrt[3]{-8}$ **e)** $\sqrt[4]{-16}$

a) To find $\sqrt{36}$ on the TI-83 or TI-83+, press $\boxed{\text{2nd}}$ $\boxed{\sqrt{}}$ 3 6 $\boxed{)}$ $\boxed{\text{ENTER}}$. ($\sqrt{}$ is the second operation associated with the $\boxed{x^2}$ key.) Note that the TI-83 and the TI-83+ supply a left parenthesis with the radical symbol and we close the expression with a right parenthesis. The TI-82 does not supply a left parenthesis so the $\boxed{)}$ keystroke above should not be used on this grapher.

b) To find $-\sqrt{36}$ on the TI-83 or TI-83+, press $\boxed{(-)}$ $\boxed{\text{2nd}}$ $\boxed{\sqrt{}}$ 3 6 $\boxed{)}$ $\boxed{\text{ENTER}}$. The right parenthesis should not be included on a TI-82.

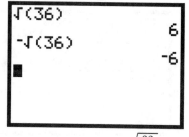

c) We will use the xth-root feature from the MATH menu to find $\sqrt[5]{\dfrac{32}{243}}$. We will also use ▷Frac to express the result as a fraction. Press 5 $\boxed{\text{MATH}}$ 5 $\boxed{(}$ 3 2 $\boxed{\div}$ 2 4 3 $\boxed{)}$ $\boxed{\text{MATH}}$ 1 $\boxed{\text{ENTER}}$. The first 5 is the index of the radical, and the second 5 is used to select item 5, the xth-root, from the MATH menu.

d) We will use the cube-root feature from the MATH menu to find $\sqrt[3]{-8}$. On a TI-83 or a TI-83+ press $\boxed{\text{MATH}}$ 4 $\boxed{(-)}$
8 $\boxed{)}$ $\boxed{\text{ENTER}}$. On a TI-82 the right parenthesis should not be included.

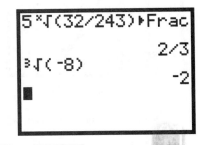

e) To enter $\sqrt[4]{-16}$ press 4 $\boxed{\text{MATH}}$ 5 $\boxed{(-)}$ 1 6 $\boxed{\text{ENTER}}$. When the TI-83 or TI-83+ is set in REAL mode, we get an error message indicating that the answer is nonreal.

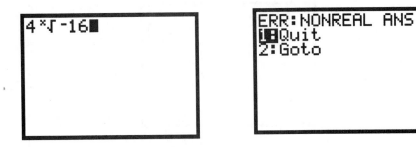

On the TI-82 we also get an error message.

SOLVING EQUATIONS GRAPHICALLY

We can use the Intersect feature from the CALC menu to solve equations.

Section R.7, Example 1 Solve: $2(5 - 3x) = 8 - 3(x + 2)$.

On the equation-editor screen clear any existing entries and then enter $y_1 = 2(5 - 3x)$ and $y_2 = 8 - 3(x + 2)$. The solution of the original equation is the first coordinate of the point of intersection of the graphs of y_1 and y_2. Find the point of intersection as described on page 9 of this manual.

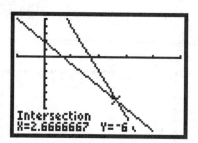

The first coordinate of the point of intersection is 2.6666667. This is a decimal approximation of the solution. This number is stored in the calculator as X. If it is a rational number we can find fractional notation for the exact solution using the ▷Frac feature. Press $\boxed{\text{2nd}}$ $\boxed{\text{QUIT}}$ to go to the home screen. Then press $\boxed{\text{X, T, }\Theta, n}$ $\boxed{\text{MATH}}$ 1 $\boxed{\text{ENTER}}$. We see that the solution is 8/3.

Chapter 1
Graphs, Functions, and Models

FINDING FUNCTION VALUES

When a formula for a function is given, function values can be found in several ways.

Section 1.1, Example 4 (b) For $f(x) = 2x^2 - x + 3$, find $f(-7)$.

Method 1: Substitute the inputs directly in the formula. Press 2 $\boxed{(}$ $\boxed{(-)}$ 7 $\boxed{)}$ $\boxed{x^2}$ $\boxed{-}$ $\boxed{(}$ $\boxed{(-)}$ 7 $\boxed{)}$ $\boxed{+}$ 3 $\boxed{\text{ENTER}}$.
Although it is not necessary to use the second set of parentheses, they allow the expression to be read more easily so we include them here.

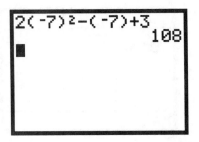

Method 2: Enter $y_1 = 2x^2 - x + 3$ on the "Y =" screen. Then press $\boxed{\text{2nd}}$ $\boxed{\text{QUIT}}$ to go to the home screen. To use the TI-83 or TI-83+ to find $f(-7)$, the value of y_1 when $x = -7$, press $\boxed{(-)}$ 7 $\boxed{\text{STO} \triangleright}$ $\boxed{\text{X, T, } \Theta, n}$ $\boxed{\text{ALPHA}}$ $\boxed{:}$ $\boxed{\text{VARS}}$ $\boxed{\triangleright}$ 1 1 $\boxed{\text{ENTER}}$. (: is the ALPHA operation associated with the $\boxed{.}$ key.) This series of keystrokes stores -7 as the value of x and then substitutes it in the function y_1. To use the TI-82 to find $f(-7)$ press $\boxed{(-)}$ 7 $\boxed{\text{STO} \triangleright}$ $\boxed{\text{X, T, } \Theta}$ $\boxed{\text{2nd}}$ $\boxed{:}$ $\boxed{\text{2nd}}$ $\boxed{\text{Y-VARS}}$ 1 1 $\boxed{\text{ENTER}}$. (: is the second operation associated with the $\boxed{.}$ key.)

Method 3: Enter $y_1 = 2x^2 - x + 3$ on the "Y =" screen and press $\boxed{\text{2nd}}$ $\boxed{\text{QUIT}}$ to go to the home screen. To find $f(-7)$ on the TI-83 or TI-83+ press $\boxed{\text{VARS}}$ $\boxed{\triangleright}$ 1 1 $\boxed{(}$ $\boxed{(-)}$ 7 $\boxed{)}$ $\boxed{\text{ENTER}}$. On the the TI-82 press $\boxed{\text{2nd}}$ $\boxed{\text{Y-VARS}}$ 1 1 $\boxed{(}$ $\boxed{(-)}$ 7 $\boxed{)}$ $\boxed{\text{ENTER}}$. Note that this entry closely resembles function notation.

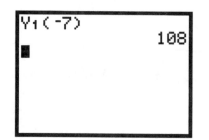

Method 4: The TABLE feature can also be used to find function values. Enter $y_1 = 2x^2 - x + 3$ on the "Y =" screen. Then set up a table Ask mode, by pressing [2nd] [TBLSET], moving the cursor over "Indpnt: Ask," and pressing [ENTER]. In ASK mode, you supply x-values and the grapher returns the corresponding y-values. The settings for TblStart and ΔTbl are irrelevant in this mode. Press [2nd] [TABLE] to display the TABLE screen. Then press [(−)] 7 [ENTER] to find $f(-7)$.

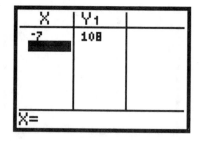

Method 5: We can also use the Value feature from the CALC menu to find $f(-7)$. To do this, graph $y_1 = 2x^2 - x + 3$ in a window that includes the x-value -7. We will use the standard window. Then press [2nd] [CALC] 1 or [2nd] [CALC] [ENTER] to access the CALC menu and select item 1, Value. Now supply the desired x-value by pressing [(−)] 7. Press [ENTER] to see X = −7, Y = 108 at the bottom of the screen, Thus, $f(-7) = 108$.

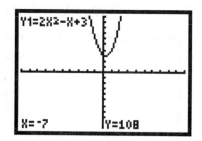

GRAPHS OF FUNCTIONS

The TI-82, TI-83, and TI-83+ do not use function notation. To graph a function, first replace the function notation with y. For example, to graph $f(x) = x^2 - 5$ replace $f(x)$ with y. Then enter the equation $y = x^2 - 5$ on the equation-editor screen and graph it as described on page 8 of this manual.

LINEAR REGRESSION

We can use the Linear Regression feature in the STAT CALC menu to fit a linear equation to a set of data.

Section 1.3, Example 1 The following table shows the number of apartment households in the United States, in millions, for years since 1970.

Years, x	Number of Apartment Households (in millions)
1970, 0	8.5
1975, 5	9.9
1980, 10	10.8
1985, 15	12.9
1990, 20	14.2
1997, 27	14.5

(a) Fit a regression line to the data using the linear regression feature on a grapher.

(b) Use the linear model to predict the number of apartment households in 2003.

(a) We will enter the data as ordered pairs on the STAT list editor screen as described on pages 4 and 5 of this manual.

The grapher's linear regression feature can be used to fit a linear equation to the data. Once the data have been entered in the lists, on the TI-83 or the TI-83+ press $\boxed{\text{STAT}}$ $\boxed{\triangleright}$ 4 $\boxed{\text{ENTER}}$ to select LinReg($ax + b$) from the STAT CALC menu and to display the coefficients a and b of the regression equation $y = ax + b$. On the TI-82 press $\boxed{\text{STAT}}$ $\boxed{\triangleright}$ 5 $\boxed{\text{ENTER}}$.

```
LinReg
y=ax+b
a=.2402037351
b=8.717385399
r²=.9516135878
r=.9755068364
■
```

The TI-82 always displays a value for r along with the coefficients of the regression equation. If the diagnostics have been turned on in the TI-83 or TI-83+, values for r^2 and r will be displayed. These numbers indicate how well the regression line fits the data.

If you wish to select DiagnosticOn mode on the TI-83 or TI-83+, press $\boxed{\text{2nd}}$ $\boxed{\text{CATALOG}}$ and use $\boxed{\triangledown}$ to position the triangular selection cursor beside DiagnosticOn. To alleviate the tedium of scrolling through many items to reach

DiagnosticOn, press $\boxed{\text{D}}$ after pressing $\boxed{\text{2nd}}$ $\boxed{\text{CATALOG}}$ to move quickly to the first catalog item that begins with the letter D. (D is the ALPHA operation associated with the $\boxed{x^{-1}}$ key.) Then use $\boxed{\triangledown}$ to scroll to DiagnosticOn. Note that it is not necessary to press $\boxed{\text{ALPHA}}$ before $\boxed{\text{D}}$ when the catalog is displayed. Press $\boxed{\text{ENTER}}$ to paste this instruction to the home screen and then press $\boxed{\text{ENTER}}$ a second time to set the mode. To select DiagnosticOff mode, press $\boxed{\text{2nd}}$ $\boxed{\text{CATALOG}}$, position the selection cursor beside DiagnosticOff, press $\boxed{\text{ENTER}}$ to paste this instruction to the home screen, and then press $\boxed{\text{ENTER}}$ again to set this mode. Note that this procedure does not apply to the TI-82.

```
DiagnosticOn
          Done
```

```
DiagnosticOff
           Done
■
```

Immediately after the regression equation is found it can be copied to the equation-editor screen as Y_1. Note that any previous entry in Y_1 must have been cleared first. Press $\boxed{\text{Y} =}$ and position the cursor beside Y_1. Then on the TI-83 and TI-83+ press $\boxed{\text{VARS}}$ 5 $\boxed{\triangleright}$ $\boxed{\triangleright}$ 1. On the TI-82 press $\boxed{\text{VARS}}$ 5 $\boxed{\triangleright}$ $\boxed{\triangleright}$ 7. These keystrokes select Statistics from the VARS menu, then select the EQ (Equation) submenu, and finally select the RegEq (Regression Equation) from this submenu.

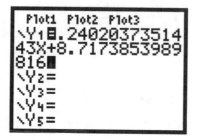

Before the regression equation is found, it is possible to select a y-variable to which it will be stored on the equation editor screen on the TI-83 and TI-83+. After the data have been stored in the lists and the equation previously entered as Y_1 has been cleared, $\boxed{\text{STAT}}$ $\boxed{\triangleright}$ 4 $\boxed{\text{VARS}}$ $\boxed{\triangleright}$ 1 1 $\boxed{\text{ENTER}}$. The coefficients of the regression equation will be displayed on the home screen, and the regression equation will also be stored as Y_1 on the equation-editor screen. This procedure does not apply to the TI-82.

```
LinReg(ax+b) Y1■
```

(b) To predict the number of apartment households in 2003, evaluate the regression equation for $x = 33$. (2003 is 33 years after 1970.) Use any of the methods for evaluating a function presented earlier in this chapter. (See pages 17 and 18 of this manual.) We will use function notation on the home screen.

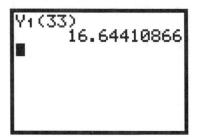

When $x = 33, y \approx 16.6$, so we predict that there will be about 16.6 million apartment households in the United States in 2003.

We can also plot the data points along with the graph of the regression equation. To do this we first turn on the STAT PLOT feature as described on pages 5 and 6 of this manual. Now select a viewing window. We will press ZOOM 9 to activate the ZoomStat operation which automatically defines a viewing window that displays all of the points and also displays the graph.

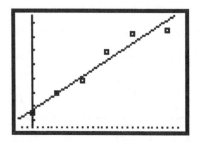

Turn off the STAT PLOT as described on page 6 of this manual before graphing other functions.

THE MAXIMUM AND MINIMUM FEATURES

Section 1.4, Example 2 Use a grapher to determine any relative maxima or minima of the function $f(x) = 0.1x^3 - 0.6x^2 - 0.1x + 2$.

First graph $y_1 = 0.1x^3 - 0.6x^2 - 0.1x + 2$ in a window that displays the relative extrema of the function. Trial and error reveals that one good choice is $[-4, 6, -3, 3]$. Observe that a relative maximum occurs near $x = 0$ and a relative minimum occurs near $x = 4$.

To find the relative maximum, first press 2nd CALC 4 or 2nd CALC ▽ ▽ ▽ ENTER to select the Maximum feature from the CALC menu. We are prompted to select a left bound for the relative maximum. This is called a lower bound on the TI-82. This means that we must choose an x-value that is to the left of the x-value of the point where the relative maximum occurs. This can be done by using the left- and right-arrow keys to move the cursor to a point to the left of the relative maximum or, on the TI-83 and TI-83+, by keying in an appropriate value.

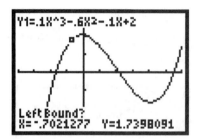

Once this is done, press ENTER. Now we are prompted to select a right bound. This is called an upper bound on the TI-82. We move the cursor to a point to the right of the relative maximum or, on the TI-83 and TI-83+, we can key in an appropriate value.

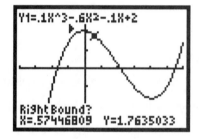

Press ENTER again. Finally we are prompted to guess the x-value at which the relative maximum occurs. Move the cursor close to the relative maximum point or, on the TI-83 and TI-83+, key in an x-value.

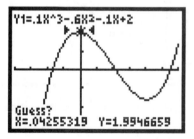

Press ENTER a third time. We see that a relative maximum function value of approximately 2.004 occurs when $x \approx -0.082$.

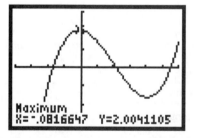

To find the relative minimum, select the Minimum feature from the CALC menu by pressing 2nd CALC 3 or 2nd CALC ▽ ▽ ENTER. Select left (or lower) and right (or upper) bounds for the relative minimum and guess the

x-value at which it occurs as described above. We see that a relative minimum function value of approximately -1.604 occurs when $x \approx 4.082$.

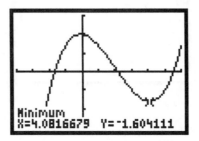

GRAPHING FUNCTIONS DEFINED PIECEWISE

Operations from the TEST menu are used to enter functions that are defined piecewise. (TEST is the second operation associated with the $\boxed{\text{MATH}}$ key.) Select DOT mode from the MODE menu when graphing such functions. On the TI-83, DOT mode can also be selected by choosing the DOT style on the "Y =" screen. (See page 14 of this manual.) Any style selected on the TI-83 "Y =" screen overrides a MODE selection.

Section 1.4, Example 5 Graph

$$f(x) = \begin{cases} 4, & \text{for } x \leq 0, \\ 4 - x^2, & \text{for } 0 < x \leq 2, \\ 2x - 6, & \text{for } x > 2. \end{cases}$$

Press $\boxed{\text{Y} =}$ and clear any functions that have previously been entered. With the cursor beside "Y1 =" enter the function as described on page 111 of the text by pressing $\boxed{(}$ $\boxed{4}$ $\boxed{)}$ $\boxed{(}$ $\boxed{\text{X, T, }\Theta, n}$ $\boxed{\text{2nd}}$ $\boxed{\text{TEST}}$ $\boxed{6}$ $\boxed{0}$ $\boxed{)}$ $\boxed{+}$ $\boxed{(}$ $\boxed{4}$ $\boxed{-}$ $\boxed{\text{X, T, }\Theta, n}$ $\boxed{x^2}$ $\boxed{)}$ $\boxed{(}$ $\boxed{0}$ $\boxed{\text{2nd}}$ $\boxed{\text{TEST}}$ $\boxed{5}$ $\boxed{\text{X, T, }\Theta, n}$ $\boxed{)}$ $\boxed{(}$ $\boxed{\text{X, T, }\Theta, n}$ $\boxed{\text{2nd}}$ $\boxed{\text{TEST}}$ $\boxed{6}$ $\boxed{2}$ $\boxed{)}$ $\boxed{+}$ $\boxed{(}$ $\boxed{2}$ $\boxed{\text{X, T, }\Theta, n}$ $\boxed{-}$ $\boxed{6}$ $\boxed{)}$ $\boxed{(}$ $\boxed{\text{X, T, }\Theta, n}$ $\boxed{\text{2nd}}$ $\boxed{\text{TEST}}$ $\boxed{3}$ $\boxed{2}$ $\boxed{)}$. Select a window and then press $\boxed{\text{GRAPH}}$. The window $[-5, 5, -3, 6]$ is shown here.

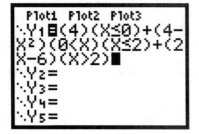
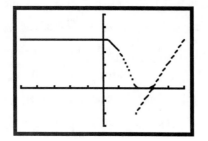

THE GREATEST INTEGER FUNCTION

The greatest integer function is found in the MATH NUM menu and is denoted "int." To find int(1.9) on the TI-83 or T-83+ press $\boxed{\text{MATH}}$ $\boxed{\triangleright}$ $\boxed{5}$ $\boxed{1}$ $\boxed{.}$ $\boxed{9}$ $\boxed{)}$ $\boxed{\text{ENTER}}$. Note that the grapher supplies a left parenthesis and we close the parentheses after entering 1.9. To find int(1.9) on the TI-82 press $\boxed{\text{MATH}}$ $\boxed{\triangleright}$ $\boxed{4}$ $\boxed{1}$ $\boxed{.}$ $\boxed{9}$ $\boxed{\text{ENTER}}$. No parentheses are required in this case on the TI-82.

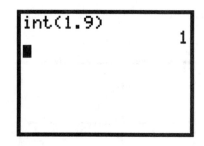

We can also graph the greatest integer function.

Section 1.4, Example 7 Graph $f(x) = \text{int}(x)$.

With the grapher set in DOT mode, press $\boxed{\text{Y} =}$ and clear any previously entered functions. Position the cursor beside "Y1 =" and select the greatest integer function from the MATH NUM menu as follows. On the TI-83 press $\boxed{\text{MATH}}$ $\boxed{\triangleright}$ 5 $\boxed{\text{X, T, } \Theta, n}$ $\boxed{)}$ and on the TI-82 press $\boxed{\text{MATH}}$ $\boxed{\triangleright}$ 4 $\boxed{\text{X, T, } \Theta}$. Select a window and press $\boxed{\text{GRAPH}}$. The window $[-6, 6, -6, 6]$ is shown here.

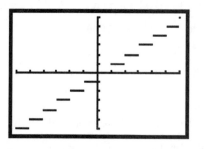

THE ALGEBRA OF FUNCTIONS

The grapher can be used to evaluate and graph combinations of functions.

Section 1.4, Example 8 (b) Given that $f(x) = x + 1$ and $g(x) = \sqrt{x + 3}$, find $(f + g)(6)$.

Press $\boxed{\text{Y} =}$ and enter $y_1 = x + 1$, $y_2 = \sqrt{x + 3}$, and $y_3 = y_1 + y_2$. To enter $y_3 = y_1 + y_2$ on the TI-83 or TI-83+ press $\boxed{\text{VARS}}$ $\boxed{\triangleright}$ 1 1 $\boxed{+}$ $\boxed{\text{VARS}}$ $\boxed{\triangleright}$ 1 2. On the TI-82 press $\boxed{\text{2nd}}$ $\boxed{\text{Y-VARS}}$ 1 1 $\boxed{+}$ $\boxed{\text{2nd}}$ $\boxed{\text{Y-VARS}}$ 1 2. Note that $y_3 = f(x) + g(x)$, or $(f + g)(x)$. Use y_3 to find $(f + g)(6)$ employing one of the methods for finding function values described on pages 17 and 18 of this manual. We find that $(f + g)(6) = 10$.

To view the graphs of $f(x)$, $g(x)$, and $(f + g)(x)$ enter y_1, y_2, and y_3 as above, select a window, and press $\boxed{\text{GRAPH}}$. These graphs appear on page 115 of the text. It is possible to deselect one or two of these functions and display the graph(s) of the remaining function(s). For example, to display only the graph of y_3 without deleting the equations of y_1 and y_2, press $\boxed{\text{Y} =}$. Then move the cursor to y_1, position it over the equals sign, and press $\boxed{\text{ENTER}}$. This deselects or turns off y_1. Do the same for y_2. Now press $\boxed{\text{GRAPH}}$ and see only the graph of y_3.

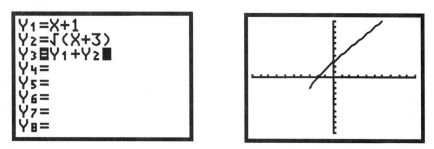

To select or turn on a function again, repeat this process. Note that the equals sign on a selected function is highlighted.

GRAPHING CIRCLES

If the center and radius of a circle are known, the circle can be graphed using the Circle feature from the DRAW menu.

Section 1.7, Exercise 37 Graph $(x - 1)^2 + (y - 5)^2 = 36$.

The center of this circle is (1,5) and its radius is 6. To graph it using the Circle feature from the DRAW menu first press $\boxed{Y =}$ and clear all previously entered equations. Then select a square window. (See page 150 of the text for a discussion on squaring the viewing window.) We will use $[-12, 12, -4, 12]$, Xscl $= 2$, Yscl $= 2$. Press $\boxed{2\text{nd}}$ $\boxed{\text{QUIT}}$ to go to the home screen. Then press $\boxed{2\text{nd}}$ $\boxed{\text{DRAW}}$ 9 to display "Circle(." Enter the coordinates of the center and the radius, separating the entries by commas, and close the parentheses: 1 $\boxed{,}$ 5 $\boxed{,}$ 6 $\boxed{)}$ $\boxed{\text{ENTER}}$.

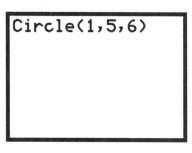

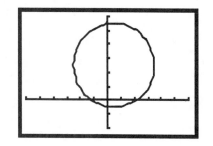

Chapter 2
Functions and Equations: Zeros and Solutions

THE ZERO FEATURE/THE ROOT FEATURE

The Zero feature of the TI-83 or TI-83+ or the Root feature of the TI-82 can be used to find the zeros of a function or to solve an equation in the form $f(x) = 0$.

Section 2.1, Example 1 Find the zero of $f(x) = 5x - 9$.

On the equation-editor screen, clear any existing entries and then enter $y_1 = 5x - 9$. Now graph the function in a viewing window that shows the x-intercept clearly. The standard window is a good choice.

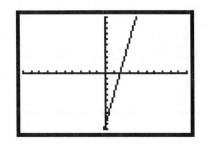

Press 2nd CALC to display the CALC menu. Then press 2 to select the Zero feature on the TI-83 or TI-83+ or the Root feature on the TI-82. We are first prompted to select a left bound on the TI-83 or TI-83+ or a lower bound on the TI-82. This means that we must choose an x-value that is to the left of the x-intercept. This can be done by using the left- and right-arrow keys to move the cursor to a point on the curve to the left of the x-intercept or, on the TI-83 or TI-83+, by keying in a value less than the first coordinate of the intercept.

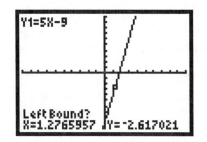

Once this is done press ENTER . Now we are prompted to select a right bound that is to the right of the x-intercept. This is called an upper bound on the TI-82. Again, this can be done by using the arrow keys to move the cursor to a point on the curve to the right of the x-intercept or, on the TI-83 or TI-83+, by keying in a value greater than the first coordinate of the intercept.

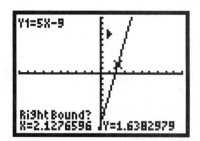

Press | ENTER | again. Finally we are prompted to make a guess as to the value of the zero. Move the cursor to a point close to the zero or key in a value.

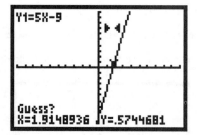

Press | ENTER | a third time. We see that $y = 0$ when $x = 1.8$, so 1.8 is the zero of the function.

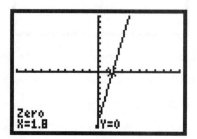

If a function has more than one zero, the Zero feature or Root feature can be used as many times as necessary to find all of them.

OPERATIONS WITH COMPLEX NUMBERS

Operations with complex numbers can be performed on the TI-83 and the TI-83+. These operations cannot be performed on the TI-82. First set the grapher in the complex $a + bi$ mode by pressing | MODE |, positioning the cursor over $a + bi$, and pressing | ENTER |.

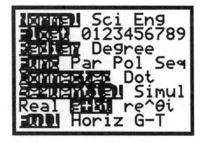

Section 2.1, Example 4

(a) Add: $(8 + 6i) + (3 + 2i)$.

To find this sum go to the home screen and press 8 [+] 6 [2nd] [i] [+] 3 [+] 2 [2nd] [i] [ENTER]. (The number i is the second operation associated with the [·] key.) Note that it is not necessary to include parentheses when we are adding.

(b) Subtract: $(4 + 5i) - (6 - 3i)$.

Press 4 [+] 5 [2nd] [i] [−] [(] 6 [−] 3 [2nd] [i] [)] [ENTER]. Note that the parentheses must be included as shown so that the entire number $6 - 3i$ is subtracted.

```
8+6i+3+2i
              11+8i
4+5i-(6-3i)
               -2+8i
■
```

Section 2.1, Example 5

(a) Multiply: $\sqrt{-16} \cdot \sqrt{-25}$.

Press [2nd] [√] [(−)] 1 6 [)] [2nd] [√] [(−)] 2 5 [)] [ENTER].

(b) Multiply: $(1 + 2i)(1 + 3i)$.

Press [(] 1 [+] 2 [2nd] [i] [)] [(] 1 [+] 3 [2nd] [i] [)] [ENTER].

(c) Multiply: $(3 - 7i)^2$.

Press [(] 3 [−] 7 [2nd] [i] [)] [x^2] [ENTER].

```
√(-16)√(-25)
                -20
(1+2i)(1+3i)
               -5+5i
(3-7i)²
              -40-42i
■
```

QUADRATIC REGRESSION

Quadratic functions can be fit to data using the quadratic regression operation from the STAT CALC menu. The operations of entering data, making scatterplots, and graphing and evaluating quadratic regression functions are the same as for linear regression functions.

Section 2.5, Example 1 *Leisure Time* The following table shows the median number of hours of leisure time that Americans had each week in various years.

Year	Median Number of Leisure Hours per Week
0, 1973	26.2
7, 1980	19.2
14, 1987	16.6
20, 1993	18.8
24, 1997	19.5

(a) Make a scatterplot of the data, letting x represent the number of years since 1973, and determine whether a linear function, a quadratic function, or neither seems to fit the data.

(b) Use a grapher to fit the type of function determined in part (a) to the data.

(c) Graph the equation with the scatterplot.

(d) Use the function found in part (c) to estimate the number of leisure hours per week in 1978; in 1990; in 2005.

(a) Clear any existing entries on the equation-editor screen. Then enter the data in L_1 and L_2 and make a scatterplot as described on pages 4 - 6 of this manual. We have used a ZoomStat window here. It appears that a quadratic function fits the data.

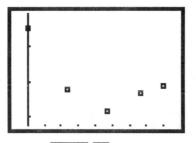

(b) To fit a quadratic function to the data, press $\boxed{\text{STAT}}$ $\boxed{\triangleright}$ to view the STAT CALC menu. Then select QuadReg by pressing 5 on the TI-83 or TI-83+ or 6 on the TI-82 followed by $\boxed{\text{ENTER}}$. The coefficients of a quadratic equation $y = ax^2 + bx + c$ are displayed. Note that at least three data points are required for quadratic regression.

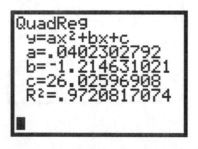

(c) The regression equation can be copied to the "Y =" screen as described on page 20 of this manual. The TI-83 and TI-83+ also offer the usual option of selecting a y-variable name before the regression equation is found. Once the regression equation is entered in the "Y =" screen, it can be graphed with the scatterplot.

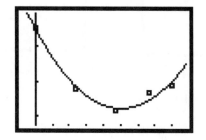

Be sure to turn off the STAT PLOT as described on page 6 of this manual before graphing future equations.

(d) To estimate the number of leisure hours per week in 1978, 1990, and 2005, we evaluate the regression function for 5, 17, and 32, respectively. We can use any of the methods for evaluating a function found on pages 17 and 18 of this manual. Here we show a table set in Ask mode.

X	Y₁	
5	20.959	
17	17.004	
32	28.354	

X=

CHECKING SOLUTIONS OF INEQUALITIES

We can perform a partial check of the solution of an inequality using operations from the TEST menu.

Section 2.7, Example 2 Solve: $-3 < 2x + 5 \le 7$.

The solution set is found algebraically in the text. It is $\{x| -4 < x \le 1\}$, or $(-4, 1]$. We can perform a partial check of this solution by graphing $y = (-3 < 2x + 5) \text{ and } (2x + 5 \le 7)$ in Dot mode. The value of y will be 1 for those x-values which make y a true statement. It will be 0 for those x-values for which y is false. To enter the expression for y, position the cursor beside Y₁ on the Y = screen. Then press (((−) 3 2nd TEST 5 2 X, T, Θ, n + 5) 2nd TEST ▷ 1 (2 X, T, Θ, n + 5 2nd TEST 6 7) . (TEST is the second operation associated with the MATH key.) The keystrokes 2nd TEST 5 display the TEST submenu of the TEST menu and paste the symbol "<" from that menu to the equation-editor screen. The keystrokes 2nd TEST ▷ 1 display the LOGIC submenu of the TEST menu and paste "and" from that menu to the equation-editor screen.

Now select a window and press GRAPH . We use the window $[-10, 10, -1, 2]$.

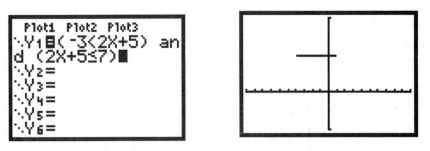

We see that $y = 1$ for x-values from -4 to 1, confirming that all x-values from -4 to 1 are in the solution set. The algebraic solution indicates that the endpoint 1 is also in the solution set.

Chapter 3
Polynomial and Rational Functions

POWER MODELS

A power model $y = ax^b$ can be fit to data using the power regression feature from the STAT CALC menu.

Section 3.1, Example 4 (a) *Cholesterol Level and the Risk of Heart Attack.* The data in the following table show the relationship of cholesterol level in men to the risk of a heart attack.

Cholesterol Level, x	Men Per 10,000 Who Suffer a Heart Attack
100	30
200	65
250	100
275	130
300	180

(a) Use a grapher to fit a power function to the data.

Enter the data in lists as described on pages 4 and 5 of this manual. Then select power regression from the STAT CALC menu on the TI-83 or TI-83+ by pressing $\boxed{\text{STAT}}\ \boxed{\triangleright}\ \boxed{\text{ALPHA}}\ \boxed{\text{A}}\ \boxed{\text{ENTER}}$. (A is the green alphabetic operation associated with the $\boxed{\text{MATH}}$ key.) On the TI-82 press $\boxed{\text{STAT}}\ \boxed{\triangleright}\ \boxed{\text{ALPHA}}\ \boxed{\text{B}}\ \boxed{\text{ENTER}}$. (B is the alphabetic operation associated with the $\boxed{\text{MATRX}}$ key.) The grapher displays the coefficient a and the exponent b for the power function $y = ax^b$.

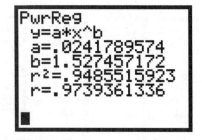

This function can be copied to the Y = screen using one of the methods described on page 20 of this manual. Then it can be graphed. It can also be evaluated using one of the methods on pages 17 and 18.

CUBIC AND QUARTIC REGRESSION

We can fit third-degree, or cubic, functions and fourth-degree, or quartic, functions to data on a grapher.

Section 3.1, Example 5 (a) The table below shows the number of farms, in millions, for years after 1900. Model the data with both cubic and quartic functions. Let the first coordinate of each data point be the number of years after 1900.

Years after 1900	Number of Farms, in millions
10, 1910	6.4
20, 1920	6.5
30, 1930	6.3
40, 1940	6.1
50, 1950	5.4
59, 1959	3.7
69, 1969	2.7
78, 1978	2.3
87, 1987	2.1
97, 1997	1.9

Enter the data in lists as described on pages 4 and 5 of this manual. To select cubic regression from the STAT CALC menu on the TI-83 or TI-83+ press $\boxed{\text{STAT}}$ $\boxed{\triangleright}$ 6 $\boxed{\text{ENTER}}$. On the TI-82 press $\boxed{\text{STAT}}$ $\boxed{\triangleright}$ 7 $\boxed{\text{ENTER}}$. The grapher displays the coefficients of a cubic function $y = ax^3 + bx^2 + cx + d$.

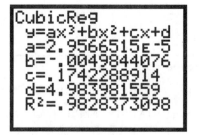

To model the data with a quartic function select quartic regression from the STAT CALC menu. On the TI-83 or TI-83+ press $\boxed{\text{STAT}}$ $\boxed{\triangleright}$ 7 $\boxed{\text{ENTER}}$. On the TI-82 press $\boxed{\text{STAT}}$ $\boxed{\triangleright}$ 8 $\boxed{\text{ENTER}}$. The grapher displays the coefficients of a quartic function $y = ax^4 + bx^3 + cx^2 + dx + e$.

```
QuarticReg
 y=ax⁴+bx³+…+e
 a=1.5229297E-7
 b=-3.092184E-6
 c=-.0026500648
 d=.1117312855
↓e=5.463775105
■
```

```
QuarticReg
 y=ax⁴+bx³+…+e
↑b=-3.092184E-6
 c=-.0026500648
 d=.1117312855
 e=5.463775105
 R²=.9836750763
```

A scatterplot of the data can be graphed as described on pages 5 and 6 of this manual. This function can be copied to the Y = screen using one of the methods described on page 20 of this manual. Then it can be graphed along with the scatterplot. It can also be evaluated using one of the methods on pages 17 and 18.

GRAPHING RATIONAL FUNCTIONS

Section 3.4, Example 1 Consider $f(x) = \dfrac{1}{x-3}$ and graph f.

In the text the domain is found to be $\{x | x \neq 3\}$, or $(-\infty, 3) \cup (3, \infty)$. Thus, there is not a point on the graph with an

x-coordinate of 3. Graphing the function in Connected mode can lead to an incorrect graph in which a line connects he last point plotted to the left of $x = 3$ with the last point plotted to the right of $x = 3$. This line can be eliminated by using Dot mode as described on page 14 of this manual. Selecting a ZDecimal window from the ZOOM menu will also produce a graph in which this line does not appear. To do this, first enter $y = \dfrac{1}{x - 3}$ on the Y = screen and then press $\boxed{\text{ZOOM}}$ 4. The resulting window dimensions and graph are shown below.

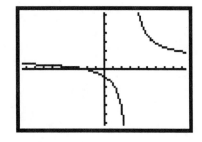

Section 3.4, Example 10 Graph: $g(x) = \dfrac{x - 2}{x^2 - x - 2}$.

As explained in the text, the graph of $g(x)$ is the graph of $y = \dfrac{1}{x + 1}$ with the point $\left(2, \dfrac{1}{3}\right)$ missing. The window used in the text to produce the graph with a "hole" at $\left(2, \dfrac{1}{3}\right)$ is obtained using the ZDecimal feature from the ZOOM menu. After entering $y = \dfrac{x - 2}{x^2 - x - 2}$ on the Y = screen, press $\boxed{\text{ZOOM}}$ 4 to select this window and display the graph.

Chapter 4
Exponential and Logarithmic Functions

THE COMPOSITION OF FUNCTIONS

We can evaluate composite functions on a grapher.

Section 4.1, Example 1 (a) Given that $f(x) = 2x - 5$ and $g(x) = x^2 - 3x + 8$, find $(f \circ g)(7)$ and $(g \circ f)(7)$.

On the equation-editor screen enter $y_1 = 2x - 5$ and $y_2 = x^2 - 3x + 8$. Then $(f \circ g)(7) = (y_1 \circ y_2)(7)$, or $y_1(y_2(7))$ and $(g \circ f)(7) = (y_2 \circ y_1)(7)$, or $y_2(y_1(7))$. To find these function values press $\boxed{\text{2nd}}$ $\boxed{\text{QUIT}}$ to go to the home screen. Then enter $y_1(y_2(7))$ on the TI-83 or TI-83+ by pressing $\boxed{\text{VARS}}$ $\boxed{\triangleright}$ 1 1 $\boxed{(}$ $\boxed{\text{VARS}}$ $\boxed{\triangleright}$ 1 2 $\boxed{(}$ 7 $\boxed{)}$ $\boxed{)}$ $\boxed{\text{ENTER}}$. On the TI-82 press $\boxed{\text{2nd}}$ $\boxed{\text{Y-VARS}}$ 1 1 $\boxed{(}$ $\boxed{\text{2nd}}$ $\boxed{\text{Y-VARS}}$ 1 2 $\boxed{(}$ 7 $\boxed{)}$ $\boxed{)}$ $\boxed{\text{ENTER}}$. Now enter $y_2(y_1(7))$ on the TI-83 or TI-83+ by pressing $\boxed{\text{VARS}}$ $\boxed{\triangleright}$ 1 2 $\boxed{(}$ $\boxed{\text{VARS}}$ $\boxed{\triangleright}$ 1 1 $\boxed{(}$ 7 $\boxed{)}$ $\boxed{)}$ $\boxed{\text{ENTER}}$. On the TI-82 press $\boxed{\text{2nd}}$ $\boxed{\text{Y-VARS}}$ 1 2 $\boxed{(}$ $\boxed{\text{2nd}}$ $\boxed{\text{Y-VARS}}$ 1 1 $\boxed{(}$ 7 $\boxed{)}$ $\boxed{)}$ $\boxed{\text{ENTER}}$.

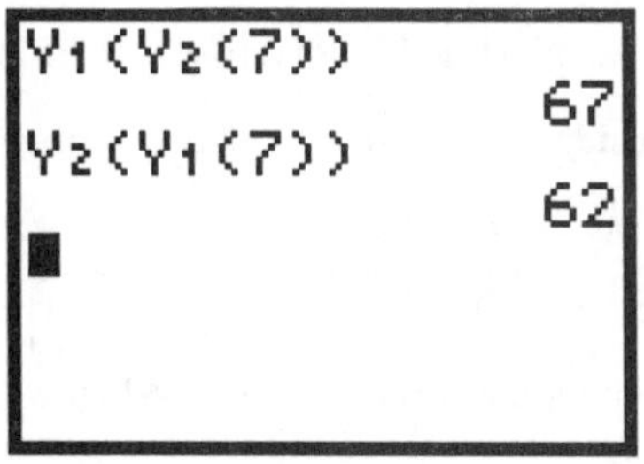

```
Y₁(Y₂(7))
               67
Y₂(Y₁(7))
               62
■
```

GRAPHING AN INVERSE FUNCTION

The DrawInv operation can be used to graph a function and its inverse on the same screen. A formula for the inverse function need not be found in order to do this. The grapher must be set in Func mode when this operation is used.

Section 4.1, Example 7 Graph $f(x) = 2x - 3$ and $f^{-1}(x)$ using the same set of axes.

Enter $y_1 = 2x - 3$ and either clear or deselect all other functions on the "Y =" screen. Then press $\boxed{\text{2nd}}$ $\boxed{\text{DRAW}}$ 8 to select the DrawInv operation. (DRAW is the second operation associated with the $\boxed{\text{PRGM}}$ key.) On the TI-83 or TI-83+ follow these keystrokes with $\boxed{\text{VARS}}$ $\boxed{\triangleright}$ 1 1 to select function y_1. On the TI-82 y_1 is selected by pressing $\boxed{\text{2nd}}$ $\boxed{\text{Y-VARS}}$ 1 1. Press $\boxed{\text{ENTER}}$ to see the graph of the function and its inverse. The graphs are shown here in the standard window.

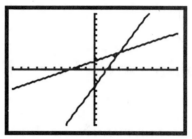

EVALUATING e^x, Log x, and Ln x

Use the grapher's scientific keys to evaluate e^x, $\log x$, and $\ln x$ for specific values of x.

Section 4.2, Example 6 (a), (b) Find the value of e^3 and $e^{-0.23}$. Round to four decimal places.

To find e^3 press $\boxed{\text{2nd}}$ $\boxed{e^x}$ $\boxed{3}$ $\boxed{)}$ $\boxed{\text{ENTER}}$. (e^x is the second operation associated with the $\boxed{\text{LN}}$ key.) On the TI-82 the keystroke $\boxed{)}$ should not be included. The grapher returns 20.08553692. Thus, $e^3 \approx 20.0855$. To find $e^{-0.23}$ press $\boxed{\text{2nd}}$ $\boxed{e^x}$ $\boxed{(-)}$ $\boxed{\cdot}$ $\boxed{2\ 3}$ $\boxed{)}$ $\boxed{\text{ENTER}}$. On the TI-82 the keystroke $\boxed{)}$ should not be included. The grapher returns .7945336025, so $e^{-0.23} \approx 0.7945$.

Section 4.3, Example 4 Find the values of log 645,778, log 0.0000239, and log (-3). Round to four decimal places.

To find log 645,778 press $\boxed{\text{LOG}}$ $\boxed{6\ 4\ 5\ 7\ 7\ 8}$ $\boxed{)}$ $\boxed{\text{ENTER}}$ and read 5.810083246. Thus, log $645,778 \approx 5.8101$. On the TI-82 the keystroke $\boxed{)}$ should not be included. To find log 0.0000239 press $\boxed{\text{LOG}}$ $\boxed{\cdot}$ $\boxed{0\ 0\ 0\ 0\ 2\ 3\ 9}$ $\boxed{)}$ $\boxed{\text{ENTER}}$. The grapher returns -4.621602099, so $\log 0.0000239 \approx -4.6216$. On the TI-82 the keystroke $\boxed{)}$ should not be included. When the TI-83 is set in Real mode the keystrokes $\boxed{\text{LOG}}$ $\boxed{(-)}$ $\boxed{3}$ $\boxed{)}$ $\boxed{\text{ENTER}}$ produce the message ERR: NONREAL ANS indicating that the result of this calculation is not a real number. When we press $\boxed{\text{LOG}}$ $\boxed{(-)}$ $\boxed{3}$ $\boxed{\text{ENTER}}$ on the TI-82 the message ERR: DOMAIN is returned. This indicates that -3 is not in the domain of the function $\log x$.

Section 4.3, Example 5 (a), (b), (c) Find the values of ln 645,778, ln 0.0000239, and ln (-5). Round to four decimal places.

To find ln 645,778 and ln 0.0000239 repeat the keystrokes used above to find log 645,778 and log 0.0000239 but press $\boxed{\text{LN}}$ rather than $\boxed{\text{LOG}}$. We find that ln $645,778 \approx 13.3782$ and $\ln 0.0000239 \approx -10.6416$. When the TI-83 is set in Real mode the keystrokes $\boxed{\text{LN}}$ $\boxed{(-)}$ $\boxed{5}$ $\boxed{)}$ $\boxed{\text{ENTER}}$ produce the message ERR: NONREAL ANS indicating that the result of this calculation is not a real number. When we press $\boxed{\text{LN}}$ $\boxed{(-)}$ $\boxed{5}$ $\boxed{\text{ENTER}}$ on the TI-82 the message ERR: DOMAIN is returned indicating that -5 is not in the domain of the function $\ln x$.

USING THE CHANGE OF BASE FORMULA

To find a logarithm with a base other than 10 or e we use the change-of-base formula, $\log_b M = \dfrac{\log_a M}{\log_a b}$, where a and b are any logarithmic bases and M is any positive number.

Section 4.3, Example 6 Find $\log_5 8$ using common logarithms.

We let $a = 10$, $b = 5$, and $M = 8$ and substitute in the change-of-base formula. On the TI-83 and TI-83+ press $\boxed{\text{LOG}}$ 8

$\fbox{)}$ $\fbox{$\div$}$ $\fbox{LOG}$ 5 $\fbox{)}$ $\fbox{ENTER}$. Note that the parentheses must be closed in the numerator to enter the expression correctly. We also close the parentheses in the denominator for completeness. On the TI-82 press $\fbox{LOG}$ 8 $\fbox{$\div$}$ $\fbox{LOG}$ 5 $\fbox{ENTER}$. No parentheses are required on this grapher. The result is about 1.2920. We could have let $a = e$ and used natural logarithms to find $\log_5 8$ as well.

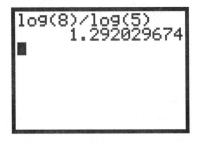

Section 4.3, Example 9 Graph $y = \log_5 x$.

To use a grapher we must first change the base to e or 10. Here we use e. Let $a = e$, $b = 5$, and $M = x$ and substitute in the change-of-base formula. Enter $y_1 = \dfrac{\ln x}{\ln 5}$ on the Y = screen, select a window, and press $\fbox{GRAPH}$. Note that since the TI-83 and the TI-83+ force the use of parentheses with the ln function, the parentheses in the numerator must be closed on this grapher: $\ln(x)/\ln(5)$. The right parenthesis following the 5 is optional but we include it for completeness.

 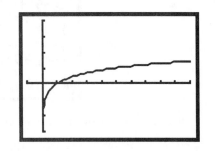

EXPONENTIAL AND LOGARITHMIC REGRESSION

In addition to the types of polynomial regression discussed earlier, exponential and logarithmic functions can be fit to data. The operations of entering data, making scatterplots, and graphing and evaluating these functions are the same as for linear regression functions. So are the procedures for copying a regression equation to the Y = screen, graphing it, and using it to find function values. Note that the coefficient of correlation, r, will be displayed on the TI-83 or TI-83+ only if DiagnosticOn has been selected from the Catalog.

Section 4.6, Example 6 (a) *Credit Card Volume.* The total credit card volume for Visa, MasterCard, American Express, and Discover has increased dramatically in recent years.

Year, x	Credit Card Volume (in billions)
1988, 0	$261.0
1989, 1	296.3
1990, 2	338.4
1991, 3	361.0
1992, 4	403.1
1993, 5	476.7
1994, 6	584.8
1995, 7	701.2
1996, 8	798.3
1997, 9	885.2

(a) Use a grapher to fit an exponential function to the data.

Enter the data in lists as described on pages 4 and 5 of this manual. Then select exponential regression from the STAT CALC menu on the TI-83 or TI-83+ by pressing $\boxed{\text{STAT}}$ $\boxed{\triangleright}$ $\boxed{0}$ $\boxed{\text{ENTER}}$. On the TI-82 press $\boxed{\text{STAT}}$ $\boxed{\triangleright}$ $\boxed{\text{ALPHA}}$ $\boxed{\text{A}}$ $\boxed{\text{ENTER}}$. (A is the alphabetic operation associated with the $\boxed{\text{MATH}}$ key.) The grapher displays the coefficient a and the base b for the exponential function $y = a \cdot b^x$.

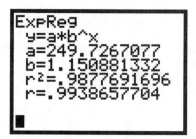

A scatterplot of the data can be graphed as described on pages 5 and 6 of this manual. This function can be copied to the Y = screen using one of the methods described on page 20 of this manual. Then it can be graphed along with the scatterplot. It can also be evaluated using one of the methods on pages 17 and 18.

Section 4.6, Exercise 26 (a) *Forgetting.* In an art class, students were tested at the end of the course on a final exam. Then they were retested with an equivalent test at subsequent time intervals. Their scores after time t, in months, are given in the following table.

Time, t (in months)	Score, y
1	84.9%
2	84.6%
3	84.4%
4	84.2%
5	84.1%
6	83.9%

(a) Use a grapher to fit a logarithmic function $y = a + b \ln x$ to the data.

After entering the data in lists as described on pages 4 and 5 of this manual, press $\boxed{\text{STAT}}$ $\boxed{\triangleright}$ to view the STAT CALC menu. Select LnReg by pressing 9 on the TI-83 or TI-83+ or 0 on the TI-82 followed by $\boxed{\text{ENTER}}$. The values of a and b

for the logarithmic function $y = a + b \ln x$ are displayed along with the coefficient of correlation r. The TI-83 also displays r^2.

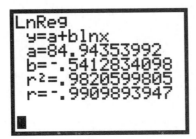

LOGISTIC REGRESSION

A logistic function can be fit to data using the TI-83 or TI-83+. The TI-82 does not have this capability.

Section 4.6, Exercise 28 (a) *Effect of Advertising.* A company introduces a new software product on a trial run in a city. They advertised the product on television and found the following data relating the percent P of people who bought the product after x ads were run.

Number of Ads, x	Percent Who Bought, P
0	0.2
10	0.7
20	2.7
30	9.2
40	27
50	57.6
60	83.3
70	94.8
80	98.5
90	99.6

(a) Use a grapher to fit a logistic function $P(x) = \dfrac{a}{1 + be^{-kx}}$ to the data.

After entering the data in lists as described on pages 4 and 5 of this manual, press $\boxed{\text{STAT}}$ $\boxed{\triangleright}$ to view the STAT CALC menu. Select Logistic by pressing $\boxed{\text{ALPHA}}$ $\boxed{\text{B}}$ $\boxed{\text{ENTER}}$. The values of a, b, and c for the logistic function $y = \dfrac{c}{1 + ae^{-bx}}$ are displayed.

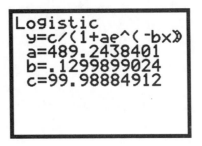

Chapter 5
The Trigonometric Functions

FINDING TRIGONOMETRIC FUNCTION VALUES OF REAL NUMBERS

The grapher's SIN, COS, and TAN operations can be used to find trigonometric function values of any real number. The grapher must be set in Radian mode when this is done.

Section 5.2, Example 5 Find each of the following function values using a grapher. Round the answers to four decimal places.

a) $\cos \dfrac{2\pi}{5}$　　b) $\tan(-3)$　　c) $\sin 24.9$　　d) $\sin \dfrac{\pi}{7}$

a) On a TI-83 or TI-83+ set in Radian mode, press $\boxed{\text{COS}}$ 2 $\boxed{\text{2nd}}$ $\boxed{\pi}$ $\boxed{\div}$ 5 $\boxed{)}$ $\boxed{\text{ENTER}}$. (π is the second operation associated with the $\boxed{\wedge}$ key.) Although it is not necessary to close the parentheses, we do it for completeness. On the TI-82 add a left parenthesis before pressing 2. We find that $\cos \dfrac{2\pi}{5} \approx 0.3090$.

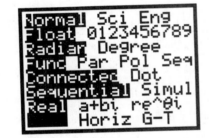

b) To find $\tan(-3)$ on the TI-83 or TI-83+ press $\boxed{\text{TAN}}$ $\boxed{(-)}$ 3 $\boxed{)}$ $\boxed{\text{ENTER}}$. The right parenthesis should be omitted on the TI-82. We find that $\tan(-3) \approx 0.1425$.

c) To find $\sin 24.9$ on the TI-83 or TI-83+ press $\boxed{\text{SIN}}$ 2 4 $\boxed{.}$ 9 $\boxed{)}$ $\boxed{\text{ENTER}}$. Omit the right parenthesis on the TI-82. We find that $\sin 24.9 \approx -0.2306$.

d) The secant, cosecant, and cotangent functions can be found by taking the reciprocals of the cosine, sine, and tangent functions, respectively. This can be done either by entering the reciprocal or by using the $\boxed{x^{-1}}$ key. To find $\sec \dfrac{\pi}{7}$ we can enter the reciprocal of $\cos \dfrac{\pi}{7}$ on a TI-83 or TI-83+ set in Radian mode by pressing 1 $\boxed{\div}$ $\boxed{\text{COS}}$ $\boxed{\text{2nd}}$ $\boxed{\pi}$ $\boxed{\div}$ 7 $\boxed{)}$

$\boxed{\text{ENTER}}$. On the TI-82 press 1 $\boxed{\div}$ $\boxed{\text{COS}}$ $\boxed{(}$ $\boxed{\text{2nd}}$ $\boxed{\pi}$ $\boxed{\div}$ 7 $\boxed{)}$ $\boxed{\text{ENTER}}$. To find $\sec\dfrac{\pi}{7}$ using the $\boxed{x^{-1}}$ key on the TI-83 or TI-83+ press $\boxed{\text{COS}}$ $\boxed{\text{2nd}}$ $\boxed{\pi}$ $\boxed{\div}$ 7 $\boxed{)}$ $\boxed{x^{-1}}$ $\boxed{\text{ENTER}}$. On the TI-82 press $\boxed{(}$ $\boxed{\text{COS}}$ $\boxed{(}$ $\boxed{\text{2nd}}$ $\boxed{\pi}$ $\boxed{\div}$ 7 $\boxed{)}$ $\boxed{)}$ $\boxed{x^{-1}}$ $\boxed{\text{ENTER}}$. The result is $\sec\dfrac{\pi}{7} \approx 1.1099$.

The output for the TI-83 and TI-83+ is shown on the left below, and the TI-82 output is on the right. Both graphers are set in Radian mode.

```
1/cos(π/7)
        1.109916264
cos(π/7)-1
        1.109916264
■
```

```
1/cos (π/7)
        1.109916264
(cos (π/7))-1
        1.109916264
```

CONVERTING BETWEEN D°M′S″ AND DECIMAL DEGREE MEASURE

We can convert D°M′S″ notation to decimal notation and vice versa on the TI-82, TI-83, and TI-83+.

Section 5.3, Example 2 Convert 5°42′30″ to decimal degree notation.

On the TI-83 or TI-83+ enter 5°42′30″ by pressing 5 $\boxed{\text{2nd}}$ $\boxed{\text{ANGLE}}$ 1 4 2 $\boxed{\text{2nd}}$ $\boxed{\text{ANGLE}}$ 2 3 0 $\boxed{\text{ALPHA}}$ $\boxed{''}$ $\boxed{\text{ENTER}}$. (ANGLE is the second operation associated with the $\boxed{\text{MATRX}}$ key on the TI-83 and the second operation associated with the $\boxed{\text{APPS}}$ key on the TI-83+. ″ is the ALPHA operation associated with the $\boxed{+}$ key.) On the TI-82 enter 5°42′30″ as 5′42′30′ by pressing 5 $\boxed{\text{2nd}}$ $\boxed{\text{ANGLE}}$ 2 4 2 $\boxed{\text{2nd}}$ $\boxed{\text{ANGLE}}$ 2 3 0 $\boxed{\text{2nd}}$ $\boxed{\text{ANGLE}}$ 2 $\boxed{\text{ENTER}}$. (ANGLE is the second operation associated with the $\boxed{\text{MATRX}}$ key on the TI-82.) In either case the grapher returns 5.708333333, so 5°42′30″ $\approx$ 5.71°.

Section 5.3, Example 3 Convert 72.18° to D°M′S″ notation.

We use the ▷D°M′S″ feature from the ANGLE menu to do this conversion. Press 7 2 $\boxed{\cdot}$ 1 8 $\boxed{\text{2nd}}$ $\boxed{\text{ANGLE}}$ 4 $\boxed{\text{ENTER}}$. The grapher returns 72°10′48″.

The conversions in Examples 2 and 3 are shown for the TI-83 and TI-83+ on the left below and for the TI-82 on the right.

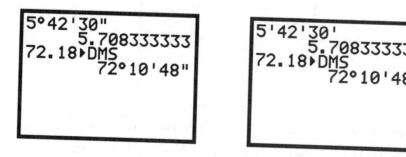

```
5°42'30"
        5.708333333
72.18▶DMS
        72°10'48"
```

```
5'42'30'
        5.708333333
72.18▶DMS
        72°10'48"
```

CONVERTING BETWEEN DEGREE AND RADIAN MEASURE

We can use the grapher to convert from degree to radian measure and vice versa. The grapher should be set in Radian mode when converting from degree to radian measure and in Degree mode when converting from radian to degree measure.

Section 5.3, Example 5 Convert each of the following to radians.

a) 120°   b) −297.25°

a) Set the grapher in Radian mode. Press 1 2 0 | 2nd | | ANGLE | 1 | ENTER | to enter 120°. The grapher returns a decimal approximation of the radian measure. We see that 120° ≈ 2.09 radians.

b) With the grapher set in Radian mode press | (−) | 2 9 7 | · | 2 5 | 2nd | | ANGLE | 1 | ENTER |. We see that −297.25° ≈ −5.19 radians.

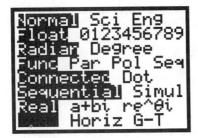

Section 5.3, Example 6 Convert each of the following to degrees.

a) $\frac{3\pi}{4}$ radians   b) 8.5 radians

a) Set the grapher in Degree mode. Then press | (| 3 | 2nd | | π | | ÷ | 4 |) | | 2nd | | ANGLE | 3 | ENTER | to enter $\frac{3\pi}{4}$ radians. (π is the second operation associated with the | ∧ | key). The grapher returns 135, so $3\pi/4$ radians = 135°. Note that the parentheses are necessary in order to enter the entire expression in radian measure. Without the parentheses, the grapher reads only the denominator, 4, in radian measure and an incorrect result occurs.

b) With the grapher set in Degree mode press 8 | · | 5 | 2nd | | ANGLE | 3 | ENTER |. The grapher returns 487.0141259, so 8.5 radians ≈ 487.01°.

FINDING TRIGONOMETRIC FUNCTION VALUES OF ANGLES

The grapher's SIN, COS, and TAN operations can be used to find the values of trigonometric functions of angles measured in degrees.

Section 5.5, Example 5 Find the trigonometric function value, rounded to four decimal places, of each of the following.

a) tan 29.7°   b) sec 48°   c) sin 84°10′39″

a) On a TI-83 or TI-83+ set in Degree mode, press $\boxed{\text{TAN}}$ 2 9 $\boxed{\cdot}$ 7 $\boxed{)}$ $\boxed{\text{ENTER}}$. Although it is not necessary to close the parentheses, we do it for completeness. The right parenthesis should be omitted on the TI-82. If the grapher is set in Radian mode, press $\boxed{\text{2nd}}$ $\boxed{\text{ANGLE}}$ $\boxed{\text{ENTER}}$ after the 7 to copy the degree symbol after the angle. This indicates to the grapher that the angle is given in degrees. We find that tan 29.7° ≈ 0.5704.

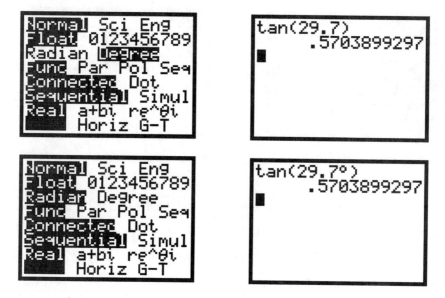

b) The secant, cosecant, and cotangent functions can be found by taking the reciprocals of the cosine, sine, and tangent functions, respectively. This can be done either by entering the reciprocal or by using the $\boxed{x^{-1}}$ key. To find sec 48° we can enter the reciprocal of cos 48° on a TI-83 or TI-83+ set in Degree mode by pressing 1 $\boxed{\div}$ $\boxed{\text{COS}}$ 4 8 $\boxed{)}$ $\boxed{\text{ENTER}}$. The right parenthesis should be omitted on the TI-82. To find sec 48° using the $\boxed{x^{-1}}$ key on the TI-83 or TI-83+ press $\boxed{\text{COS}}$ 4 8 $\boxed{)}$ $\boxed{x^{-1}}$ $\boxed{\text{ENTER}}$. On the TI-82 press $\boxed{(}$ $\boxed{\text{COS}}$ 4 8 $\boxed{)}$ $\boxed{x^{-1}}$ $\boxed{\text{ENTER}}$. If the grapher is set in Radian mode, press $\boxed{\text{2nd}}$ $\boxed{\text{ANGLE}}$ $\boxed{\text{ENTER}}$ after the 8 to copy the degree symbol after the angle. The result is sec 48° ≈ 1.4945.

The output for the TI-83 and TI-83+ is shown on the left below, and the TI-82 output is on the right. Both graphers are set in Degree mode.

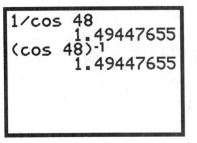

c) With the grapher set in Degree mode, press $\boxed{\text{SIN}}$ followed by 84°10′39″ entered as described above in Converting Between D°M′S″ and Decimal Degree Measure for the grapher being used. Then press $\boxed{\text{ENTER}}$. We find that sin 84°10′39″ ≈ 0.9948.

FINDING ANGLES

The inverse trigonometric function keys provide a quick way to find an angle given a trigonometric function value for that angle.

Section 5.5, Example 6 Find the acute angle, to the nearest tenth of a degree, whose sine value is approximately 0.20113.

Although the TABLE feature can be used to approximate this angle, it is faster to use the inverse sine key. With the grapher set in Degree mode, on the TI-83 or TI-83+ press $\boxed{\text{2nd}}$ $\boxed{\text{SIN}^{-1}}$ $\boxed{.}$ 2 0 1 1 3 $\boxed{)}$ $\boxed{\text{ENTER}}$. (SIN^{-1} is the second operation associated with the $\boxed{\text{SIN}}$ key.) Although it is not necessary to close the parentheses in this case, we do it for completeness. On the TI-82 the right parenthesis should be omitted. We find that the desired acute angle is approximately 11.6°.

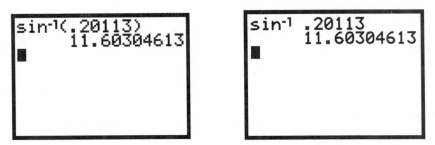

Section 5.5, Exercise 39 Find the acute angle, to the nearest tenth of a degree, whose cotangent value is 2.127.

Angles whose secant, cosecant, or cotangent values are known can be found using the reciprocals of the cosine, sine, and tangent functions, respectively. Since $\cot\theta = \dfrac{1}{\tan\theta} = 2.127$, we have $\tan\theta = \dfrac{1}{2.127}$, or $(2.127)^{-1}$. To find θ on the TI-83 or TI-83+, press $\boxed{\text{2nd}}$ $\boxed{\text{TAN}^{-1}}$ 1 $\boxed{\div}$ 2 $\boxed{.}$ 1 2 7 $\boxed{)}$ $\boxed{\text{ENTER}}$ or $\boxed{\text{2nd}}$ $\boxed{\text{TAN}^{-1}}$ 2 $\boxed{.}$ 1 2 7 $\boxed{x^{-1}}$ $\boxed{)}$ $\boxed{\text{ENTER}}$. (TAN^{-1} is the second operation associated with the $\boxed{\text{TAN}}$ key.) On the TI-82 press $\boxed{\text{2nd}}$ $\boxed{\text{TAN}^{-1}}$ $\boxed{(}$ 1 $\boxed{\div}$ 2 $\boxed{.}$ 1 2 7 $\boxed{)}$ $\boxed{\text{ENTER}}$ or $\boxed{\text{2nd}}$ $\boxed{\text{TAN}^{-1}}$ 2 $\boxed{.}$ 1 2 7 $\boxed{x^{-1}}$ $\boxed{\text{ENTER}}$. Note that the parentheses are necessary in the first set of keystrokes for each grapher. The left parenthesis must be keyed in on the TI-82 while it appears on the TI-83 and TI-83+ along with "tan⁻¹." Without parentheses we would be finding the angle whose tangent is 1 and then dividing that angle by 2.127. We find that

$\theta \approx 25.2°$.

```
tan-1(1/2.127)
        25.18036384
tan-1(2.127-1)
        25.18036384
■
```

```
tan-1 (1/2.127)
        25.18036384
tan-1 2.127-1
        25.18036384
```

Chapter 6
Trigonometric Identities, Inverse Functions, and Equations

FINDING INVERSE FUNCTION VALUES

We can use a grapher to find inverse function values in both radians and degrees.

Section 6.4, Example 2 (a), (e) Approximate $\cos^{-1}(-0.2689)$ and $\csc^{-1} 8.205$ in both radians and degrees.

To find inverse function values in radians, first set the grapher in Radian mode. Then, to approximate $\cos^{-1}(-0.2689)$ on the TI-83 or TI-83+, press $\boxed{\text{2nd}}$ $\boxed{\text{COS}^{-1}}$ $\boxed{(-)}$ $\boxed{\cdot}$ 2 6 8 9 $\boxed{)}$ $\boxed{\text{ENTER}}$. Although it is not necessary to close the parentheses in this case, we do it for completeness. The right parenthesis should be omitted on the TI-82. The grapher returns 1.84304711, so $\cos^{-1}(-0.2689) \approx 1.8430$ radians.

To find $\csc^{-1} 8.205$, recall the identity $\csc \theta = \dfrac{1}{\sin \theta}$. Then $\csc^{-1} 8.205 = \sin^{-1}\left(\dfrac{1}{8.205}\right)$. On the TI-83 or TI-83+ press $\boxed{\text{2nd}}$ $\boxed{\text{SIN}^{-1}}$ 1 $\boxed{\div}$ 8 $\boxed{\cdot}$ 2 0 5 $\boxed{)}$ $\boxed{\text{ENTER}}$ or $\boxed{\text{2nd}}$ $\boxed{\text{SIN}^{-1}}$ 8 $\boxed{\cdot}$ 2 0 5 $\boxed{x^{-1}}$ $\boxed{)}$ $\boxed{\text{ENTER}}$. On the TI-82 press $\boxed{\text{2nd}}$ $\boxed{\text{SIN}^{-1}}$ $\boxed{(}$ 1 $\boxed{\div}$ 8 $\boxed{\cdot}$ 2 0 5 $\boxed{)}$ $\boxed{\text{ENTER}}$ or $\boxed{\text{2nd}}$ $\boxed{\text{SIN}^{-1}}$ 8 $\boxed{\cdot}$ 2 0 5 $\boxed{x^{-1}}$ $\boxed{\text{ENTER}}$. The readout is .1221806653, so $\csc^{-1} 8.205 \approx 0.1222$ radians.

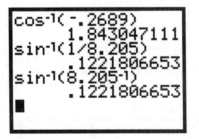

To find inverse function values in degrees, set the grapher in degree mode. Then use the keystrokes above to find that $\cos^{-1}(-0.2689) \approx 105.6°$ and $\csc^{-1} 8.205 \approx 7.0°$.

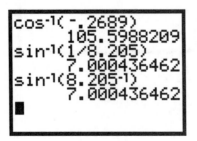

We also use reciprocal relationships to find function values for arcsecant and arccotangent.

SINE REGRESSION

The SinReg operation on the TI-83 and TI-83+ can be used to fit a sine curve $y = a\sin(bx + c) + d$ to a set of data. The TI-82 does not have this capability. At least four data points are required and there must be at least two data points per period. The output of SinReg is always in radians, regardless of the Radian/Degree mode setting. To see the graph, however, we must set the grapher in Radian mode.

The operations of entering data, making scatterplots, and graphing and evaluating the regression function are the same as for linear regression functions. Reread the material on pages 5, 6, 20, and 21 of this manual to review these procedures.

Section 6.5, Exercise 57 (a) Sales of certain products fluctuate in cycles. The data in the following table show the total sales of skis per month for a business in a northern climate.

Month, x	Total Sales, y (in thousands of dollars)
August, 8	0
November, 11	7
February, 2	14
May, 5	7
August, 8	0

Using the sine regression feature on a grapher, fit a sine function of the form $y = A\sin(Bx - C) + D$ to this set of data.

Enter the data in L_1 and L_2 as described in Chapter 1 of this manual. Press $\boxed{\text{STAT}}$ $\boxed{\triangleright}$ to view the STAT CALC menu. Then select SinReg by pressing $\boxed{\text{ALPHA}}$ C. If the data is entered in a combination of lists other than L_1 and L_2 their names must be entered separated by a comma. Since we have used L_1 and L_2 this is not necessary in this case. We also have the usual TI-83 option of specifying a $y =$ variable to which the regression equation can be stored. To select y_1, for example, press $\boxed{\text{VARS}}$ $\boxed{\triangleright}$ 1 1. Now press $\boxed{\text{ENTER}}$ to see the coefficients a, b, c, and d of the sine regression function $y = a\sin(bx + c) + d$

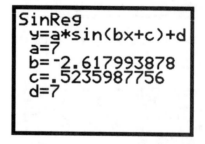

Chapter 7
Applications of Trigonometry

FINDING TRIGONOMETRIC NOTATION FOR COMPLEX NUMBERS

The TI-82, TI-83, or TI-83+ can be used to find trigonometric notation for a complex number.

Section 7.4, Example 3 (a) Find trigonometric notation for $1 + i$.

Trigonometric notation for a complex number has the form $r(\cos\theta + i\sin\theta)$. On the TI-83 and TI-8+ we can find r using the abs feature from the MATH CPX menu. Press $\boxed{\text{MATH}}$ $\boxed{\triangleright}$ $\boxed{\triangleright}$ to display this menu. Then press 5 to copy "abs" to the home screen. (We could also use $\boxed{\triangledown}$ to highlight 5 and then press $\boxed{\text{ENTER}}$.) Then press 1 $\boxed{+}$ $\boxed{\text{2nd}}$ $\boxed{i}$ $\boxed{)}$ $\boxed{\text{ENTER}}$. The grapher returns $|1 + i|$, the value of r. It is approximately 1.414213562. This is a decimal approximation for $\sqrt{2}$.

Now use the MATH CPX menu again to find θ in degrees. First select Degree mode. Then press $\boxed{\text{MATH}}$ $\boxed{\triangleright}$ $\boxed{\triangleright}$ to display the MATH CPX menu. Select item 4, "angle," by pressing 4 or by using $\boxed{\triangledown}$ to highlight 4 and then pressing $\boxed{\text{ENTER}}$. Then press 1 $\boxed{+}$ $\boxed{\text{2nd}}$ $\boxed{i}$ $\boxed{)}$ $\boxed{\text{ENTER}}$. The grapher returns 45, so the angle θ is 45°. We can use the same procedure to find θ in radians after Radian mode has been selected.

```
abs(1+i)
           1.414213562
angle(1+i)
                    45
■
```

On the TI-82 we express $1 + i$ as the pair $(1, 1)$ where the first number is the real part of $1 + i$ and the second number is the imaginary part. To find r press $\boxed{\text{2nd}}$ $\boxed{\text{ANGLE}}$ 5 to select "R▷Pr(" from the ANGLE menu. Then press 1 $\boxed{,}$ 1 $\boxed{)}$ $\boxed{\text{ENTER}}$. The grapher returns 1.414213562, a decimal approximation for $\sqrt{2}$.

We use "R▷Pθ(" from the ANGLE menu to find θ. With the grapher set in Degree mode, press $\boxed{\text{2nd}}$ $\boxed{\text{ANGLE}}$ 6 1 $\boxed{,}$ 1 $\boxed{)}$ $\boxed{\text{ENTER}}$. We see that θ is 45°. We can use the same procedure to find θ in radians after Radian mode has been selected.

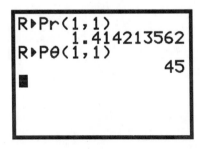

```
R▶Pr(1,1)
           1.414213562
R▶Pθ(1,1)
                    45
■
```

Chapter 8
Systems of Equations and Matrices

MATRICES AND ROW-EQUIVALENT OPERATIONS

Matrices with up to 99 rows or columns can be entered on the grapher. As many as ten matrices can be entered on the TI-83 or TI-83+ while the TI-82 accepts as many as five at one time. Row-equivalent operations can be performed on matrices on the grapher.

Section 8.3, Example 1 Solve the following system:

$$
\begin{aligned}
2x - y + 4z &= -3, \\
x - 2y - 10z &= -6, \\
3x \quad\quad + 4z &= 7.
\end{aligned}
$$

First we enter the augmented matrix

$$
\begin{bmatrix}
2 & -1 & 4 & -3 \\
1 & -2 & -10 & -6 \\
3 & 0 & 4 & 7
\end{bmatrix}
$$

on the grapher. Begin by pressing $\boxed{\text{2nd}}$ $\boxed{\text{MATRX}}$ $\boxed{\triangleright}$ $\boxed{\triangleright}$ to display the MATRIX EDIT menu on the TI-83+. (MATRX is the second operation associated with the $\boxed{x^{-1}}$ key.) On the TI-83 and the TI-82 simply press $\boxed{\text{MATRX}}$ $\boxed{\triangleright}$ $\boxed{\triangleright}$. Then select the matrix to be defined. We will select matrix [**A**] by pressing 1. Now the MATRIX EDIT screen appears. The dimensions of the matrix are displayed on the top line of this screen, with the cursor on the row dimension. Enter the dimensions of the augmented matrix, 3 x 4, by pressing 3 $\boxed{\text{ENTER}}$ 4 $\boxed{\text{ENTER}}$. Now the cursor moves to the element in the first row and first column of the matrix. Enter the elements of the first row by pressing 2 $\boxed{\text{ENTER}}$ $\boxed{(-)}$ 1 $\boxed{\text{ENTER}}$ 4 $\boxed{\text{ENTER}}$ $\boxed{(-)}$ 3 $\boxed{\text{ENTER}}$. The cursor moves to the element in the second row and first column of the matrix. Enter the elements of the second and third rows of the augmented matrix by typing each in turn followed by $\boxed{\text{ENTER}}$ as above. Note that the screen only displays three columns of the matrix. The arrow keys can be used to move the cursor to any element at any time.

Row-equivalent operations are performed by making selections from the MATRIX MATH menu. To view this menu press $\boxed{\text{2nd}}$ $\boxed{\text{QUIT}}$ to leave the MATRIX EDIT screen. Then press $\boxed{\text{2nd}}$ $\boxed{\text{MATRX}}$ $\boxed{\triangleright}$ on the TI-83+ or $\boxed{\text{MATRX}}$ $\boxed{\triangleright}$ on the TI-83 or TI-82. Now on the TI-83 or TI-83+ press $\boxed{\triangledown}$ fifteen times or $\boxed{\triangle}$ one time to see the four row-equivalent operations, C: rowSwap(, D: row+(, E: *row(, and F: *row+(. On the TI-82 press the $\boxed{\triangledown}$ key ten times to see these operations. They are items 8, 9, 0, and A on the TI-82 MATRIX MATH menu. These operations interchange two rows of a matrix, add two rows, multiply a row by a number, and multiply a row by a number and add it to a second row, respectively.

We will use the grapher to perform the row-equivalent operations that were done algebraically in the text. First, to interchange row 1 and row 2 of matrix [**A**], with the MATRIX MATH menu displayed on the TI-83 or TI-83+, press ALPHA C to select rowSwap. On the TI-82 press 8 to select this operation. Then press 2nd MATRX 1 on the TI-83+ or MATRX 1 on the TI-83 or TI-82 to select [**A**]. Follow this with a comma and the rows to be interchanged, ⸴ 1 ⸴ 2) ENTER .

```
rowSwap([A],1,2)
[[1  -2  -10  -6]
 [2  -1   4   -3]
 [3   0   4    7 ]]
■
```

The grapher will not store the matrix produced using a row-equivalent operation, so when several operations are to be performed in succession it is helpful to store the result of each operation as it is produced. For example, to store the matrix resulting from interchanging the first and second rows of [**A**] as matrix [**B**] on the TI-83+ press STO▷ 2nd MATRX 2 ENTER immediately after interchanging the rows. Press STO▷ MATRX 2 ENTER on the TI-83 or TI-82. This can also be done before ENTER is pressed at the end of the rowSwap.

Next we multiply the first row of [**B**] by −2, add it to the second row and store the result as [**B**] again on the TI-83+ by pressing 2nd MATRX ▷ ALPHA F (−) 2 ⸴ 2nd MATRX 2 ⸴ 1 ⸴ 2) STO▷ 2nd MATRX 2 ENTER . It is not necessary to press 2nd before MATRX on the TI-83 and TI-82. Also, on the TI-82, press A rather than F . These keystrokes select *row+(from the MATRIX MATH menu; then they specify that the value of the multiplier is −2, the matrix being operated on is [**B**], and that a multiple of row 1 is being added to row 2; finally they store the result as [**B**].

To multiply row 1 by −3, add it to row 3, and store the result as [**B**] on the TI-83+ press 2nd MATRX ▷ ALPHA F (−) 3 ⸴ 2nd MATRX 2 ⸴ 1 ⸴ 3) STO▷ 2nd MATRX 2 ENTER . It is not necessary to press 2nd before MATRX on the TI-83 and TI-82. Also, on the TI-82, press A rather than F .

```
*row+(-3,[B],1,3
)→[B]
[[1  -2  -10  -6]
 [0   3   24   9 ]
 [0   6   34  25]]
```

Now multiply the second row by 1/3 and store the result as [**B**] again. On the TI-83+ press 2nd MATRX ▷ ALPHA E 1 (÷) 3 ⸴ 2nd MATRX 2 ⸴ 2) STO▷ 2nd MATRX 2 ENTER . It is not necessary to press 2nd before

MATRX on the TI-83 and TI-82. Also, on the TI-82, press 0 rather than ALPHA E. These keystrokes select *row(from the MATRIX MATH menu; then they specify that the value of the multiplier is 1/3, the matrix being operated on is [**B**], and row 2 is being multiplied; finally they store the result as [**B**]. The keystrokes 1 (÷) 3 could be replaced with 3 x^{-1}.

```
*row(1/3,[B],2)→
[B]
 [[1  -2 -10 -6]
  [0  1   8   3 ]
  [0  6   34  25]]
```

Multiply the second row by −6 and add it to the third row using *row+(. On the TI-83+ press 2nd MATRX ▷ ALPHA F (−) 6 , 2nd MATRX 2 , 2 , 3) STO▷ 2nd MATRX 2 ENTER. It is not necessary to press 2nd before MATRX on the TI-83 and TI-82. Also, on the TI-82, press A rather than F.

On the TI-82 the entry in the third row, second column is 1E−13. This is an approximation of 0 that occurs because of the manner in which the grapher performs calculations and should be treated as 0. In fact, it would be a good idea to return to the MATRIX EDIT screen at this point to replace this entry of [**B**] with 0. Press MATRX ▷ ▷ 2 to display [**B**]. Then move the cursor to the third row, second column and press 0 ENTER. Now press 2nd QUIT to leave this screen.

```
*row+(-6,[B],2,3
)→[B]
 [[1  -2 -10 -6]
  [0  1   8   3 ]
  [0  0  -14  7 ]]
```

Finally, multiply the third row by −1/14 on the TI-83+ by pressing 2nd MATRX ▷ ALPHA E (−) 1 (÷) 1 4 , 2nd MATRX 2 , 3) ENTER. It is not necessary to press 2nd before MATRX on the TI-83 and TI-82. Also, on the TI-82, press 0 rather than ALPHA E. The keystrokes (−) 1 (÷) 1 4 could be replaced with (−) 1 4 x^{-1}.

```
*row(-1/14,[B],3
)
[[1  -2 -10 -6 ]
 [0  1   8   3  ]
 [0  0   1  -.5]]
```

Write the system of equations that corresponds to the final matrix. Then use back-substitution to solve for x, y, and z as illustrated in the text.

Instead of stopping with row-echelon form as we did above, we can continue to apply row-equivalent operations until the matrix is in reduced row-echelon form as in Example 3 in Section 8.3 of the text. Reduced row-echelon form of a matrix can be found directly on the TI-83 and TI-83+ by using the rref(operation from the MATRIX MATH menu. For example, to find reduced row-echelon form for matrix $\mathbf{A}$ in Example 1 above, after entering [A] and leaving the MATRIX EDIT screen on the TI-83+ press $\boxed{\text{2nd}}$ $\boxed{\text{MATRX}}$ $\boxed{\triangleright}$ $\boxed{\text{ALPHA}}$ $\boxed{\text{B}}$ $\boxed{\text{2nd}}$ $\boxed{\text{MATRX}}$ 1 $\boxed{\text{ENTER}}$. It is not necessary to press $\boxed{\text{2nd}}$ before $\boxed{\text{MATRX}}$ on the TI-83. We can read the solution of the system of equations, $(3, 7, -0.5)$ directly from the resulting matrix. The TI-82 does not have a rref(operation.

```
rref([A]
     [[1 0 0 3  ]
      [0 1 0 7  ]
      [0 0 1 -.5]]
```

MATRIX OPERATIONS

We can use the grapher to add and subtract matrices, to multiply a matrix by a scalar, and to multiply matrices.

Section 8.4, Example 1 (a) Find $\mathbf{A} + \mathbf{B}$ for

a) $\mathbf{A} = \begin{bmatrix} -5 & 0 \\ 4 & \frac{1}{2} \end{bmatrix}$, $\mathbf{B} = \begin{bmatrix} 6 & -3 \\ 2 & 3 \end{bmatrix}$.

Enter $\mathbf{A}$ and $\mathbf{B}$ on the MATRIX EDIT screen as [A] and [B] as described earlier in this chapter of the Graphing Calculator Manual. Press $\boxed{\text{2nd}}$ $\boxed{\text{QUIT}}$ to leave this screen. Then press $\boxed{\text{2nd}}$ $\boxed{\text{MATRX}}$ 1 $\boxed{+}$ $\boxed{\text{2nd}}$ $\boxed{\text{MATRX}}$ 2 $\boxed{\text{ENTER}}$ to display the sum. It is not necessary to press $\boxed{\text{2nd}}$ before $\boxed{\text{MATRX}}$ on the TI-83 and TI-82.

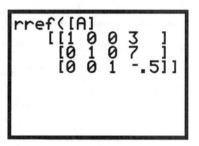

```
[A]+[B]
     [[1  -3 ]
      [6  3.5]]
```

Section 8.4, Example 2 Find $C - D$ for each of the following.

a) $C = \begin{bmatrix} 1 & 2 \\ -2 & 0 \\ -3 & -1 \end{bmatrix}$, $D = \begin{bmatrix} 1 & -1 \\ 1 & 3 \\ 2 & 3 \end{bmatrix}$ b) $C = \begin{bmatrix} 5 & -6 \\ -3 & 4 \end{bmatrix}$, $D = \begin{bmatrix} -4 \\ 1 \end{bmatrix}$

a) Enter **C** and **D** on the MATRIX EDIT screen as [**C**] and [**D**]. Press $\boxed{\text{2nd}}$ $\boxed{\text{QUIT}}$ to leave this screen. Then press $\boxed{\text{2nd}}$ $\boxed{\text{MATRX}}$ 3 $\boxed{-}$ $\boxed{\text{2nd}}$ $\boxed{\text{MATRX}}$ 4 $\boxed{\text{ENTER}}$ to display the difference on the TI-83+. It is not necessary to press $\boxed{\text{2nd}}$ before $\boxed{\text{MATRX}}$ on the TI-83 and TI-82.

```
[C]-[D]
        [[0   3 ]
         [-3  -3]
         [-5  -4]]
```

b) Enter **C** and **D** on the MATRIX EDIT screen as [**C**] and [**D**]. Press $\boxed{\text{2nd}}$ $\boxed{\text{QUIT}}$ to leave this screen. Then, on the TI-83+, press $\boxed{\text{2nd}}$ $\boxed{\text{MATRX}}$ 3 $\boxed{-}$ $\boxed{\text{2nd}}$ $\boxed{\text{MATRX}}$ 4 $\boxed{\text{ENTER}}$. It is not necessary to press $\boxed{\text{2nd}}$ before $\boxed{\text{MATRX}}$ on the TI-83 and TI-82. The grapher returns the message ERR:DIM MISMATCH, indicating that this subtraction is not possible. This is the case because the matrices have different orders.

```
ERR:DIM MISMATCH
1:Goto
2:Quit
```

Section 8.4, Example 4 Find 3**A** and (-1)**A**, for $A = \begin{bmatrix} -3 & 0 \\ 4 & 5 \end{bmatrix}$

Enter **A** on the MATRIX EDIT screen as [**A**]. Press $\boxed{\text{2nd}}$ $\boxed{\text{QUIT}}$ to leave this screen. Then to find 3**A** on the TI-83+ press 3 $\boxed{\text{2nd}}$ $\boxed{\text{MATRX}}$ 1 $\boxed{\text{ENTER}}$ and to find (-1)**A** press $\boxed{(-)}$ 1 $\boxed{\text{2nd}}$ $\boxed{\text{MATRX}}$ 1 $\boxed{\text{ENTER}}$. Note that (-1)**A** is the opposite, or additive inverse, of **A** and can also be found by pressing $\boxed{(-)}$ $\boxed{\text{2nd}}$ $\boxed{\text{MATRX}}$ 1 $\boxed{\text{ENTER}}$. It is not necessary to press $\boxed{\text{2nd}}$ before $\boxed{\text{MATRX}}$ on the TI-83 and TI-82.

```
3[A]
              [[-9  0 ]
               [12 15]]
-1[A]
              [[3   0 ]
               [-4 -5]]
■
```

Section 8.4, Example 6 (a), (d) For

$$A = \begin{bmatrix} 3 & 1 & -1 \\ 2 & 0 & 3 \end{bmatrix}, B = \begin{bmatrix} 1 & 6 \\ 3 & -5 \\ -2 & 4 \end{bmatrix}, \text{ and } C = \begin{bmatrix} 4 & -6 \\ 1 & 2 \end{bmatrix}$$

find each of the following.

a) **AB**   d) **AC**

First enter **A**, **B**, and **C** as [A], [B], and [C] on the MATRIX EDIT screen. Press $\boxed{\text{2nd}}$ $\boxed{\text{QUIT}}$ to leave this screen.

a) To find **AB** on the TI-83+ press $\boxed{\text{2nd}}$ $\boxed{\text{MATRX}}$ 1 $\boxed{\text{2nd}}$ $\boxed{\text{MATRX}}$ 2 $\boxed{\text{ENTER}}$. It is not necessary to press $\boxed{\text{2nd}}$ before $\boxed{\text{MATRX}}$ on the TI-83 and TI-82.

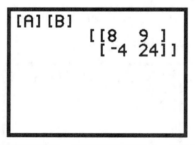

```
[A][B]
              [[8   9 ]
               [-4 24]]
```

d) To find **AC** on the TI-83+ press $\boxed{\text{2nd}}$ $\boxed{\text{MATRX}}$ 1 $\boxed{\text{2nd}}$ $\boxed{\text{MATRX}}$ 3 $\boxed{\text{ENTER}}$. It is not necessary to press $\boxed{\text{2nd}}$ before $\boxed{\text{MATRX}}$ on the TI-83 and TI-82. The grapher returns the message ERR:DIM MISMATCH, indicating that this multiplication is not possible. This is the case because the number of columns in **A** is not the same as the number of rows in **C**. Thus, the matrices cannot be multiplied in this order.

FINDING THE INVERSE OF A MATRIX

The inverse of a matrix can be found quickly on the grapher.

Section 8.5, Example 3 Find A^{-1}, where

$$A = \begin{bmatrix} -2 & 3 \\ -3 & 4 \end{bmatrix}.$$

Enter **A** as [A] on the MATRIX EDIT screen. Then press $\boxed{\text{2nd}}$ $\boxed{\text{QUIT}}$ to leave this screen. Now, on the TI-83+, press $\boxed{\text{2nd}}$ $\boxed{\text{MATRX}}$ 1 $\boxed{x^{-1}}$ $\boxed{\text{ENTER}}$. It is not necessary to press $\boxed{\text{2nd}}$ before $\boxed{\text{MATRX}}$ on the TI-83 and TI-82.

```
[A]⁻¹
        [ [4  -3]
          [3  -2] ]
```

Section 8.5, Exercise 7 Find $\mathbf{A}^{-1}$, where

$$\mathbf{A} = \begin{bmatrix} 6 & 9 \\ 4 & 6 \end{bmatrix}.$$

Enter $\mathbf{A}$ as [A] on the MATRIX EDIT screen and then press $\boxed{\text{2nd}}$ $\boxed{\text{QUIT}}$ to leave this screen. Now, on the TI-83+, press $\boxed{\text{2nd}}$ $\boxed{\text{MATRX}}$ $\boxed{1}$ $\boxed{x^{-1}}$ $\boxed{\text{ENTER}}$. It is not necessary to press $\boxed{\text{2nd}}$ before $\boxed{\text{MATRX}}$ on the TI-83 and TI-82. The grapher returns the message ERR:SINGULAR MAT, indicating that $\mathbf{A}^{-1}$ does not exist.

MATRIX SOLUTIONS OF SYSTEMS OF EQUATIONS

We can write a system of n linear equations in n variables as a matrix equation $\mathbf{AX} = \mathbf{B}$. If $\mathbf{A}$ has an inverse the solution of the system of equations is given by $\mathbf{X} = \mathbf{A}^{-1}\mathbf{B}$.

Section 8.5, Example 4 Use an inverse matrix to solve the following system of equations:

$$\begin{aligned} x + 2y - z &= -2, \\ 3x + 5y + 3z &= 3, \\ 2x + 4y + 3z &= 1. \end{aligned}$$

Enter $\mathbf{A} = \begin{bmatrix} 1 & 2 & -1 \\ 3 & 5 & 3 \\ 2 & 4 & 3 \end{bmatrix}$ and $\mathbf{B} = \begin{bmatrix} -2 \\ 3 \\ 1 \end{bmatrix}$ on the MATRIX EDIT screen as [A] and [B]. Press $\boxed{\text{2nd}}$ $\boxed{\text{QUIT}}$ to leave this screen. Then, on the TI-83+, press $\boxed{\text{2nd}}$ $\boxed{\text{MATRX}}$ $\boxed{1}$ $\boxed{x^{-1}}$ $\boxed{\text{2nd}}$ $\boxed{\text{MATRX}}$ $\boxed{2}$ $\boxed{\text{ENTER}}$. It is not necessary to press $\boxed{\text{2nd}}$ before $\boxed{\text{MATRX}}$ on the TI-83 and TI-82. The result is the 3 x 1 matrix $\begin{bmatrix} 5 \\ -3 \\ 1 \end{bmatrix}$, so the solution is $(5, -3, 1)$.

```
[A]⁻¹[B]
        [ [5 ]
          [-3]
          [1 ] ]
▪
```

GRAPHS OF INEQUALITIES

We can graph linear inequalities on the grapher, shading the region of the solution set. The grapher should be set in Func mode at this point.

Section 8.6, Example 1 Graph: $y < x + 3$.

First we graph the related equation $y = x + 3$. We use the standard window $[-10, 10, -10, 10]$. Since the inequality symbol is $<$ we know that the line $y = x + 3$ is not part of the solution set. In a hand-drawn graph we would use a dashed line to indicate this. We can select Dot mode on any of the three calculators or use the Dot GraphStyle on TI-83 or TI-83+. (See page 14 of this manual for instructions on selecting GraphStyles.) Even if Dot mode is used, however, the line appears to be solid. After determining that the solution set of the inequality consists of all points below the line, we use the grapher's SHADE operation to shade this region. SHADE is item 7 on the DRAW DRAW menu. To access it press $\boxed{\text{2nd}}$ $\boxed{\text{DRAW}}$ 7.

Now enter a lower function and an upper function. The region between them will be shaded. We want to shade the area between the bottom of the window, $y = -10$, and the line $y = x + 3$ so we enter $\boxed{(-)}$ 1 0 $\boxed{\text{,}}$ $\boxed{\text{X,T,}\Theta,n}$ $\boxed{+}$ 3 $\boxed{)}$ $\boxed{\text{ENTER}}$. We can also enter $x + 3$ as y_1. The result is shown below. Keep in mind that the line $y = x + 3$ is not included in the solution set.

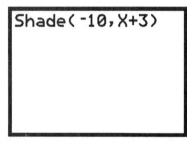
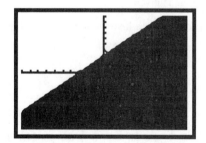

The "shade below" GraphStyle on the TI-83 or TI-83+ can also be used to shade this region. After entering the related equation, cycle through the Graph Style options on the "Y =" screen as described on page 14 of this manual until the "shade below" option appears. Then press $\boxed{\text{GRAPH}}$ to display the graph of the inequality. As mentioned above, keep in mind the fact that the line $y = x + 3$ is not included in the solution set.

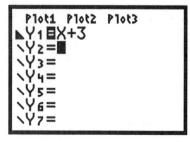
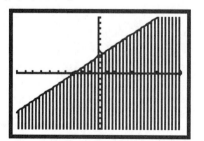

We can also use the SHADE operation to graph a system of inequalities when the solution set lies between the graphs of two functions.

Section 8.6, Exercise 37 Graph:
$$y \leq x,$$
$$y \geq 3 - x.$$

First graph the related equations $y_1 = x$ and $y_2 = 3 - x$ and determine that the solution set consists of all the points on or above the graph of $y_2 = 3 - x$ and on or below the graph of $y_1 = x$. We will shade this region by pressing $\boxed{\text{2nd}}$ $\boxed{\text{DRAW}}$ 7 3 $\boxed{-}$ $\boxed{\text{X,T,}\Theta,n}$ $\boxed{,}$ $\boxed{\text{X,T,}\Theta,n}$ $\boxed{)}$ $\boxed{\text{ENTER}}$. These keystrokes select the SHADE operation from the DRAW DRAW menu and then enter $y_2 = 3 - x$ as the lower function and $y_1 = x$ as the upper function. We could also enter these functions as y_2 and y_1, respectively.

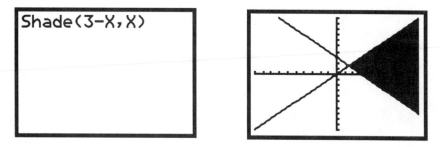

On the TI-83 and TI-83+ we can also graph systems of inequalities by shading the solution set of each inequality in the system with a different pattern. When the "shade above" or "shade below" Graph Style options are selected the TI-83 and TI-83+ rotate through four shading patterns. Vertical lines shade the first function, horizontal lines the second, negatively sloping diagonal lines the third, and positively sloping diagonal lines the fourth. These patterns repeat if more than four functions are graphed.

Section 8.6, Example 5 Graph the solution set of the system
$$x + y \leq 4,$$
$$x - y \geq 2.$$

First graph the equation $x + y = 4$, entering it in the form $y_1 = -x + 4$. We determine that the solution set of $x + y \leq 4$ consists of all points below the line $x + y = 4$, or $y_1 = -x + 4$, so we select the "shade below" GraphStyle for this function. Next graph $x - y = 2$, entering it in the form $y_2 = x - 2$. The solution set of $x - y \geq 2$ is all points below the line $x - y = 2$, or $y_2 = x - 2$, so we also choose the "shade below" GraphStyle for this function. Now press $\boxed{\text{GRAPH}}$ to display the solution sets of each inequality in the system and the region where they overlap. The region of overlap is the solution set of the system of inequalities.

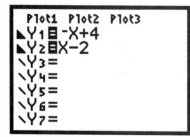

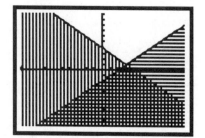

Chapter 9
Analytic Geometry Topics

Many conic sections are represented by equations that are not functions. Consequently, these equations must be entered on the TI-82, TI-83, and TI-83+ as two equations, each of which is a function.

GRAPHING PARABOLAS

To graph a parabola of the form $y^2 = 4px$ or $(y - k)^2 = 4p(x - h)$, we must first solve the equation for y.

Section 9.1, Example 4 Graph the parabola $y^2 - 2y - 8x - 31 = 0$.

In the text we used the quadratic formula to solve the equation for y:

$$y = \frac{2 \pm \sqrt{32x + 128}}{2}.$$

One way to produce the graph of the parabola is to enter $y_1 = \dfrac{2 + \sqrt{32x + 128}}{2}$ and $y_2 = \dfrac{2 - \sqrt{32x + 128}}{2}$, select a window, and press $\boxed{\text{GRAPH}}$ to see the graph. Here we use $[-12, 12, -8, 8]$. The first equation produces the top half of the parabola and the second equation produces the lower half.

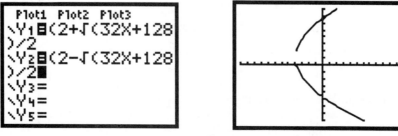

We can also enter $y_1 = \sqrt{32x + 128}$ and then enter $y_2 = \dfrac{2 + y_1}{2}$ and $y_3 = \dfrac{2 - y_1}{2}$. For example, to enter $y_2 = \dfrac{2 + y_1}{2}$ on the TI-83 or TI-83+ position the cursor beside "Y2 =" and press $\boxed{(}$ 2 $\boxed{+}$ $\boxed{\text{VARS}}$ $\boxed{\triangleright}$ 1 1 $\boxed{)}$ $\boxed{\div}$ 2. On the TI-82 press $\boxed{(}$ 2 $\boxed{+}$ $\boxed{\text{2nd}}$ $\boxed{\text{Y-VARS}}$ 1 1 $\boxed{)}$ $\boxed{\div}$ 2. Enter $y_3 = \dfrac{2 - y_1}{2}$ in a similar manner. Finally, deselect y_1 by moving the cursor to the equals sign following Y1 and pressing $\boxed{\text{ENTER}}$. The top half of the graph is produced by y_2 and the lower half by y_3. The expression for y_1 was entered to avoid entering the square root more than once. By deselecting y_1 we prevent its graph from appearing on the screen with the graph of the parabola.

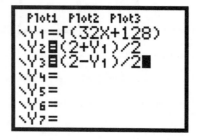

We could also use the standard equation of the parabola found in the text:

$$(y - 1)^2 = 8(x + 4).$$

Solve this equation for y.

$$y - 1 = \pm\sqrt{8(x + 4)}$$
$$y = 1 \pm \sqrt{8(x + 4)}$$

Then enter $y_1 = 1 + \sqrt{8(x + 4)}$ and $y_2 = 1 - \sqrt{8(x + 4)}$, or enter $y_1 = \sqrt{8(x + 4)}$, $y_2 = 1 + y_1$, and $y_3 = 1 - y_1$, and deselect y_1 as described above.

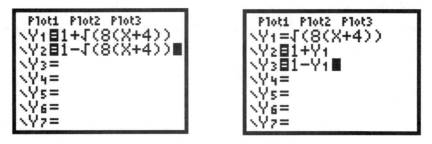

GRAPHING CIRCLES

The equation of a circle must be solved for y before it can be entered on a TI-82, TI-83, or TI-83+.

Section 9.2, Example 1 Graph the circle $x^2 + y^2 - 16x + 14y + 32 = 0$.

In the text we found the standard form for the equation of the circle and then solved for y:

$$y = -7 \pm \sqrt{81 - (x - 8)^2}.$$

We could also have solved the original equation using the quadratic formula.

One way to produce the graph is to enter $y_1 = -7 + \sqrt{81 - (x - 8)^2}$ and $y_2 = -7 - \sqrt{81 - (x - 8)^2}$, select a square window, and press $\boxed{\text{GRAPH}}$. Here we use $[-12, 24, -20, 4]$. The first equation produces the top half of the circle and the second equation produces the lower half.

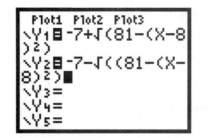 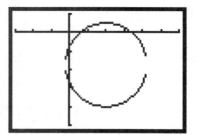

We can also enter $y_1 = \sqrt{81 - (x - 8)^2}$ and then enter $y_2 = -7 + y_1$ and $y_3 = -7 - y_1$. Then deselect y_1, select a square window, and press $\boxed{\text{GRAPH}}$. We use y_1 to eliminate the need to enter the square root more than once. Deselecting it prevents the graph of y_1 from appearing on the screen with the graph of the circle. The top half of the graph is produced by y_2 and the lower half by y_3.

```
Plot1 Plot2 Plot3
\Y₁⊟√(81-(X-8)²)

\Y₂⊟-7+Y₁
\Y₃⊟-7-Y₁■
\Y₄=
\Y₅=
\Y₆=
```

GRAPHING ELLIPSES

The equation of an ellipse must be solved for y before it can be entered on a TI-82, TI-83, or TI-83+. In Example 2 of Section 9.2 of the text the procedure for graphing an ellipse of the form $\dfrac{x^2}{a^2} + \dfrac{y^2}{b^2} = 1$ or $\dfrac{x^2}{b^2} + \dfrac{y^2}{a^2} = 1$ is described. Here we consider ellipses of the form $\dfrac{(x-h)^2}{a^2} + \dfrac{(y-k)^2}{b^2} = 1$ or $\dfrac{(x-h)^2}{b^2} + \dfrac{(y-k)^2}{a^2} = 1$

Section 9.2, Example 4 Graph the ellipse $4x^2 + y^2 + 24x - 2y + 21 = 0$.

Completing the square in the text, we found that the equation can be written as

$$\frac{(x+3)^2}{4} + \frac{(y-1)^2}{16} = 1.$$

Solve this equation for y.

$$\frac{(x+3)^2}{4} + \frac{(y-1)^2}{16} = 1$$

$$\frac{(y-1)^2}{16} = 1 - \frac{(x+3)^2}{4}$$

$$(y-1)^2 = 16 - 4(x+3)^2 \qquad \text{Multiplying by 16}$$

$$y - 1 = \pm\sqrt{16 - 4(x+3)^2}$$

$$y = 1 \pm \sqrt{16 - 4(x+3)^2}$$

Now we can produce the graph in either of two ways. One is to enter $y_1 = 1 + \sqrt{16 - 4(x+3)^2}$ and $y_2 = 1 - \sqrt{16 - 4(x+3)^2}$, select a square window, and press $\boxed{\text{GRAPH}}$. Here we use $[-9, 9, -6, 6]$. The first equation produces the top half of the ellipse and the second equation produces the lower half.

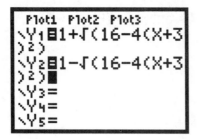
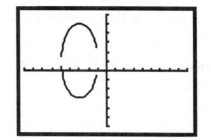

We can also enter $y_1 = \sqrt{16 - 4(x+3)^2}$ and then enter $y_2 = 1 + y_1$ and $y_3 = 1 - y_1$. Deselect y_1, select a square window, and press $\boxed{\text{GRAPH}}$. We use y_1 to eliminate the need to enter the square root more than once. Deselecting it prevents the graph of y_1 from appearing on the screen with the graph of the ellipse. The top half of the graph is produced by y_2 and the lower half by y_3.

```
Plot1  Plot2  Plot3
\Y₁=√(16-4(X+3)²
)
\Y₂⊟1+Y₁
\Y₃⊟1-Y₁█
\Y₄=
\Y₅=
\Y₆=
```

We could also begin by using the quadratic formula to solve the original equation for y.

$$4x^2 + y^2 + 24x - 2y + 21 = 0$$

$$y^2 - 2y + (4x^2 + 24x + 21) = 0$$

$$y = \frac{-(-2) \pm \sqrt{(-2)^2 - 4 \cdot 1 \cdot (4x^2 + 24x + 21)}}{2 \cdot 1}$$

$$y = \frac{2 \pm \sqrt{4 - 16x^2 - 96x - 84}}{2}$$

$$y = \frac{2 \pm \sqrt{-16x^2 - 96x - 80}}{2}$$

Then enter $y_1 = \dfrac{2 + \sqrt{-16x^2 - 96x - 80}}{2}$ and $y_2 = \dfrac{2 - \sqrt{-16x^2 - 96x - 80}}{2}$, or enter $y_1 = \sqrt{-16x^2 - 96x - 80}$,
$y_2 = \dfrac{2 + y_1}{2}$, and $y_3 = \dfrac{2 - y_1}{2}$, and deselect y_1.

```
Plot1  Plot2  Plot3
\Y₁⊟(2+√(-16X²-9
6X-80))/2
\Y₂⊟(2-√((-16²-9
6X-80))/2█
\Y₃=
\Y₄=
\Y₅=
```

```
Plot1  Plot2  Plot3
\Y₁=√(-16X²-96X-
80)
\Y₂⊟(2+Y₁)/2
\Y₃⊟(2-Y₁)/2█
\Y₄=
\Y₅=
\Y₆=
```

Select a square window and press $\boxed{\text{GRAPH}}$ to display the graph.

GRAPHING HYPERBOLAS

As with equations of circles, parabolas, and ellipses, equations of hyperbolas must be solved for y before they can be
entered on a TI-82, TI-83, or TI-83+.

Section 9.3, Example 2 Graph the hyperbola $9x^2 - 16y^2 = 144$.

First solve the equation for y.
$$9x^2 - 16y^2 = 144$$

$$-16y^2 = -9x^2 + 144$$

$$y^2 = \frac{-9x^2 + 144}{-16}$$

$$y = \pm\sqrt{\frac{-9x^2 + 144}{-16}}, \text{ or } \pm\sqrt{\frac{9x^2 - 144}{16}}$$

It is not necessary to simplify further.

Now enter $y_1 = \sqrt{\dfrac{9x^2 - 144}{16}}$ and either $y_2 = -\sqrt{\dfrac{9x^2 - 144}{16}}$ or $y_2 = -y_1$, select a square window, and press $\boxed{\text{GRAPH}}$.

Here we use $[-9, 9, -6, 6]$. The top half of the graph is produced by y_1 and the lower half by y_2.

 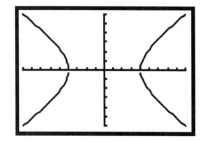

Section 9.3, Example 3 Graph the hyperbola $4y^2 - x^2 + 24y + 4x + 28 = 0$.

In the text we completed the square to get the standard form of the equation. Now solve the equation for y.

$$\frac{(y+3)^2}{1} - \frac{(x-2)^2}{4} = 1$$

$$(y+3)^2 = \frac{(x-2)^2}{4} + 1$$

$$y + 3 = \pm\sqrt{\frac{(x-2)^2}{4} + 1}$$

$$y = -3 \pm \sqrt{\frac{(x-2)^2}{4} + 1}$$

The graph can be produced in either of two ways. One is to enter $y_1 = -3 + \sqrt{\frac{(x-2)^2}{4} + 1}$ and $y_2 = -3 - \sqrt{\frac{(x-2)^2}{4} + 1}$, select a square window, and press $\boxed{\text{GRAPH}}$. Here we use $[-12, 12, -9, 9]$. The first equation produces the top half of the hyperbola and the second the lower half.

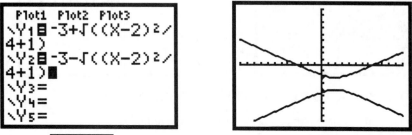

We can also enter $y_1 = \sqrt{\frac{(x-2)^2}{4} + 1}$, $y_2 = -3 + y_1$, and $y_3 = -3 - y_1$. Then deselect y_1, select a square window, and press $\boxed{\text{GRAPH}}$. Again, y_1 is used to eliminate the need to enter the square root more than once. Deselecting it prevents the graph of y_1 from appearing on the screen with the graph of the hyperbola. The top half of the graph is produced by y_2 and the lower half by y_3.

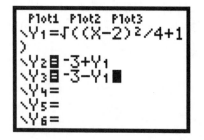

CONVERTING FROM RECTANGULAR TO POLAR COORDINATES

The grapher can be used to convert from rectangular to polar coordinates, expressing the result using either degrees or radians. The grapher will supply a positive value for r and an angle in the interval $(-180°, 180°]$, or $(-\pi, \pi]$.

Section 9.5, Example 2 (a) Convert (3,3) to polar coordinates.

To find r, regardless of the type of angle measure, press $\boxed{\text{2nd}}$ $\boxed{\text{ANGLE}}$ 5 3 $\boxed{,}$ 3 $\boxed{)}$ $\boxed{\text{ENTER}}$. The readout is 4.242640687, so $r \approx 4.2426$. This is a decimal approximation for $3\sqrt{2}$. Now, to find θ in degrees, set the grapher in Degree mode and press $\boxed{\text{2nd}}$ $\boxed{\text{ANGLE}}$ 6 3 $\boxed{,}$ 3 $\boxed{)}$ $\boxed{\text{ENTER}}$. The readout is 45, so $\theta = 45°$. Thus polar notation for (3,3) is (4.2426, 45°).

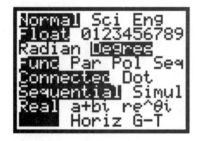
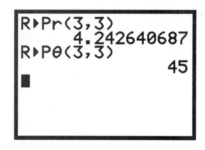

Set the grapher in Radian mode to find θ in radians. Repeat the keystrokes for finding θ above to find that $\theta \approx 0.7854$. This is a decimal approximation for $\pi/4$. Thus polar notation for (3,3) is (4.2426, 0.7854).

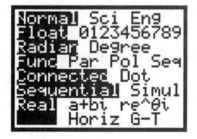
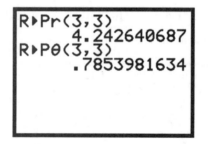

CONVERTING FROM POLAR TO RECTANGULAR COORDINATES

The grapher can also be used to convert from polar to rectangular coordinates.

Section 9.5, Example 3 Convert each of the following to rectangular coordinates.

(a) $(10, \pi/3)$ (b) $(-5, 135°)$

(a) Since the angle is given in radians, set the grapher in Radian mode. To find the x-coordinate of rectangular notation, press $\boxed{\text{2nd}}$ $\boxed{\text{ANGLE}}$ 7 1 0 $\boxed{,}$ $\boxed{\text{2nd}}$ $\boxed{\pi}$ $\boxed{\div}$ 3 $\boxed{)}$ $\boxed{\text{ENTER}}$. The readout is 5, so $x = 5$. The y-coordinate is found by pressing $\boxed{\text{2nd}}$ $\boxed{\text{ANGLE}}$ 8 1 0 $\boxed{,}$ $\boxed{\text{2nd}}$ $\boxed{\pi}$ $\boxed{\div}$ 3 $\boxed{)}$ $\boxed{\text{ENTER}}$. The readout is 8.660254038, so $y \approx 8.6603$. This is a decimal approximation of $5\sqrt{3}$. Thus, rectangular notation for $(10, \pi/3)$ is (5, 8.6603).

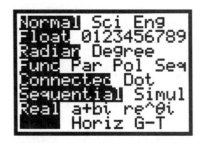
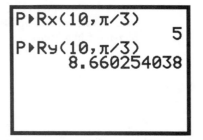

(b) The angle is given in degrees, so we set the grapher in Degree mode. To find the x-coordinate of rectangular notation, press 2nd ANGLE 7 (−) 5 · 1 3 5) ENTER . The readout is 3.535533906, so $x \approx 3.5355$. This is a decimal approximation of $\frac{5\sqrt{2}}{2}$. The y-coordinate is found by pressing 2nd ANGLE 8 (−) 5 · 1 3 5) ENTER . The readout is −3.535533906, so $y \approx -3.5355$. This is a decimal approximation of $-\frac{5\sqrt{2}}{2}$. Thus, rectangular notation for $(-5, 135°)$ is $(3.5355, -3.5355)$.

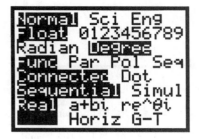
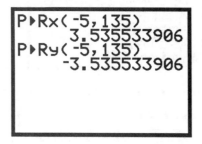

GRAPHING POLAR EQUATIONS

Polar equations can be graphed in either Radian mode or Degree mode. The equation must be written in the form $r = f(\theta)$ and the grapher must be set in Polar (Pol) mode. Typically we begin with a range of $[0, 2\pi]$ or $[0°, 360°]$, but it might be necessary to increase the range to ensure that sufficient points are plotted to display the entire graph.

Section 9.5, Example 6 Graph: $r = 1 - \sin\theta$.

First set the grapher in Polar mode by pressing MODE ▽ ▽ ▽ ▷ ▷ ENTER . We will also select Radian mode.

The equation is given in $r = f(\theta)$ form. Press Y = to enter it on the "Y =" screen. Clear any existing entries and, with the cursor beside "$r_1 =$," press 1 − SIN X,T,θ,n . (Enter θ on the TI-82 by pressing X,T,θ .) Now press WINDOW and enter the following settings:

θmin $= 0$ (Smallest value of θ to be evaluated)
θmax $= 2\pi$ (Largest value of θ to be evaluated)
θstep $= \pi/24$ (Increment in θ values)
Xmin $= -3$
Xmax $= 3$
Xscl $= 1$
Ymin $= -3$
Ymax $= 1$
Yscl $= 1$

With these settings the grapher evaluates the function from $\theta = 0$ to $\theta = 2\pi$ in increments of $\pi/24$ and displays the graph in the square window $[-3, 3, -3, 1]$. Values entered in terms of π appear on the screen as decimal approximations. Press GRAPH to display the graph.

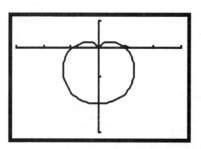

The curve can be traced with either rectangular or polar coordinates being displayed. The value of θ is also displayed when rectangular coordinates are selected. The choice of coordinates is made on the FORMAT screen. Press 2nd FORMAT on the TI-83 or TI-83+ or WINDOW $\triangleright$ on the TI-82 to display this screen. (FORMAT is the second operation associated with the ZOOM key on the TI-83 and TI-83+.) Then position the blinking cursor over RectGC to select rectangular coordinates or over PolarGC to select polar coordinates and press ENTER.

GRAPHING PARAMETRIC EQUATIONS

Plane curves described with parametric equations can be graphed on a grapher.

Section 9.8, Example 1 (a) Using a grapher, graph the plane curve given by the set of parametric equations and the restriction for the parameter.

$x = t^2,\ y = t - 1,;\ -1 \le t \le 4$

First press MODE and select Parametric (Par) mode.

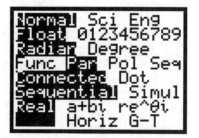

Then press Y $=$ to display the equation-editor screen. Enter $X_{1T} = t^2$ and $Y_{1T} = t - 1$. Note that, when the

$\boxed{\text{X, T, } \theta, n}$ key on the TI-83 or TI-83+ or the $\boxed{\text{X, T, } \theta}$ key on the TI-82 is pressed in Parametric mode, the variable T is produced. Now press $\boxed{\text{WINDOW}}$ and enter the following settings:

Tmin $= -1$ (Smallest value of T to be evaluated)
Tmax $= 4$ (Largest value of T to be evaluated)
Tstep $= .1$ (Increment in T values)
Xmin $= -2$
Xmax $=18$
Xscl $= 1$
Ymin $= -4$
Ymax $= 4$
Yscl $= 1$

Since $x = t^2$ and $-1 \leq t \leq 4$, we have $0 \leq x \leq 16$. Thus, we choose Xmin and Xmax to display this interval. Similarly, since $y = t - 1$, we hve $-2 \leq y \leq 3$ and we choose Ymin and Ymax to show this interval. Press $\boxed{\text{GRAPH}}$ to display the graph.

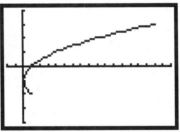

The curve can be traced as described in Example 6 from Section 9.5 above.

Chapter 10
Sequences, Series, and Combinatorics

Both the graphing capabilities and the computational capabilities of the grapher can be used when working with sequences, series, and combinatorics.

FINDING THE TERMS OF A SEQUENCE

Section 10.1, Example 2 Use a grapher to find the first 5 terms of the sequence whose general term is given by $a_n = n/(n + 1)$.

Although we could use a table, we will use the Seq feature. The grapher can be set in either Func or Seq mode when this feature is used. On the TI-83 or TI-83+ press $\boxed{\text{2nd}}$ $\boxed{\text{LIST}}$ $\boxed{\triangleright}$ to display the LIST OPS menu. Then press 5 to paste "seq(" to the home screen. On the TI-82 press $\boxed{\text{2nd}}$ $\boxed{\text{LIST}}$ 5. (LIST is the second operation associated with the $\boxed{\text{STAT}}$ key.) Then enter the general term of the sequence, replacing n with x if the grapher is in Func mode. Follow this with the variable and the numbers of the first and last terms desired. We will also use the ▷Frac feature to express the terms as fractions. Press $\boxed{\text{X, T, }\Theta, n}$ $\boxed{\div}$ $\boxed{(}$ $\boxed{\text{X, T, }\Theta, n}$ $\boxed{+}$ 1 $\boxed{)}$ $\boxed{,}$ $\boxed{\text{X, T, }\Theta, n}$ $\boxed{,}$ 1 $\boxed{,}$ 5 $\boxed{)}$ $\boxed{\text{MATH}}$ $\boxed{\text{ENTER}}$ $\boxed{\text{ENTER}}$. If the TI-83 or TI-83+ is in Func mode, pressing $\boxed{\text{X, T, }\Theta, n}$ will produce the variable x in the expression. If it is in Sequence mode the variable will be n.

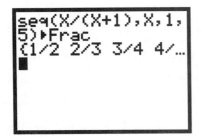

GRAPHING SEQUENCES

The grapher can be used to graph a sequence.

Section 10.1, Example 3 Graph the sequence whose general term is given by $a_n = n/(n + 1)$.

First we use the TI-83 and TI-83+ to graph the sequence. Begin by setting the grapher in Seq mode. Press $\boxed{\text{MODE}}$ $\boxed{\triangledown}$ $\boxed{\triangledown}$ $\boxed{\triangledown}$ $\boxed{\triangleright}$ $\boxed{\triangleright}$ $\boxed{\triangleright}$ $\boxed{\text{ENTER}}$. Then press $\boxed{\text{Y} =}$. Set the graph-style to "dot" beside "u(n) =" by positioning the cursor on the graph-style icon and pressing $\boxed{\text{ENTER}}$ until the dot icon appears. Now press $\boxed{\triangleright}$ $\boxed{\triangleright}$ and enter $n/(n + 1)$ beside "u(n) =" by pressing $\boxed{\text{X,T,}\theta, n}$ $\boxed{\div}$ $\boxed{(}$ $\boxed{\text{X,T,}\theta, n}$ $\boxed{+}$ 1 $\boxed{)}$. Press $\boxed{\triangledown}$ $\boxed{\cdot}$ 5 to enter the first term of the sequence, $1/(1+1)$, or .5, beside "u(nMin) =."

To graph the sequence first press $\boxed{\text{WINDOW}}$ to display the WINDOW screen. Set nMin $= 1$ and nMax $= 10$ to define the smallest and largest values of n for which terms of the sequence are calculated. Also set PlotStart $= 1$ and PlotStep $=$

1 to define the first term of the sequence to be plotted and the incremental n value. Set Xmin = 0, Xmax = 10, Xscl = 1, Ymin = 0, Ymax = 1, and Yscl = 1 to define the window dimensions and the spacing between tick marks. It will be necessary to use the $\boxed{\bigtriangledown}$ key to display and enter Ymin, Ymax, and Yscl. The window format should be set on Time. Press $\boxed{\text{2nd}}$ $\boxed{\text{FORMAT}}$ to display the WINDOW FORMAT screen. If Time is not selected, position the cursor over it and press $\boxed{\text{ENTER}}$.

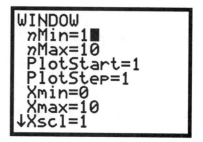

Press $\boxed{\text{GRAPH}}$ to display the graph.

Now we do Example 3 on the TI-82. Begin by setting the grapher in SEQUENCE and DOT modes. Press $\boxed{\text{MODE}}$ $\boxed{\bigtriangledown}$ $\boxed{\bigtriangledown}$ $\boxed{\bigtriangledown}$ $\boxed{\triangleright}$ $\boxed{\triangleright}$ $\boxed{\triangleright}$ $\boxed{\text{ENTER}}$ to select SEQUENCE mode, followed immediately by $\boxed{\bigtriangledown}$ $\boxed{\triangleright}$ $\boxed{\text{ENTER}}$ to select DOT mode. Now press $\boxed{\text{Y} =}$. Position the cursor beside "$U_n =$" and enter $n/(n+1)$ by pressing $\boxed{\text{2nd}}$ $\boxed{n}$ $\boxed{\div}$ $\boxed{(}$ $\boxed{\text{2nd}}$ $\boxed{n}$ $\boxed{+}$ $\boxed{1}$ $\boxed{)}$. (n is the second operation associated with the 9 key.) Then press $\boxed{\text{WINDOW}}$ to display the WINDOW screen. Press $\boxed{\bigtriangledown}$ to position the cursor beside "U_nStart =" and enter the first term of the sequence: when $n = 1$, $n/(n+1) = 1/(1+1) = 1/2$, or 0.5, so we press $\boxed{\cdot}$ $\boxed{5}$ $\boxed{\text{ENTER}}$.

To graph the sequence first press $\boxed{\text{WINDOW}}$. We have already entered U_nStart = .5. Now set V_nStart = 1 to define the initial value of n in the calculation of sequence values; set nMin = 1 and nMax = 10 to set the values of n at which plotting begins and ends at 1 and 10, respectively. Now set Xmin = 0, Xmax = 10, Xscl = 1, Ymin = 0, Ymax = 1, and Yscl = 1 to define the window dimensions and the spacing between tick marks. It will be necessary to use the $\boxed{\bigtriangledown}$ key to display and enter Xscl, Ymin, Ymax, and Yscl. The window format should be set on Time. While the WINDOW screen is displayed, highlight FORMAT at the top of the screen to display the WINDOW FORMAT screen. If Time is not selected, position the cursor over it and press $\boxed{\text{ENTER}}$. Now press $\boxed{\text{GRAPH}}$ to display the graph of the first 10 terms of the sequence.

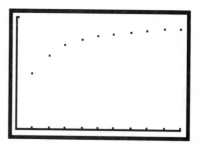

FINDING PARTIAL SUMS

We can use a grapher to find partial sums of a sequence when a formula for the general term is known.

Section 10.1, Example 6 Use a grapher to find S_1, S_2, S_3, and S_4 for the sequence whose general term is given by $a_n = n^2 - 3$.

We will use the cumSum feature on the TI-83 and TI-83+. The grapher will write the partial sums as a list. First press $\boxed{\text{2nd}}$ $\boxed{\text{LIST}}$ $\boxed{\triangleright}$ 6 to paste "cumSum(" to the home screen. Then press $\boxed{\text{2nd}}$ $\boxed{\text{LIST}}$ $\boxed{\triangleright}$ 5 to paste "seq(" into the cumSum expression. Finally press $\boxed{\text{X, T, }\Theta, n}$ $\boxed{x^2}$ $\boxed{-}$ 3 $\boxed{,}$ $\boxed{\text{X, T, }\Theta, n}$ $\boxed{,}$ 1 $\boxed{,}$ 4 $\boxed{)}$ $\boxed{)}$ $\boxed{\text{ENTER}}$. We show the result with the grapher set in Seq mode. The variable will be expressed as x if the grapher is in Func mode.

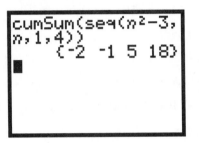

Partial sums can be found individually on the TI-82 by combining the sum and seq(features. To find S_4, for example, we enter the general term, the variable, the numbers of the first and last terms in the sum, and the increment between the desired terms. Press $\boxed{\text{2nd}}$ $\boxed{\text{LIST}}$ $\boxed{\triangleright}$ 5 $\boxed{\text{2nd}}$ $\boxed{\text{LIST}}$ 5 $\boxed{\text{X, T, }\Theta}$ $\boxed{x^2}$ $\boxed{-}$ 3 $\boxed{,}$ $\boxed{\text{X, T, }\Theta}$ $\boxed{,}$ 1 $\boxed{,}$ 4 $\boxed{,}$ 1 $\boxed{)}$.

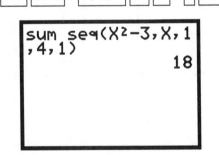

Replace 4 with 1, 2, and 3 to find S_1, S_2, and S_3, respectively. The TI-83 and TI-83+ can also compute individual partial sums. This is demonstrated in the next example.

Section 10.1, Example 7 (a) Evaluate $\displaystyle\sum_{k=1}^{5} k^3$.

In Example 6 above we have seen how to evaluate an individual sum on the TI-82. On the TI-83 or TI-83+ press $\boxed{\text{2nd}}$ $\boxed{\text{LIST}}$ $\boxed{\triangleright}$ $\boxed{\triangleright}$ 5 $\boxed{\text{2nd}}$ $\boxed{\text{LIST}}$ $\boxed{\triangleright}$ 5 $\boxed{\text{X, T, }\Theta, n}$ $\boxed{\wedge}$ 3 $\boxed{,}$ $\boxed{\text{X, T, }\Theta, n}$ $\boxed{,}$ 1 $\boxed{,}$ 5 $\boxed{)}$ $\boxed{)}$ $\boxed{\text{ENTER}}$. We show the result on a grapher set in Seq mode.

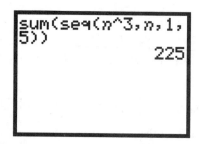

RECURSIVELY DEFINED SEQUENCES

Recursively defined sequences can also be entered on a grapher set in Seq mode.

Section 10.1, Example 7 Find the first 5 terms of the sequence defined by

$$a_1 = 5, \ a_{k+1} = 2a_k - 3, \text{ for } k \geq 1.$$

On the TI-83 or TI-83+, press $\boxed{Y =}$ and enter the recursive function beside "u(n) =" by pressing 2 $\boxed{\text{2nd}}$ $\boxed{\text{u}}$ $\boxed{(}$ $\boxed{\text{X,T,}\theta,n}$ $\boxed{-}$ 1 $\boxed{)}$ $\boxed{-}$ 3. (u is the second operation associated with the $\boxed{7}$ key.) Also set u(nMin) = 5, the first term of the sequence. Press $\boxed{\text{2nd}}$ $\boxed{\text{TblSet}}$ to display the TABLE SETUP screen and set TblStart = 1, ΔTbl = 1, and Indpnt: Auto. Now press $\boxed{\text{2nd}}$ $\boxed{\text{TABLE}}$ to display the table of values.

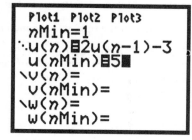
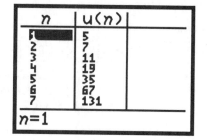

We see that $a_1 = 5$, $a_2 = 7$, $a_3 = 11$, $a_4 = 19$, and $a_5 = 35$.

On the TI-82, press $\boxed{Y =}$ and enter the recursive function beside "U_n =" by pressing 2 $\boxed{\text{2nd}}$ $\boxed{U_{n-1}}$ $\boxed{-}$ 3. (U_{n-1} is the second operation associated with the $\boxed{7}$ key.) Now press $\boxed{\text{WINDOW}}$ to display the window screen. Beside "U_nStart =" enter the first term of the sequence, 5.

Set up and display the table of values as described above, again keeping in mind that TblMin on the TI-82 corresponds to TblStart on the TI-83.

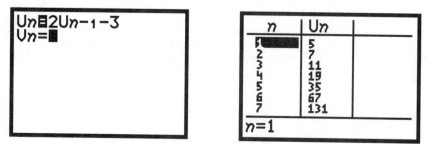

As with the TI-83 and TI-83+ we see that $a_1 = 5$, $a_2 = 7$, $a_3 = 11$, $a_4 = 19$, and $a_5 = 35$.

EVALUATING FACTORIALS, PERMUTATIONS, AND COMBINATIONS

Operations from the MATH PRB (probability) menu can be used to evaluate factorials, permutations, and combinations.

Section 10.5, Exercise 6 Evaluate 7!.

Press 7 $\boxed{\text{MATH}}$ $\boxed{\triangleright}$ $\boxed{\triangleright}$ $\boxed{\triangleright}$ 4 $\boxed{\text{ENTER}}$. These keystrokes enter 7, display the MATH PRB menu, select item 4, !, from that menu, and then cause 7! to be evaluated. The result is 5040.

Section 10.5, Exercise 9 Evaluate $\frac{9!}{5!}$.

Press 9 $\boxed{\text{MATH}}$ $\boxed{\triangleright}$ $\boxed{\triangleright}$ $\boxed{\triangleright}$ 4 $\boxed{\div}$ 5 $\boxed{\text{MATH}}$ $\boxed{\triangleright}$ $\boxed{\triangleright}$ $\boxed{\triangleright}$ 4 $\boxed{\text{ENTER}}$. The result is 3024.

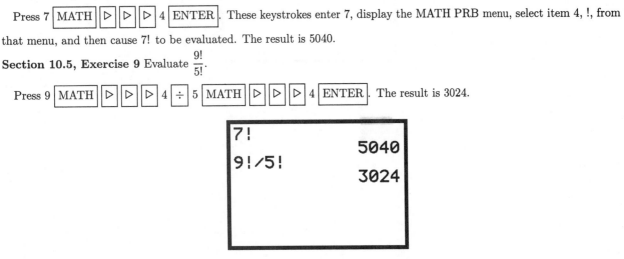

Section 10.5, Example 3 (a) Compute $_4P_4$.

Press 4 $\boxed{\text{MATH}}$ $\boxed{\triangleright}$ $\boxed{\triangleright}$ $\boxed{\triangleright}$ 2 4 $\boxed{\text{ENTER}}$. These keystrokes enter 4, for 4 objects, display the MATH PRB menu, select item 2, $_nP_r$, from that menu, enter 4, for 4 objects taken at a time, and then cause the calculation to be performed. The result is 24.

Section 10.5, Example 6 Compute $_8P_4$.

Press 8 $\boxed{\text{MATH}}$ $\boxed{\triangleright}$ $\boxed{\triangleright}$ $\boxed{\triangleright}$ 2 4 $\boxed{\text{ENTER}}$. These keystrokes enter 8, for 8 objects, display the MATH PRB menu, select item 2, $_nP_r$, from that menu, enter 4, for 4 objects taken at a time, and then cause the calculation to be performed. The result is 1680.

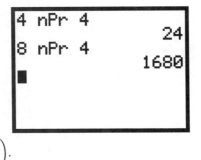

Section 10.5, Example 3 Evaluate $\binom{7}{5}$.

Press 7 $\boxed{\text{MATH}}$ $\boxed{\triangleright}$ $\boxed{\triangleright}$ $\boxed{\triangleright}$ 3 5 $\boxed{\text{ENTER}}$. These keystrokes enter 7, for 7 objects, display the MATH PRB menu, select item 3, $_nC_r$, from that menu, enter 5, for 5 objects taken at a time, and then cause the calculation to be performed. The result is 21.

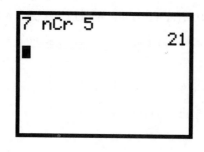

The TI-85 Graphics Calculator

Introduction to Graphs and the Graphing Calculator

GETTING STARTED

Press $\boxed{\text{ON}}$ to turn on the TI-85 graphing calculator. ($\boxed{\text{ON}}$ is the key at the bottom left-hand corner of the keypad.) You should see a blinking rectangle, or cursor, on the screen. If you do not see the cursor, try adjusting the display contrast. To do this, first press $\boxed{\text{2nd}}$. ($\boxed{\text{2nd}}$ is the yellow key in the left column of the keypad.) Then press and hold $\boxed{\triangle}$ to increase the contrast or $\boxed{\triangledown}$ to decrease the contrast. If the contrast needs to be adjusted further after the first adjustment, press $\boxed{\text{2nd}}$ again then then hold $\boxed{\triangle}$ or $\boxed{\triangledown}$ to increase or decrease the contrast, respectively.

To turn the grapher off, press $\boxed{\text{2nd}}$ $\boxed{\text{OFF}}$. (OFF is the second operation associated with the $\boxed{\text{ON}}$ key. In general, second operations are written in yellow above the keys on the keypad.) The grapher will turn itself off automatically after about five minutes without any activity.

Press $\boxed{\text{2nd}}$ $\boxed{\text{MODE}}$ to display the MODE settings. (MODE is the second operation associated with the $\boxed{\text{MORE}}$ key.) Initially you should select the settings on the left side of the display.

To change a setting on the Mode screen use $\boxed{\triangledown}$ or $\boxed{\triangle}$ to move the cursor to the line of that setting. Then use $\boxed{\triangleright}$ or $\boxed{\triangleleft}$ to move the blinking cursor to the desired setting and press $\boxed{\text{ENTER}}$. Press $\boxed{\text{CLEAR}}$ or $\boxed{\text{EXIT}}$ to leave the MODE screen. Pressing $\boxed{\text{CLEAR}}$ or $\boxed{\text{EXIT}}$ will take you to the home screen where computations are performed.

It will be helpful to read the Getting Started section of the Texas Instruments Guidebook that was packaged with your graphing calculator before proceeding.

USING A MENU

A menu is a list of options that appears when a key is pressed. Thus, multiple options, and sometimes multiple menus, may be accessed by pressing one key. For example, the following screen appears when $\boxed{\text{2nd}}$ $\boxed{\text{MATH}}$ is pressed. (MATH is the second operation associated with the $\boxed{\times}$ multiplication key.) We see several submenus at the bottom of the screen. The $\boxed{\text{F1}}$ - $\boxed{\text{F5}}$ keys at the top of the keypad are used to select options from this menu. The arrow to the right of MISC indicates that there are more choices. They can be seen by pressing $\boxed{\text{MORE}}$.

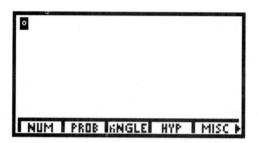

To choose the NUM submenu from the MATH menu press $\boxed{\text{F1}}$. (If you pressed $\boxed{\text{MORE}}$ to see the additional items on the MATH menu as described above, now press $\boxed{\text{MORE}}$ again to see the first five items on the menu. Then press $\boxed{\text{F1}}$ to choose NUM.) When NUM is chosen, the original submenus move up on the screen and the items on the NUM submenu appear at the bottom of the screen.

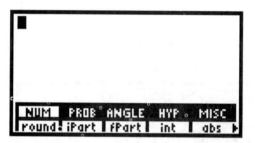

When two rows of options are displayed like this, the top row is accessed by pressing $\boxed{\text{2nd}}$ followed by one of the keys $\boxed{\text{F1}}$ - $\boxed{\text{F5}}$. These keystrokes access the second operations M1 - M5 associated with the $\boxed{\text{F1}}$ - $\boxed{\text{F5}}$ keys. The options on the bottom row are accessed by pressing one of the keys $\boxed{\text{F1}}$ - $\boxed{\text{F5}}$. Absolute value, denoted "abs," is selected from the NUM submenu and copied to the home screen, for instance, by pressing $\boxed{\text{F5}}$.

A menu can be removed from the screen by pressing $\boxed{\text{EXIT}}$. If both a menu and a submenu are displayed, press $\boxed{\text{EXIT}}$ once to remove the submenu and twice to remove both.

SETTING THE VIEWING RECTANGLE

The viewing rectangle is the portion of the coordinate plane that appears on the grapher's screen. It is defined by the minimum and maximum values of x and y: xMin, xMax, yMin, and yMax. These are referred to as the RANGE variables. The notation [xMin, xMax, yMin, yMax] is used in the text to represent these settings or dimensions. For example, $[-12,\ 12,\ -8,\ 8]$ denotes a rectangle that displays the portion of the x-axis from -12 to 12 and the portion of the y-axis from -8 to 8. In addition, the distance between tick marks on the axes is defined by the settings xScl and yScl. In this manual xScl and yScl will be assumed to be 1 unless noted otherwise. The rectangle corresponding to the settings $[-20,\ 30,\ -12,\ 20]$, xScl $= 5$, yScl $= 2$, is shown below.

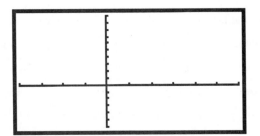

Press GRAPH F2 to display the RANGE screen and see the current settings on your grapher. The standard settings $[-10, 10, -10, 10]$, xScl = 1, yScl = 1, are shown below.

```
RANGE
 xMin=-10
 xMax=10
 xScl=1
 yMin=-10
 yMax=10
 yScl=1
y(x)= RANGE ZOOM TRACE GRAPH▶
```

To change a setting, position the cursor beside the setting you wish to change and enter the new value. For example, to change from the standard settings to $[-20, 30, -12, 20]$, xScl = 5, yScl = 2, on the RANGE screen press (−) 2 0 ENTER 3 0 ENTER 5 ENTER (−) 1 2 ENTER 2 0 ENTER 2 ENTER. You must use the (−) key on the bottom of the keypad rather than the − key in the right-hand column to enter a negative number. (−) represents "the opposite of" or "the additive inverse of" whereas − is the key for the subtraction operation. The ▽ key may be used instead of ENTER after typing each setting. To see the viewing rectangle shown above, press F5 on the top row of the keypad.

QUICK TIP: To return quickly to the standard range settings $[-10, 10, -10, 10]$, xScl = 1, yScl = 1, press GRAPH F3 F4.

PLOTTING POINTS

We can plot points on a grapher by entering their coordinates in a list and choosing an appropriate viewing rectangle.

Example 2, page 3 (Page numbers refer to pages in the text.) Use a grapher to graph the points $(-3, 5)$, $(4, 3)$, $(3, 4)$, $(-4, -2)$, $(3, -4)$, $(0, 4)$, $(-3, 0)$, and $(0, 0)$.

We choose a viewing rectangle that will display all of the points, noting that the x-coordinates range from -4 to 4 and the y-coordinates range from -4 to 5. Thus, one good choice is the standard viewing rectangle $[-10, 10, -10, 10]$.

Note that there should be no equations entered on the "y(x) =" screen. If there are entries present clear them now. To clear an entry for $y1$, for example, position the cursor beside "$y1 =$" and press CLEAR. Do this for each existing entry. If this is not done, the equations that are currently entered will be graphed along with the data points that are entered.

We will enter the coordinates of the ordered pairs on the STAT list editor screen. To clear any existing lists press STAT

$\boxed{\text{F2}}$ $\boxed{\text{ENTER}}$ $\boxed{\text{ENTER}}$ $\boxed{\text{F5}}$. Once the lists are cleared, we can enter the coordinates of the points. We will enter the first coordinates (x-coordinates) in xStat and the second coordinates (y-coordinates) in yStat. Position the cursor to the right of "x1 =." Then, to enter the point $(-3, 5)$, press $\boxed{(-)}$ 3 $\boxed{\text{ENTER}}$ 5 $\boxed{\text{ENTER}}$. Recall that the gray $\boxed{(-)}$ key in the bottom row of the keypad must be used to enter a negative number whereas the black $\boxed{-}$ key is used for the subtraction operation. Continue typing the ordered pairs with each entry followed by $\boxed{\text{ENTER}}$ The entries can be followed by $\boxed{\triangledown}$ rather than $\boxed{\text{ENTER}}$ if desired.

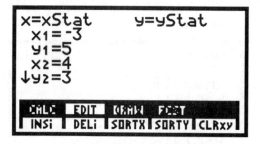

To plot the points, we select the scatterplot feature. Press $\boxed{\text{STAT}}$ $\boxed{\text{F3}}$ $\boxed{\text{F2}}$.

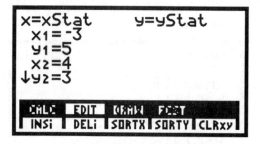

SOLUTIONS OF EQUATIONS

Example 3, page 4 Determine whether each ordered pair is a solution of $2x + 3y = 18$.

       a) $(-5, 7)$ **b)** $(3, 4)$

We can substitute each pair in the expression $2x + 3y$. If the resulting value is 18, the pair is a solution of the equation $2x + 3y = 18$. If not, the pair is not a solution. To perform the substitutions, first press $\boxed{\text{2nd}}$ $\boxed{\text{QUIT}}$ or $\boxed{\text{2nd}}$ $\boxed{\text{CLEAR}}$ to go to the home screen. To substitute -5 for x and 7 for y in $2x + 3y$, press 2 $\boxed{(}$ $\boxed{(-)}$ 5 $\boxed{)}$ $\boxed{+}$ 3 $\boxed{\times}$ 7 $\boxed{\text{ENTER}}$. The result is 11, so $(-5, 7)$ is not a solution of the equation. To substitute 3 for x and 4 for y, press 2 $\boxed{\times}$ 3 $\boxed{+}$ 3 $\boxed{\times}$ 4 $\boxed{\text{ENTER}}$. The result is 18, so $(3, 4)$ is a solution.

```
2( -5)+3*7
                              11
2*3+3*4
                              18
■
```

EDITING ENTRIES

You can recall and edit an entry if necessary. If, for instance, in entering the last expression in Example 3 above you pressed $\boxed{-}$ instead of $\boxed{+}$, first press $\boxed{\text{2nd}}$ $\boxed{\text{ENTRY}}$ to return to the last entry. (ENTRY is the second operation associated with the $\boxed{\text{ENTER}}$ key.) Then use the $\boxed{\triangleleft}$ key to move the cursor to $\boxed{-}$ and press $\boxed{+}$ to overwrite it. If you forgot to type the first 3, move the cursor to the $\boxed{+}$; then press $\boxed{\text{2nd}}$ $\boxed{\text{INS}}$ 3 to insert the 3 before the $\boxed{+}$. (INS is the second operation associated with the $\boxed{\text{DEL}}$ key.) You can continue to insert symbols immediately after the first insertion without pressing $\boxed{\text{2nd}}$ $\boxed{\text{INS}}$ again. If you typed 21 instead of 2, move the cursor to 1 and press $\boxed{\text{DEL}}$. This will delete the 1. If you notice that an entry needs to be edited before you press $\boxed{\text{ENTER}}$ to perform the computation, the editing can be done directly without recalling the entry. It is not possible to recall entries prior to the previous one on the TI-85.

THE CUSTOM MENU

The TI-85 allows you to create a custom menu containing up to 15 items selected from the Catalog. To display the custom menu, press $\boxed{\text{CUSTOM}}$.

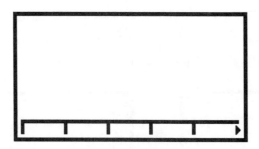

Press $\boxed{\text{MORE}}$ once to see the second menu group and press $\boxed{\text{MORE}}$ once again to see the third group.

To clear an item from the custom menu, press $\boxed{\text{2nd}}$ $\boxed{\text{CATLG-VARS}}$ $\boxed{\text{F1}}$ $\boxed{\text{F4}}$ to select BLANK from the Catalog menu. Then press one of the $\boxed{\text{F1}}$ - $\boxed{\text{F5}}$ keys corresponding to the location of the item to be cleared. To clear an item in the middle position of the first custom menu group, for instance, press $\boxed{\text{F3}}$. To clear an item in the second or third menu group, press $\boxed{\text{MORE}}$ once or twice before pressing one of the $\boxed{\text{F1}}$ - $\boxed{\text{F5}}$ keys. A new item added to a custom menu will replace the item currently in that location, so it is not necessary to clear an item before one is added in its place.

We will put "▷ Frac" in position F1 in a custom menu to illustrate the procedure. The "▷ Frac operation converts decimal notation for a rational number to fractional notation. Press $\boxed{\text{2nd}}$ $\boxed{\text{CATALOG}}$ $\boxed{\text{F3}}$ $\boxed{\text{ALPHA}}$ $\boxed{\text{A}}$ to display the catalog and go to the first item in that menu that begins with A. Now use the $\boxed{\triangle}$ key to position the triangular selection cursor beside "▷ Frac." Then press $\boxed{\text{F1}}$ to copy the operation to position F1 in the custom menu.

```
CATALOG
▶▶Frac
  ▶Hex
  ▶Oct
  ▶Pol
  ▶Rec
▛▜5E▟ ▛▜5E▛ ▐USTM E▛MN▛
▐▶Frac▐     ▐     ▐     ▐   ▶
```

THE TABLE FEATURE

The TI-85 does not have a TABLE feature. However, there are several table programs for the TI-85 on the Texas Instruments web site, www.ti.com. These programs can be downloaded to your grapher.

GRAPHING EQUATIONS

After entering an equation and setting a viewing rectangle, you can view the graph of the equation.

Example 6, page 7 Graph using a grapher: $y = \dfrac{1}{2}x + 1$.

We will enter the equation on the equation-editor, or "y(x) =," screen. Press $\boxed{\text{GRAPH}}$ $\boxed{\text{F1}}$ to go to this screen. Clear any entries that are present as described on page 83 of this manual. Next enter the equation by positioning the cursor beside "y1 =" and pressing $\boxed{(}$ $\boxed{1}$ $\boxed{\div}$ $\boxed{2}$ $\boxed{)}$ $\boxed{\text{F1}}$ $\boxed{+}$ 1. Note that the parentheses must be used. If they are not, the expression $1/2x + 1$ will be interpreted as $\dfrac{1}{2x} + 1$.

The standard $[-10, 10, -10, 10]$ viewing rectangle is a good choice for this graph. Access the RANGE screen by pressing $\boxed{\text{2nd}}$ $\boxed{\text{F2}}$ and enter these dimensions. Then press $\boxed{\text{F5}}$ to see the graph or, immediately after entering the equation, simply press $\boxed{\text{2nd}}$ $\boxed{\text{F3}}$ $\boxed{\text{F4}}$ to select the standard viewing rectangle and see the graph.

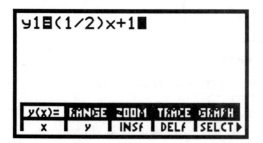

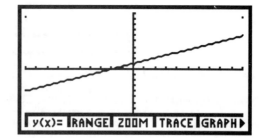

FINDING POINTS OF INTERSECTION

We can use the ISECT (Intersect) feature from the GRAPH MATH menu to find the point(s) of intersection of two graphs.

Example 9, page 9 Use a grapher to find the point of intersection of the graphs of $x - y = -5$ and $y = 4x + 10$.

We begin by entering the equations on the equation-editor screen. Since equations must be entered in the form "y =", we solve the first equation for y, obtaining $y = x + 5$. Then press $\boxed{\text{GRAPH}}$ $\boxed{\text{F1}}$ to go to the equation-editor screen. Clear any existing entries. Enter $y_1 = x + 5$ by positioning the cursor beside "y1 =" and pressing $\boxed{\text{F1}}$ $\boxed{+}$ 5, or $\boxed{\text{x-VAR}}$ $\boxed{+}$ 5. Next press $\boxed{\text{ENTER}}$ or $\boxed{\bigtriangledown}$ to position the cursor beside "y2 =" and enter $y_2 = 4x + 10$ by pressing 4 $\boxed{\text{F1}}$ $\boxed{+}$ 1 0, or 4 $\boxed{\text{x-VAR}}$ $\boxed{+}$ 1 0. Now graph the equations. We begin by using the standard viewing rectangle and see that it is a good choice because it shows the point of intersection of the graphs.

We we will use the ISECT (Intersect) feature from the GRAPH MATH menu to find the coordinates of that point. To select this feature press $\boxed{\text{GRAPH}}$ $\boxed{\text{MORE}}$ $\boxed{\text{F1}}$ $\boxed{\text{MORE}}$ $\boxed{\text{F5}}$. Use the $\boxed{\triangleleft}$ or $\boxed{\triangleright}$ key to move the cursor near the point of intersection and press $\boxed{\text{ENTER}}$ $\boxed{\text{ENTER}}$. The coordinates of the point of intersection appear at the bottom of the screen.

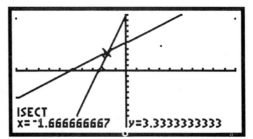

We see that the graphs intersect at the point $(-1.666666667, 3.3333333333)$. This is a decimal approximation for the point of intersection. If the coordinates are rational numbers, their exact values can be found using the "▷ Frac" feature from the MATH MISC menu.

To do this first press $\boxed{\text{2nd}}$ $\boxed{\text{QUIT}}$ to go to the home screen. The x- and y-coordinates of the point of intersection are stored in the calculator as x and y, respectively. To convert the decimal approximation for x to a rational number, press $\boxed{\text{x-VAR}}$ $\boxed{\text{2nd}}$ $\boxed{\text{MATH}}$ $\boxed{\text{F5}}$ $\boxed{\text{MORE}}$ $\boxed{\text{F1}}$ $\boxed{\text{ENTER}}$. (MATH is the second operation associated with the $\boxed{\times}$ multiplication key.) These keystrokes tell the grapher to use x, and then they access the MISC submenu of the MATH menu, copy "▷ Frac" to the home screen, and display the conversion. If ▷ Frac has been placed in position F1 of your Custom menu as described on page 85 of this manual, the keystrokes $\boxed{\text{2nd}}$ $\boxed{\text{MATH}}$ $\boxed{\text{F5}}$ $\boxed{\text{MORE}}$ can be replaced by $\boxed{\text{CUSTOM}}$. To convert y to a rational number when the MATH MISC menu is displayed, press $\boxed{\text{2nd}}$ $\boxed{\text{ALPHA}}$ $\boxed{\text{Y}}$ $\boxed{\text{F1}}$ $\boxed{\text{ENTER}}$. (Y is the alphabetic operation associated with the 0 numeric key.) To use the Custom menu press $\boxed{\text{CUSTOM}}$ before $\boxed{\text{F1}}$. We see that the point of intersection is $\left(-\dfrac{5}{3}, \dfrac{10}{3} \right)$.

Chapter R
Basic Concepts of Algebra

ABSOLUTE VALUE

Section R.1, Example 3 Find the distance between -2 and 3.

The distance between -2 and 3 is $|-2-3|$, or $|3-(-2)|$. Absolute value notation is denoted "abs" on the grapher and is found in the MATH NUM menu.

To enter $|-2-3|$ first press $\boxed{\text{2nd}}$ $\boxed{\text{MATH}}$ $\boxed{\text{F1}}$ to display the MATH NUM menu. Then press $\boxed{\text{F5}}$ $\boxed{(}$ $\boxed{(-)}$ $\boxed{2}$ $\boxed{-}$ $\boxed{3}$ $\boxed{)}$ $\boxed{\text{ENTER}}$. To enter $|3-(-2)|$ press $\boxed{\text{2nd}}$ $\boxed{\text{MATH}}$ $\boxed{\text{F1}}$ $\boxed{\text{F5}}$ $\boxed{(}$ $\boxed{3}$ $\boxed{-}$ $\boxed{(}$ $\boxed{(-)}$ $\boxed{2}$ $\boxed{)}$ $\boxed{)}$ $\boxed{\text{ENTER}}$. Note that the expression inside the absolute value symbols must be enclosed in parentheses so that the absolute value of the entire expression will be found. The parentheses around -2 in the second expression are not necessary, but they allow the expression to be more easily read so we have included them here.

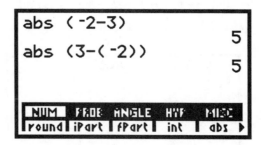

SCIENTIFIC NOTATION

To enter a number in scientific notation, first type the decimal portion of the number; then press $\boxed{\text{EE}}$; finally type the exponent, which can be at most two digits. For example, to enter 1.789×10^{-11} in scientific notation, press 1 $\boxed{.}$ $7\,8\,9$ $\boxed{\text{EE}}$ $\boxed{(-)}$ $1\,1$ $\boxed{\text{ENTER}}$. To enter 6.084×10^{23} in scientific notation, press 6 $\boxed{.}$ $0\,8\,4$ $\boxed{\text{EE}}$ $2\,3$ $\boxed{\text{ENTER}}$. The decimal portion of each number appears before a small E while the exponent follows the E.

```
1.789E-11
                 1.789E-11
6.084E23
                 6.084E23
■

 NUM   PROB  ANGLE  HYP   MISC
round iPart  fPart  int   abs  ▶
```

The grapher can be used to perform computations in scientific notation.

Section R.2, Example 7 *Distance to a Star.* Alpha Centauri is about 4.3 light-years from Earth. One light-year is the distance that light travels in one year and is about 5.88×10^{12} miles. How many miles is it from Earth to Alpha Centauri? Express your answer in scientific notation.

To solve this problem we find the product $4.3 \times (5.88 \times 10^{12})$. Press 4 $\boxed{.}$ 3 $\boxed{\times}$ 5 $\boxed{.}$ $8\,8$ $\boxed{\text{EE}}$ $1\,2$ $\boxed{\text{ENTER}}$. The result is 2.5284×10^{13} miles.

```
4.3*5.88E12
                    2.5284E13
■



 NUM   PROB  ANGLE  HYP   MISC
 round  iPart  fPart   int    abs  ▶
```

ORDER OF OPERATIONS

Section R.2, Example 8 (b) Calculate: $\dfrac{10 \div (8-6) + 9 \cdot 4}{2^5 + 3^2}$.

In order to divide the entire numerator by the entire denominator, we must enclose both the numerator and the denominator in parentheses. That is, we enter $(10 \div (8-6) + 9 \cdot 4) \div (2^5 + 3^2)$. Press $\boxed{(}$ $1\,0$ $\boxed{\div}$ $\boxed{(}$ 8 $\boxed{-}$ 6 $\boxed{)}$ $\boxed{+}$ 9 $\boxed{\times}$ 4 $\boxed{)}$ $\boxed{\div}$ $\boxed{(}$ 2 $\boxed{\wedge}$ 5 $\boxed{+}$ 3 $\boxed{x^2}$ $\boxed{)}$ $\boxed{\text{ENTER}}$. Note that 3^2 can be entered either as 3 $\boxed{x^2}$ or as 3 $\boxed{\wedge}$ 2.

```
(10/(8−6)+9*4)/(2^5+3
2)
                            1
■



 NUM   PROB  ANGLE  HYP   MISC
 round  iPart  fPart   int    abs  ▶
```

THE PATH GRAPH STYLE

The TI-85 does not have the capability to produce a path graph style.

SELECTING THE DrawDot GRAPH FORMAT

When graphing an equation in which a variable appears in a denominator, the DrawDot graph format should be used. To select this format press $\boxed{\text{GRAPH}}$ $\boxed{\text{MORE}}$ $\boxed{\text{F3}}$ to display the Graph Format screen and use $\boxed{\triangledown}$ and $\boxed{\triangleright}$ to position the blinking cursor over "DrawDot." Then press $\boxed{\text{ENTER}}$.

To return to the DrawLine format, press $\boxed{\text{GRAPH}}$ $\boxed{\text{MORE}}$ $\boxed{\text{F3}}$, position the cursor over DrawLine, and press $\boxed{\text{ENTER}}$.

RADICAL NOTATION

We can use the square-root and xth-root features to simplify radical expressions.

Section R.6, Example 1 Simplify each of the following.

a) $\sqrt{36}$ b) $-\sqrt{36}$ c) $\sqrt[5]{\dfrac{32}{243}}$ d) $\sqrt[3]{-8}$ e) $\sqrt[4]{-16}$

a) To find $\sqrt{36}$ press $\boxed{\text{2nd}}$ $\boxed{\sqrt{}}$ 3 6 $\boxed{\text{ENTER}}$. ($\sqrt{}$ is the second operation associated with the $\boxed{x^2}$ key.)

b) To find $-\sqrt{36}$ press $\boxed{(-)}$ $\boxed{\text{2nd}}$ $\boxed{\sqrt{}}$ 3 6 $\boxed{\text{ENTER}}$.

```
√36
                          6
-√36
                         -6
```

c) We will use the xth-root feature from the MATH MISC menu to find $\sqrt[5]{\dfrac{32}{243}}$. We will also use ▷Frac to express the result as a fraction. Press 5 $\boxed{\text{2nd}}$ $\boxed{\text{MATH}}$ $\boxed{\text{F5}}$ $\boxed{\text{MORE}}$ $\boxed{\text{F4}}$ $\boxed{(}$ 3 2 $\boxed{\div}$ 2 4 3 $\boxed{)}$ $\boxed{\text{F1}}$ $\boxed{\text{ENTER}}$. Note that the parentheses must be used. If they are not, the expression is interpreted as $\dfrac{\sqrt[5]{32}}{243}$.

(d) We will also use the MATH MISC menu to find $\sqrt[3]{-8}$. Press 3 $\boxed{\text{2nd}}$ $\boxed{\text{MATH}}$ $\boxed{\text{F5}}$ $\boxed{\text{MORE}}$ $\boxed{\text{F4}}$ $\boxed{(-)}$ 8 $\boxed{\text{ENTER}}$.

```
5 ×√(32/243)▶Frac
                        2/3
3 ×√ -8
                         -2

 NUM   FROB  ANGLE  HYP  MISC
▶Frac   %  ▷Eval  ×√  eval
```

e) To enter $\sqrt[4]{-16}$ press 4 $\boxed{\text{2nd}}$ $\boxed{\text{MATH}}$ $\boxed{\text{F5}}$ $\boxed{\text{MORE}}$ $\boxed{\text{F4}}$ $\boxed{(-)}$ 1 6 $\boxed{\text{ENTER}}$. The TI-85 returns a result in the form (a, b). This number is not a real number. Numbers of this type will be discussed in Chapter 2.

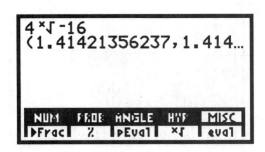

SOLVING EQUATIONS GRAPHICALLY

We can use the ISECT (Intersect) feature from the GRAPH MATH menu to solve equations.

Section R.7, Example 1 Solve: $2(5 - 3x) = 8 - 3(x + 2)$.

On the equation-editor screen clear any existing entries and then enter $y_1 = 2(5 - 3x)$ and $y_2 = 8 - 3(x + 2)$. The solution of the original equation is the first coordinate of the point of intersection of the graphs of y_1 and y_2. Find the point of intersection as described on page 86 of this manual.

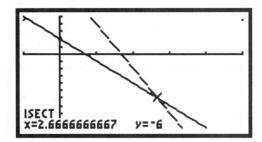

The first coordinate of the point of intersection is 2.6666666667. This is a decimal approximation of the solution. This number is stored in the calculator as x. If it is a rational number we can find fractional notation for the exact solution using the ▷Frac feature. Press $\boxed{\text{2nd}}$ $\boxed{\text{QUIT}}$ to go to the home screen. Then press $\boxed{\text{x-VAR}}$ $\boxed{\text{2nd}}$ $\boxed{\text{MATH}}$ $\boxed{\text{F5}}$ $\boxed{\text{MORE}}$ $\boxed{\text{F1}}$ $\boxed{\text{ENTER}}$. If you have put ▷ Frac in position F1 of your custom menu as described on page 85 of this manual, press $\boxed{\text{x-VAR}}$ $\boxed{\text{CUSTOM}}$ $\boxed{\text{F1}}$ $\boxed{\text{ENTER}}$. We see that the solution is 8/3.

$$\boxed{\begin{array}{l} \text{x▶Frac} \\ \qquad\qquad\qquad\qquad 8/3 \\ \blacksquare \\[1em] \hline \textbf{NUM} \quad \text{PROB} \quad \text{ANGLE} \quad \text{HYP} \quad \boxed{\textbf{MISC}} \\ \boxed{\text{▶Frac}} \quad \% \quad \boxed{\text{▷Eval}} \quad \text{×√} \quad \boxed{\text{eval}} \end{array}}$$

Chapter 1
Graphs, Functions, and Models

FINDING FUNCTION VALUES

When a formula for a function is given, function values can be found in several ways.

Section 1.1, Example 4 (b) For $f(x) = 2x^2 - x + 3$, find $f(-7)$.

Method 1: Substitute the inputs directly in the formula. Press 2 $\boxed{(}$ $\boxed{(-)}$ 7 $\boxed{)}$ $\boxed{x^2}$ $\boxed{-}$ $\boxed{(}$ $\boxed{(-)}$ 7 $\boxed{)}$ $\boxed{+}$ 3 $\boxed{\text{ENTER}}$.
Although it is not necessary to use the second set of parentheses, they allow the expression to be read more easily so we include them here.

```
2(-7)2-(-7)+3
                    108
```

Method 2: Enter $y_1 = 2x^2 - x + 3$ on the "y(x) =" screen. Then press $\boxed{\text{2nd}}$ $\boxed{\text{QUIT}}$ to go to the home screen. To find $f(-7)$, the value of y_1 when $x = -7$, press $\boxed{(-)}$ 7 $\boxed{\text{STO} \triangleright}$ $\boxed{\text{x-VAR}}$ $\boxed{\text{2nd}}$ $\boxed{:}$ $\boxed{\text{2nd}}$ $\boxed{\text{alpha}}$ $\boxed{\text{Y}}$ $\boxed{\text{ALPHA}}$ $\boxed{\text{ALPHA}}$ 1 $\boxed{\text{ENTER}}$. (: is the second operation associated with the $\boxed{.}$ key. alpha is the second operation associated with the $\boxed{\text{ALPHA}}$ key.) This series of keystrokes stores -7 as the value of x and then substitutes it in the function y_1.

```
-7→x:y1
                    108
■
```

Method 3: We can also use the Eval feature from the GRAPH menu to find $f(-7)$. To do this, graph $y_1 = 2x^2 - x + 3$ in a viewing rectangle that includes the x-value -7. We will use the standard viewing rectangle. Then press $\boxed{\text{MORE}}$ $\boxed{\text{MORE}}$ $\boxed{\text{F1}}$ to select Eval. Now supply the desired x-value by pressing $\boxed{(-)}$ 7. Press $\boxed{\text{ENTER}}$ to see X = -7, Y = 108 at the bottom of the screen, Thus, $f(-7) = 108$.

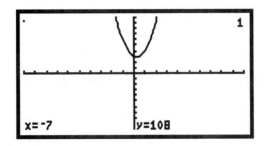

GRAPHS OF FUNCTIONS

The TI-85 does not use function notation. To graph a function, first replace the function notation with y. For example, to graph $f(x) = x^2 - 5$ replace $f(x)$ with y. Then enter the equation $y = x^2 - 5$ on the equation-editor screen and graph it as described on page 86 of this manual.

LINEAR REGRESSION

We can use the Linear Regression feature in the STAT CALC menu to fit a linear equation to a set of data.

Section 1.3, Example 1 The following table shows the number of apartment households in the United States, in millions, for years since 1970.

Years, x	Number of Apartment Households (in millions)
1970, 0	8.5
1975, 5	9.9
1980, 10	10.8
1985, 15	12.9
1990, 20	14.2
1997, 27	14.5

(a) Fit a regression line to the data using the linear regression feature on a grapher.

(b) Use the linear model to predict the number of apartment households in 2003.

(a) We will enter the data as ordered pairs on the STAT list editor screen as described on pages 83 and 84 of this manual.

```
x=xStat        y=yStat
 x1=0
 y1=8.5
 x2=5
↓y2=9.9

 CALC   EDIT  ORMW  FCST
 INSi  DELi SORTX SORTY CLRxy
```

The grapher's linear regression feature can be used to fit a linear equation to the data. Once the data have been entered in the lists press [2nd] [F1] [ENTER] [ENTER] [F2] to select LINR (linear regression) from the STAT CALC menu and to display the coefficients a and b of the regression equation $y = a + bx$ along with "corr," the coefficient of correlation and n, the number of data points.

```
LinR
 a=8.71738539898
 b=.240203735144
 corr=.975506836378
 n=6

 CALC  EXIT  DRAW  FCST
 1-VAR LINR  LNR  EXPR PWRR ▶
```

Immediately after the regression equation is found it can be copied to the equation-editor screen as y_1. Note that any previous entry in y_1 must have been cleared first. Press GRAPH F1 and position the cursor beside $y_1 =$. Then press 2nd VARS MORE MORE F3. (VARS is the second operation associated with the 3 numeric key.) These keystrokes select Statistics from the VARS menu. Use the ▽ key to position the cursor beside RegEq and press ENTER to paste it in y_1.

```
y1◻RegEq▪



 y(x)= RANGE ZOOM TRACE GRAPH
  x     y   INSf  DELf SELCT▶
```

(b) To predict the number of apartment households in 2003, evaluate the regression equation for $x = 33$. (2003 is 33 years after 1970.) Use any of the methods for evaluating a function presented earlier in this chapter. (See page 93 of this manual.) We will store 33 as x and evaluate y_1.

```
33→x:y1
             16.6441086587



```

When $x = 33$, $y \approx 16.6$, so we predict that there will be about 16.6 million apartment households in the United States in 2003.

We can also plot the data points along with the graph of the regression equation. Recall that the equation was copied to the equation-editor screen in part(a). First select a viewing rectangle. We will use $[-3, 30, 7, 16]$. Then press STAT F3 to see the graph of the regression equation followed by F2 to add the scatterplot of the data points.

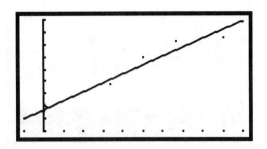

THE FMAX AND FMIN FEATURES

Section 1.4, Example 2 Use a grapher to determine any relative maxima or minima of the function $f(x) = 0.1x^3 - 0.6x^2 - 0.1x + 2$.

First graph $y_1 = 0.1x^3 - 0.6x^2 - 0.1x + 2$ in a viewing rectangle that displays the relative extrema of the function. Trial and error reveals that one good choice is $[-4, 6, -3, 3]$. Observe that a relative maximum occurs near $x = 0$ and a relative minimum occurs near $x = 4$.

To find the relative maximum, first press $\boxed{\text{MORE}}$ $\boxed{\text{F1}}$ $\boxed{\text{MORE}}$ $\boxed{\text{F2}}$ to select the FMAX feature from the GRAPH MATH menu. Move the cursor near the relative maximum point and press $\boxed{\text{ENTER}}$. We see that a relative maximum function value of approximately 2.004 occurs when $x \approx -0.0817$.

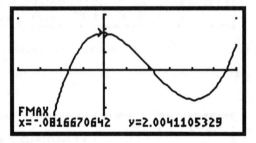

To find the relative minimum, select the FMIN feature from the GRAPH MATH menu by pressing $\boxed{\text{GRAPH}}$ $\boxed{\text{MORE}}$ $\boxed{\text{F1}}$ $\boxed{\text{MORE}}$ $\boxed{\text{F1}}$. Move the cursor near the relative minimum and press $\boxed{\text{ENTER}}$. We see that a relative minimum function value of approximately -1.604 occurs when $x \approx 4.082$.

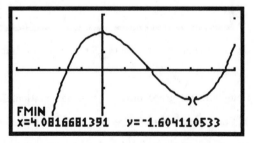

GRAPHING FUNCTIONS DEFINED PIECEWISE

Operations from the TEST menu are used to enter functions that are defined piecewise. (TEST is the second operation associated with the 2 numeric key.) Select the DrawDot graph format from the GRAPH FORMT menu. (See page 90 of this manual for the procedure.)

Section 1.4, Example 5 Graph

$$f(x) = \begin{cases} 4, & \text{for } x \leq 0, \\ 4 - x^2, & \text{for } 0 < x \leq 2, \\ 2x - 6, & \text{for } x > 2. \end{cases}$$

Press $\boxed{\text{GRAPH}}$ $\boxed{\text{F1}}$ to select "y(x) =" and clear any functions that have previously been entered. With the cursor beside "$y1 =$" enter the function as described in the middle of page 102 of the text by pressing $\boxed{(}$ $\boxed{4}$ $\boxed{)}$ $\boxed{(}$ $\boxed{x\text{-VAR}}$ $\boxed{\text{2nd}}$ $\boxed{\text{TEST}}$ $\boxed{\text{F4}}$ $\boxed{0}$ $\boxed{)}$ $\boxed{+}$ $\boxed{(}$ $\boxed{4}$ $\boxed{-}$ $\boxed{x\text{-VAR}}$ $\boxed{x^2}$ $\boxed{)}$ $\boxed{(}$ $\boxed{0}$ $\boxed{\text{F2}}$ $\boxed{x\text{-VAR}}$ $\boxed{)}$ $\boxed{(}$ $\boxed{x\text{-VAR}}$ $\boxed{\text{F4}}$ $\boxed{2}$ $\boxed{)}$ $\boxed{+}$ $\boxed{(}$ $\boxed{2}$ $\boxed{x\text{-VAR}}$ $\boxed{-}$ $\boxed{6}$ $\boxed{)}$ $\boxed{(}$ $\boxed{x\text{-VAR}}$ $\boxed{\text{F3}}$ $\boxed{2}$ $\boxed{)}$. Select a viewing rectangle and then press $\boxed{\text{F5}}$ to graph the function.

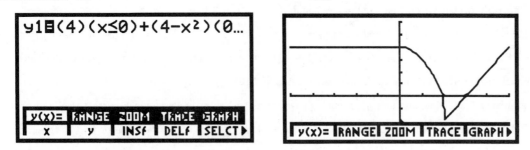

THE GREATEST INTEGER FUNCTION

The greatest integer function is found in the MATH NUM menu and is denoted "int." To find int(1.9) press $\boxed{\text{2nd}}$ $\boxed{\text{MATH}}$ $\boxed{\text{F1}}$ $\boxed{\text{F4}}$ $\boxed{1}$ $\boxed{.}$ $\boxed{9}$ $\boxed{\text{ENTER}}$.

We can also graph the greatest integer function.

Section 1.4, Example 7 Graph $f(x) = \text{int}(x)$.

With the grapher set in DrawDot mode, press $\boxed{\text{GRAPH}}$ $\boxed{\text{F1}}$ to select y(x) = and clear any previously entered functions. Position the cursor beside "$y1 =$" and select the greatest integer function from the MATH NUM menu as follows. Press $\boxed{\text{2nd}}$ $\boxed{\text{MATH}}$ $\boxed{\text{F1}}$ to select NUM. Then press $\boxed{\text{F4}}$ to select "int" followed by $\boxed{x\text{-VAR}}$. Now press $\boxed{\text{GRAPH}}$ to return to the menu that allows you to select a viewing rectangle and graph the function.

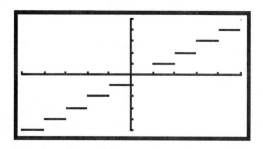

THE ALGEBRA OF FUNCTIONS

The grapher can be used to evaluate and graph combinations of functions.

Section 1.4, Example 8 (b) Given that $f(x) = x + 1$ and $g(x) = \sqrt{x+3}$, find $(f+g)(6)$.

Press $\boxed{\text{GRAPH}}$ $\boxed{\text{F1}}$ to select "y(x) =" and enter $y_1 = x + 1$, $y_2 = \sqrt{x+3}$, and $y_3 = y_1 + y_2$. To enter $y_3 = y_1 + y_2$ press $\boxed{\text{F2}}$ 1 $\boxed{+}$ $\boxed{\text{F2}}$ 2. Note that $y_3 = f(x) + g(x)$, or $(f+g)(x)$. Use y_3 to find $(f+g)(6)$ using one of the methods for finding function values described on page 93 of this manual. We find that $(f+g)(6) = 10$.

To view the graphs of $f(x)$, $g(x)$, and $(f+g)(x)$ enter y_1, y_2, and y_3 as above, select a viewing rectangle, and press $\boxed{\text{F5}}$ to select GRAPH. These graphs appear on page 115 of the text. It is possible to deselect one or two of these functions and display the graph(s) of the remaining function(s). For example, to display only the graph of y_3 without deleting the equations of y_1 and y_2, press $\boxed{\text{GRAPH}}$ $\boxed{\text{F1}}$ to select "y(x) =." Then move the cursor to y_1 and press $\boxed{\text{F5}}$ to choose SELCT. This deselects or turns off y_1. Do the same for y_2. Now press $\boxed{\text{2nd}}$ $\boxed{\text{M5}}$ to select GRAPH and see only the graph of y_3.

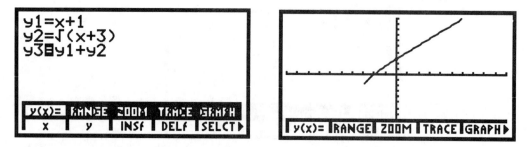

To select or turn on a function again, repeat this process. The SELCT operation reverses the selection status of a function. That is, it deselects a selected function and selects a deselected function. Note that the equals sign on a selected function is highlighted.

GRAPHING CIRCLES

If the center and radius of a circle are known, the circle can be graphed using the Circl feature.

Section 1.7, Exercise 37 Graph $(x-1)^2 + (y-5)^2 = 36$.

The center of this circle is (1,5) and its radius is 6. To graph it first press $\boxed{\text{GRAPH}}$ $\boxed{\text{F1}}$ to select "y(x) =" and clear all previously entered equations. Then select a square viewing rectangle. We will use $[-12, 12, -2, 12]$. (See page 150 of the text for a discussion of squaring the viewing rectangle.) Press [2nd] [QUIT] to go to the home screen. Now press [2nd] [CATALOG] [C] [ENTER]. Enter the coordinates of the center and the radius, separating the entries by commas, and close the parentheses: 1 [,] 5 [,] 6 [)] [ENTER].

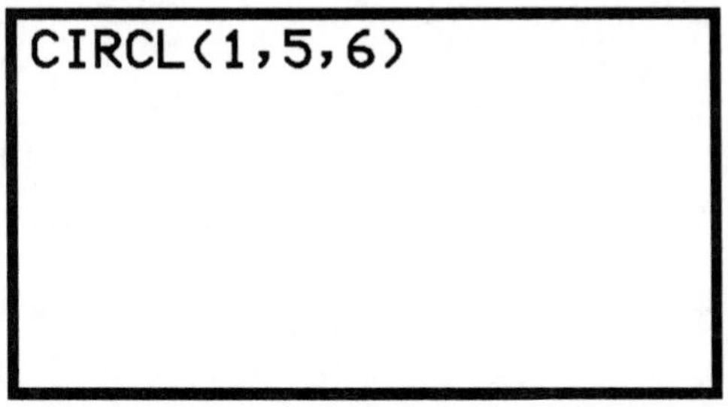

```
CIRCL(1,5,6)
```

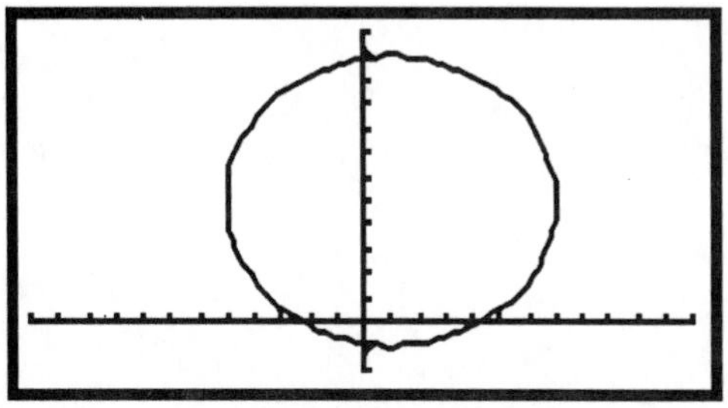

The software used to produce the the graph above causes distortion. Nevertheless, when the circle is graphed on a grapher in a square viewing rectangle, there is no distortion.

A circle graphed from the home screen can be cleared from the graph screen by pressing [GRAPH] [MORE] [F2] to access the DRAW menu. Then press [MORE] [F5] to select the CLDRW (clear drawing) operation. The graph will also be cleared when another function is subsequently entered on the "y(x) =" screen and graphed.

A circle can also graphed using the DRAW feature, but this method does not yield as accurate a graph as the method above.

Chapter 2
Functions and Equations: Zeros and Solutions

THE ROOT FEATURE

The Root feature of the TI-85 can be used to find the zeros of a function or to solve an equation in the form $f(x) = 0$.

Section 2.1, Example 1 Find the zero of $f(x) = 5x - 9$.

On the equation-editor screen, clear any existing entries and then enter $y_1 = 5x - 9$. Now graph the function in a viewing rectangle that shows the x-intercept clearly. The standard viewing rectangle is a good choice.

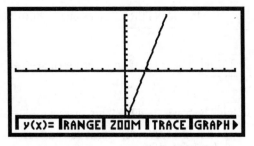

Press $\boxed{\text{MORE}}$ $\boxed{\text{F1}}$ to display the GRAPH MATH menu. Then press $\boxed{\text{F3}}$ to select the Root feature. Position the cursor near the zero and press $\boxed{\text{ENTER}}$. We see that $y = 0$ when $x = 1.8$, so 1.8 is the zero of the function.

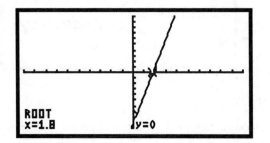

If a function has more than one zero, the Root feature can be used as many times as necessary to find all of them.

OPERATIONS WITH COMPLEX NUMBERS

A complex number $a + bi$ is represented on the TI-85 as (a, b). Operations with complex numbers can be performed on the grapher.

Section 2.1, Example 4

(a) Add: $(8 + 6i) + (3 + 2i)$.

To find this sum press $\boxed{\text{2nd}}$ $\boxed{\text{QUIT}}$ to go to the home screen and then press $\boxed{(}$ $\boxed{8}$ $\boxed{,}$ $\boxed{6}$ $\boxed{)}$ $\boxed{+}$ $\boxed{(}$ $\boxed{3}$ $\boxed{,}$ $\boxed{2}$ $\boxed{)}$ $\boxed{\text{ENTER}}$. The grapher returns (11, 8), indicating that the sum is $11 + 8i$.

(b) Subtract: $(4 + 5i) - (6 - 3i)$.

Press $\boxed{(}$ $\boxed{4}$ $\boxed{,}$ $\boxed{5}$ $\boxed{)}$ $\boxed{-}$ $\boxed{(}$ $\boxed{6}$ $\boxed{,}$ $\boxed{-}$ $\boxed{3}$ $\boxed{)}$ $\boxed{\text{ENTER}}$. The grapher returns $(-2, 8)$, indicating that the difference is $-2 + 8i$.

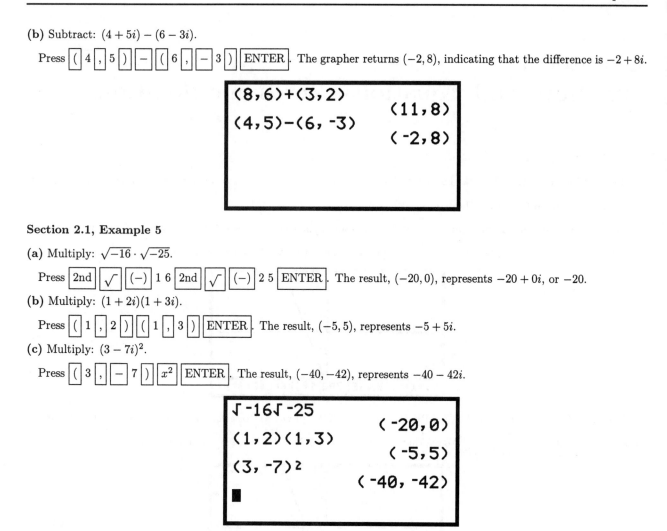

Section 2.1, Example 5

(a) Multiply: $\sqrt{-16} \cdot \sqrt{-25}$.

Press $\boxed{\text{2nd}}$ $\boxed{\sqrt{}}$ $\boxed{(-)}$ $1\,6$ $\boxed{\text{2nd}}$ $\boxed{\sqrt{}}$ $\boxed{(-)}$ $2\,5$ $\boxed{\text{ENTER}}$. The result, $(-20, 0)$, represents $-20 + 0i$, or -20.

(b) Multiply: $(1 + 2i)(1 + 3i)$.

Press $\boxed{(}$ $\boxed{1}$ $\boxed{,}$ $\boxed{2}$ $\boxed{)}$ $\boxed{(}$ $\boxed{1}$ $\boxed{,}$ $\boxed{3}$ $\boxed{)}$ $\boxed{\text{ENTER}}$. The result, $(-5, 5)$, represents $-5 + 5i$.

(c) Multiply: $(3 - 7i)^2$.

Press $\boxed{(}$ $\boxed{3}$ $\boxed{,}$ $\boxed{-}$ $\boxed{7}$ $\boxed{)}$ $\boxed{x^2}$ $\boxed{\text{ENTER}}$. The result, $(-40, -42)$, represents $-40 - 42i$.

QUADRATIC REGRESSION

Quadratic functions can be fit to data using the quadratic regression operation from the STAT CALC menu. The operations of entering data, making scatterplots, and graphing and evaluating quadratic regression functions are the same as for linear regression functions.

Section 2.5, Example 1 *Leisure Time* The following table shows the median number of hours of leisure time that Americans had each week in various years.

Year	Median Number of Leisure Hours per Week
0, 1973	26.2
7, 1980	19.2
14, 1987	16.6
20, 1993	18.8
24, 1997	19.5

(a) Make a scatterplot of the data, letting x represent the number of years since 1973, and determine whether a linear function, a quadratic function, or neither seems to fit the data.

(b) Use a grapher to fit the type of function determined in part (a) to the data.

(c) Graph the equation with the scatterplot.

(d) Use the function found in part (c) to estimate the number of leisure hours per week in 1978; in 1990; in 2005.

(a) Clear any existing entries on the equation-editor screen. Then enter the data in xStat and yStat and make a scatterplot as described on pages 83 and 84 of this manual. We have used a viewing rectangle with dimensions [0, 25, 10, 30], Xscl = 5, Yscl = 5. It appears that a quadratic function fits the data.

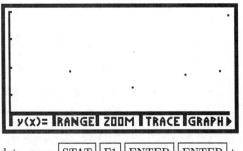

(b) To fit a quadratic function to the data, press $\boxed{\text{STAT}}$ $\boxed{\text{F1}}$ $\boxed{\text{ENTER}}$ $\boxed{\text{ENTER}}$ to view the STAT CALC menu. Then select P2Reg (quadratic regression) by pressing $\boxed{\text{MORE}}$ $\boxed{\text{F1}}$. The coefficients of a quadratic equation $y = ax^2 + bx + c$ are displayed using set notation. Note that at least three data points are required for quadratic regression.

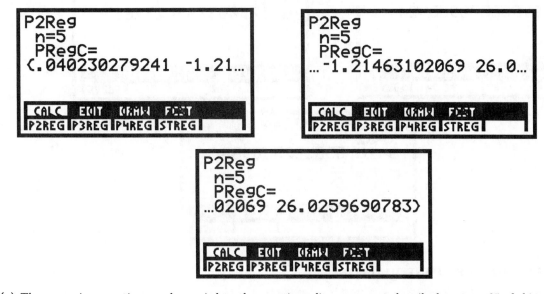

(c) The regression equation can be copied to the equation editor screen as described on page 95 of this manual. Then press $\boxed{\text{2nd}}$ $\boxed{\text{F5}}$ $\boxed{\text{STAT}}$ $\boxed{\text{F3}}$ to see the graph of the regression equation followed by $\boxed{\text{F2}}$ to add the scatterplot of the data points.

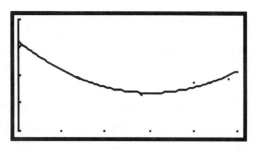

(d) To estimate the number of leisure hours per week in 1978, 1990, and 2005, we evaluate the regression function for 5, 17, and 32, respectively. We could use any of the methods for evaluating a function found on page 93 of this manual. We could also use the FORECAST feature as we will illustrate here.

First press $\boxed{\text{2nd}}$ $\boxed{\text{QUIT}}$ to go to the home screen. Then press $\boxed{\text{STAT}}$ $\boxed{\text{F4}}$ to display the FORECAST screen. Enter 5 beside "$x =$" by pressing 5 $\boxed{\text{ENTER}}$. Then, with the cursor beside "$y =$," press $\boxed{\text{F5}}$. We see that Americans had about 21.0 leisure hours per week in 1978. Now to evaluate the regression function for $x = 17$, press $\boxed{\triangle}$ to position the cursor beside "$x =$" and press 1 7 $\boxed{\text{ENTER}}$ $\boxed{\text{F5}}$. Americans had approximately 17.0 leisure hours per week in 1990. Next evaluate the function for $x = 32$ by pressing $\boxed{\triangle}$ 3 2 $\boxed{\text{ENTER}}$ $\boxed{\text{F5}}$. We predict that Americans will have about 28.4 leisure hours per week in 2005.

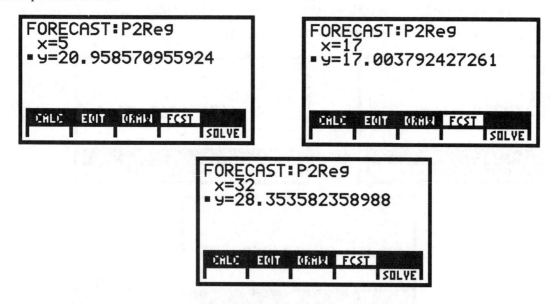

CHECKING SOLUTIONS OF INEQUALITIES

We can perform a partial check of the solution of an inequality using operations from the TEST menu.

Section 2.7, Example 2 Solve: $-3 < 2x + 5 \leq 7$.

The solution set is found algebraically in the text. It is $\{x| -4 < x \leq 1\}$, or $(-4, 1]$. We can perform a partial check of this solution by graphing $y = (-3 < 2x + 5)$ *and* $(2x + 5 \leq 7)$ in the DrawDot graph format. The value of y will be 1 for those x-values which make y a true statement. It will be 0 for those x-values for which y is false. To enter the expression for y, position the cursor beside y_1 on the y(x) = screen. Then press [(] [(−)] 3 [2nd] [TEST] [F2] 2 [x-VAR] [+] 5 [)] [2nd] [CATALOG]. Use the [▽] key to position the triangular selection cursor beside "and" and then press [ENTER] to paste it into the expression on the y(x) = screen. The press [(] 2 [x-VAR] [+] 5 [2nd] [TEST] [F4] 7 [)]. (TEST is the second operation associated with the 2 numeric key.) The keystrokes [2nd] [TEST] [F2] display the TEST menu and paste the symbol "<" from that menu to the equation-editor screen. The keystrokes [2nd] [TEST] [F4] display the TEST menu again and paste the symbol "≤" into the equation-editor screen.

Now select a viewing rectangle and press [F5] to see the graph. We use the viewing rectangle $[-10, 10, -1, 2]$.

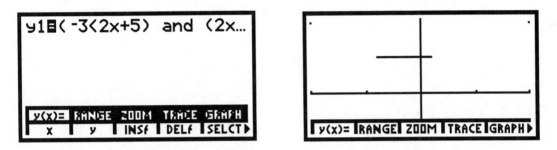

We see that $y = 1$ for x-values from -4 to 1, confirming that all x-values from -4 to 1 are in the solution set. The algebraic solution indicates that the endpoint 1 is also in the solution set.

Chapter 3
Polynomial and Rational Functions

POWER MODELS

A power model $y = ax^b$ can be fit to data using the power regression feature from the STAT CALC menu.

Section 3.1, Example 4 (a) *Cholesterol Level and the Risk of Heart Attack.* The data in the following table show the relationship of cholesterol level in men to the risk of a heart attack.

Cholesterol Level, x	Men Per 10,000 Who Suffer a Heart Attack
100	30
200	65
250	100
275	130
300	180

(a) Use a grapher to fit a power function to the data.

Enter the data in lists as described on pages 83 and 84 of this manual. Then select PwrR (power regression) from the STAT CALC menu by pressing $\boxed{\text{STAT}}$ $\boxed{\text{F1}}$ $\boxed{\text{ENTER}}$ $\boxed{\text{ENTER}}$ $\boxed{\text{F5}}$. The grapher displays the coefficient a and the exponent b for the power function $y = ax^b$.

```
PwrR
 a=.024178957415
 b=1.52745717151
 corr=.973936133593
 n=5

 CALC  EDIT  CALC  FDST
1-VAR LINR  LNR  EXPR  PWRR ▶
```

This function can be copied to the $y(x) =$ screen as described on page 95 of this manual. Then it can be graphed. It can also be evaluated using one of the methods on pages 93 and 104.

CUBIC AND QUARTIC REGRESSION

We can fit third-degree, or cubic, functions and fourth-degree, or quartic, functions to data on a grapher.

Section 3.1, Example 5 (a) The table below shows the number of farms, in millions, for years after 1900. Model the data with both cubic and quartic functions. Let the first coordinate of each data point be the number of years after 1900.

Years after 1900	Number of Farms, in millions
10, 1910	6.4
20, 1920	6.5
30, 1930	6.3
40, 1940	6.1
50, 1950	5.4
59, 1959	3.7
69, 1969	2.7
78, 1978	2.3
87, 1987	2.1
97, 1997	1.9

Enter the data in lists as described on pages 83 and 84 of this manual. Go to the home screen and select P3Reg (cubic regression) from the STAT CALC menu by pressing $\boxed{\text{STAT}}$ $\boxed{\text{F1}}$ $\boxed{\text{ENTER}}$ $\boxed{\text{ENTER}}$ $\boxed{\text{MORE}}$ $\boxed{\text{F2}}$. The grapher displays the coefficients of a cubic function $y = ax^3 + bx^2 + cx + d$. Use the $\boxed{\triangleright}$ key to see all of the coefficients.

To model the data with a quartic function select P4Reg (quartic regression) from the STAT CALC menu. From the home screen press $\boxed{\text{STAT}}$ $\boxed{\text{F1}}$ $\boxed{\text{ENTER}}$ $\boxed{\text{ENTER}}$ $\boxed{\text{MORE}}$ $\boxed{\text{F3}}$. The grapher displays the coefficients of a quartic function $y = ax^4 + bx^3 + cx^2 + dx + e$. Use the $\boxed{\triangleright}$ key to see all of the coefficients.

A scatterplot of the data can be graphed as described on page 84 of this manual. This function can be copied to the $y(x) =$ screen as described on page 95 of this manual. Then it can be graphed along with the scatterplot. It can also be evaluated using one of the methods on pages 93 and 104.

GRAPHING RATIONAL FUNCTIONS

Section 3.4, Example 1 Consider $f(x) = \dfrac{1}{x - 3}$ and graph f.

In the text the domain is found to be $\{x | x \neq 3\}$, or $(-\infty, 3) \cup (3, \infty)$. Thus, there is not a point on the graph with an

x-coordinate of 3. Graphing the function in the DrawLine graph format can lead to an incorrect graph in which a line connects he last point plotted to the left of $x = 3$ with the last point plotted to the right of $x = 3$. This line can be eliminated by using the DrawDot graph format as described on page 90 of this manual. Selecting a ZDECM viewing rectangle from the ZOOM menu will also produce a graph in which this line does not appear. To do this, first enter $y = \dfrac{1}{x - 3}$ on the y(x) = screen and then press 2nd F3 MORE F4. The resulting range dimensions and graph are shown below.

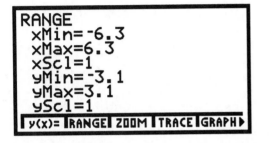 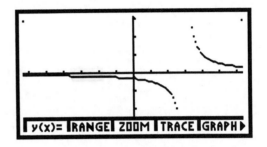

Section 3.4, Example 10 Graph: $g(x) = \dfrac{x - 2}{x^2 - x - 2}$.

As explained in the text, the graph of $g(x)$ is the graph of $y = \dfrac{1}{x + 1}$ with the point $\left(2, \dfrac{1}{3}\right)$ missing. The viewing rectangle used in the text to produce the graph with a "hole" at $\left(2, \dfrac{1}{3}\right)$ is obtained using the ZDECM feature from the ZOOM menu. After entering $y = \dfrac{x - 2}{x^2 - x - 2}$ on the y(x) = screen, press 2nd F3 MORE F4 to select this viewing rectangle and display the graph.

Chapter 4
Exponential and Logarithmic Functions

THE COMPOSITION OF FUNCTIONS

We can evaluate composite functions on a grapher.

Section 4.1, Example 1 (a) Given that $f(x) = 2x - 5$ and $g(x) = x^2 - 3x + 8$, find $(f \circ g)(7)$ and $(g \circ f)(7)$.

On the equation-editor screen enter $y_1 = 2x - 5$ and $y_2 = x^2 - 3x + 8$. Then $(f \circ g)(7) = (y_1 \circ y_2)(7)$, or $y_1(y_2(7))$ and $(g \circ f)(7) = (y_2 \circ y_1)(7)$, or $y_2(y_1(7))$. To find these function values press $\boxed{\text{2nd}}$ $\boxed{\text{QUIT}}$ to go to the home screen. Then find $(f \circ g)(7)$ by pressing 7 $\boxed{\text{STO▷}}$ $\boxed{\text{x-VAR}}$ $\boxed{\text{2nd}}$ $\boxed{:}$ $\boxed{\text{2nd}}$ $\boxed{\text{alpha}}$ $\boxed{\text{Y}}$ $\boxed{\text{ALPHA}}$ $\boxed{\text{ALPHA}}$ 2 $\boxed{\text{STO▷}}$ $\boxed{\text{x-VAR}}$ $\boxed{\text{2nd}}$ $\boxed{:}$ $\boxed{\text{2nd}}$ $\boxed{\text{alpha}}$ $\boxed{\text{Y}}$ $\boxed{\text{ALPHA}}$ $\boxed{\text{ALPHA}}$ 1 $\boxed{\text{ENTER}}$. To find $(g \circ f)(7)$ we can press $\boxed{\text{2nd}}$ $\boxed{\text{ENTRY}}$ to recall the previous entry and then edit it to interchange the 1 and the 2. We could also press 7 $\boxed{\text{STO▷}}$ $\boxed{\text{x-VAR}}$ $\boxed{\text{2nd}}$ $\boxed{:}$ $\boxed{\text{2nd}}$ $\boxed{\text{alpha}}$ $\boxed{\text{Y}}$ $\boxed{\text{ALPHA}}$ $\boxed{\text{ALPHA}}$ 1 $\boxed{\text{STO▷}}$ $\boxed{\text{x-VAR}}$ $\boxed{\text{2nd}}$ $\boxed{:}$ $\boxed{\text{2nd}}$ $\boxed{\text{alpha}}$ $\boxed{\text{Y}}$ $\boxed{\text{ALPHA}}$ $\boxed{\text{ALPHA}}$ 2 $\boxed{\text{ENTER}}$.

```
7→x:y2→x:y1
                          67
7→x:y1→x:y2
                          62
```

GRAPHING AN INVERSE FUNCTION

The DrInv operation on the TI-85 can be used to graph a function and its inverse on the same screen. A formula for the inverse function need not be found in order to do this. The grapher must be set in Func mode when this operation is used.

Section 4.1, Example 7 Graph $f(x) = 2x - 3$ and $f^{-1}(x)$ using the same set of axes.

Be sure the graph format is set to DrawLine and then enter $y_1 = 2x - 3$ and either clear or deselect all other functions on the "y(x) =" screen. Press $\boxed{\text{2nd}}$ $\boxed{\text{M5}}$ to select GRAPH. Then press $\boxed{\text{MORE}}$ $\boxed{\text{F2}}$ to select DRAW and $\boxed{\text{MORE}}$ $\boxed{\text{MORE}}$ $\boxed{\text{F2}}$ to select the DrInv operation. Press $\boxed{\text{2nd}}$ $\boxed{\text{alpha}}$ $\boxed{\text{Y}}$ 1 $\boxed{\text{ENTER}}$ to see the graph of the function and its inverse.

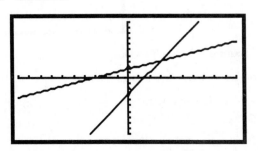

```
DrInv y1
```

EVALUATING e^x, Log x, and Ln x

Use the grapher's scientific keys to evaluate e^x, $\log x$, and $\ln x$ for specific values of x.

Section 4.2, Example 6 (a), (b) Find the value of e^3 and $e^{-0.23}$. Round to four decimal places.

To find e^3 press $\boxed{\text{2nd}}$ $\boxed{e^x}$ 3 $\boxed{\text{ENTER}}$. (e^x is the second operation associated with the $\boxed{\text{LN}}$ key.) The grapher returns 20.0855369232. Thus, $e^3 \approx 20.0855$. To find $e^{-0.23}$ press $\boxed{\text{2nd}}$ $\boxed{e^x}$ $\boxed{(-)}$ $\boxed{\cdot}$ 2 3 $\boxed{\text{ENTER}}$. The grapher returns .794533602503, so $e^{-0.23} \approx 0.7945$.

Section 4.3, Example 4 (a), (b), (c) Find the values of log 645,778, log 0.0000239, and log (-3). Round to four decimal places.

To find log 645,778 press $\boxed{\text{LOG}}$ 6 4 5 7 7 8 $\boxed{\text{ENTER}}$ and read 5.81008324563. Thus, log $645{,}778 \approx 5.8101$. To find log 0.0000239 press $\boxed{\text{LOG}}$ $\boxed{\cdot}$ 0 0 0 0 2 3 9 $\boxed{\text{ENTER}}$. The grapher returns -4.62160209905, so log $0.0000239 \approx -4.6216$. When we press $\boxed{\text{LOG}}$ $\boxed{(-)}$ 3 $\boxed{\text{ENTER}}$ the result is a non-real complex number. This indicates that -3 is not in the domain of the function $\log x$.

Section 4.3, Example 5 (a), (b), (c) Find the values of ln 645,778, ln 0.0000239, and ln (-5). Round to four decimal places.

To find ln 645,778 and ln 0.0000239 repeat the keystrokes used above to find log 645,778 and log 0.0000239 but press $\boxed{\text{LN}}$ rather than $\boxed{\text{LOG}}$. We find that ln $645{,}778 \approx 13.3782$ and ln $0.0000239 \approx -10.6416$. When we press $\boxed{\text{LN}}$ $\boxed{(-)}$ 5 $\boxed{\text{ENTER}}$ the result is a non-real complex number, indicating that -5 is not in the domain of the function $\ln x$.

USING THE CHANGE OF BASE FORMULA

To find a logarithm with a base other than 10 or e we use the change-of-base formula, $\log_b M = \dfrac{\log_a M}{\log_a b}$, where a and b are any logarithmic bases and M is any positive number.

Section 4.3, Example 6 Find $\log_5 8$ using common logarithms.

We let $a = 10$, $b = 5$, and $M = 8$ and substitute in the change-of-base formula. Press $\boxed{\text{LOG}}$ 8 $\boxed{\div}$ $\boxed{\text{LOG}}$ 5 $\boxed{\text{ENTER}}$. The result is about 1.2920. We could have let $a = e$ and used natural logarithms to find $\log_5 8$ as well.

```
log 8/log 5
              1.29202967422
ln 8/ln 5
              1.29202967422
■
```

Section 4.3, Example 9 Graph $y = \log_5 x$.

To use a grapher we must first change the base to e or 10. Here we use e. Let $a = e$, $b = 5$, and $M = x$ and substitute in the change-of-base formula. Enter $y_1 = \dfrac{\ln x}{\ln 5}$ on the "y(x) =" screen, select a viewing rectangle, and select GRAPH from the menus.

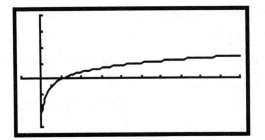

EXPONENTIAL AND LOGARITHMIC REGRESSION

In addition to the types of polynomial regression discussed earlier, exponential and logarithmic functions can be fit to data. The operations of entering data, making scatterplots, and graphing and evaluating these functions are the same as for linear regression functions. So are the procedures for copying a regression equation to the y(x) = screen, graphing it, and using it to find function values.

Section 4.6, Example 6 (a) *Credit Card Volume.* The total credit card volume for Visa, MasterCard, American Express, and Discover has increased dramatically in recent years.

Year, x	Credit Card Volume (in billions)
1988, 0	$261.0
1989, 1	296.3
1990, 2	338.4
1991, 3	361.0
1992, 4	403.1
1993, 5	476.7
1994, 6	584.8
1995, 7	701.2
1996, 8	798.3
1997, 9	885.2

(a) Use a grapher to fit an exponential function to the data.

Enter the data in lists as described on pages 83 and 84 of this manual. Then press 2nd QUIT to go to the home screen and select EXPR (exponential regression) from the STAT CALC menu by pressing STAT F1 ENTER ENTER F4. The grapher displays the coefficient a and the base b for the exponential function $y = a \cdot b^x$.

```
ExpR
 a=249.726707746
 b=1.15088133212
 corr=.993865770444
 n=10

CALC  EDIT  DRAW  FCST
1-VAR  LINR  LNR  EXPR  PWRR ▶
```

A scatterplot of the data can be graphed as described on page 84 of this manual. This function can be copied to the y(x) = screen as described on page 95 of this manual. Then it can be graphed along with the scatterplot. It can also be evaluated using one of the methods on pages 93 and 104.

Section 4.6, Exercise 26 (a) *Forgetting.* In an art class, students were tested at the end of the course on a final exam. Then they were retested with an equivalent test at subsequent time intervals. Their scores after time t, in months, are given in the following table.

Time, t (in months)	Score, y
1	84.9%
2	84.6%
3	84.4%
4	84.2%
5	84.1%
6	83.9%

(a) Use a grapher to fit a logarithmic function $y = a + b \ln x$ to the data.

After entering the data in lists as described on pages 83 and 84 of this manual, press $\boxed{\text{2nd}}$ $\boxed{\text{QUIT}}$ to go to the home screen. Then press $\boxed{\text{STAT}}$ $\boxed{\text{F1}}$ $\boxed{\text{ENTER}}$ $\boxed{\text{ENTER}}$ to view the STAT CALC menu. Select LNR (logarithmic regression) by pressing $\boxed{\text{F3}}$. The values of a and b for the logarithmic function $y = a + b \ln x$ are displayed.

```
LnR
 a=84.9435399216
 b=-.541283409758
 corr=-.990989394703
 n=6


CALC   EDIT  ［RAW］  F［ST
1-VAR  LINR  LNR   EXPR  PWRR ▶
```

LOGISTIC REGRESSION

THe TI-85 does not have the capability to fit a logistic function to data.

Chapter 5
The Trigonometric Functions

FINDING TRIGONOMETRIC FUNCTION VALUES OF REAL NUMBERS

The grapher's SIN, COS, and TAN operations can be used to find trigonometric function values of any real number. The grapher must be set in Radian mode when this is done.

Section 5.2, Example 5 Find each of the following function values using a grapher. Round the answers to four decimal places.

a) $\cos \dfrac{2\pi}{5}$ b) $\tan(-3)$ c) $\sin 24.9$ d) $\sin \dfrac{\pi}{7}$

a) With the grapher set in Radian mode, press $\boxed{\text{COS}}$ $\boxed{(}$ 2 $\boxed{\text{2nd}}$ $\boxed{\pi}$ $\boxed{\div}$ 5 $\boxed{)}$ $\boxed{\text{ENTER}}$. (π is the second operation associated with the $\boxed{\wedge}$ key.) We find that $\cos \dfrac{2\pi}{5} \approx 0.3090$.

b) To find $\tan(-3)$ press $\boxed{\text{TAN}}$ $\boxed{(-)}$ 3 $\boxed{\text{ENTER}}$. We find that $\tan(-3) \approx 0.1425$.

c) To find $\sin 24.9$ press $\boxed{\text{SIN}}$ 2 4 $\boxed{.}$ 9 $\boxed{\text{ENTER}}$. We find that $\sin 24.9 \approx -0.2306$.

d) The secant, cosecant, and cotangent functions can be found by taking the reciprocals of the cosine, sine, and tangent functions, respectively. This can be done either by entering the reciprocal or by using the x^{-1} operation. To find $\sec \dfrac{\pi}{7}$ we can enter the reciprocal of $\cos \dfrac{\pi}{7}$ by pressing 1 $\boxed{\div}$ $\boxed{\text{COS}}$ $\boxed{(}$ $\boxed{\text{2nd}}$ $\boxed{\pi}$ $\boxed{\div}$ 7 $\boxed{)}$ $\boxed{\text{ENTER}}$. To find $\sec \dfrac{\pi}{7}$ using the x^{-1} operation press $\boxed{(}$ $\boxed{\text{COS}}$ $\boxed{(}$ $\boxed{\text{2nd}}$ $\boxed{\pi}$ $\boxed{\div}$ 7 $\boxed{)}$ $\boxed{)}$ $\boxed{\text{2nd}}$ $\boxed{x^{-1}}$ $\boxed{\text{ENTER}}$. (x^{-1} is the second operation associated with the $\boxed{\text{EE}}$ key.) The result is $\sec \dfrac{\pi}{7} \approx 1.1099$.

```
1/cos (π/7)
            1.10991626417
(cos (π/7))⁻¹
            1.10991626417
```

CONVERTING BETWEEN D°M′S″ AND DECIMAL DEGREE MEASURE

The ANGLE feature can be used to convert D°M′S″ notation to decimal notation and vice versa. ANGLE is accessed by pressing $\boxed{\text{2nd}}$ $\boxed{\text{MATH}}$ $\boxed{\text{F3}}$.

Section 5.3, Example 2 Convert 5°42′30″ to decimal degree notation.

Enter 5°42′30″ as 5′42′30′ by pressing 5 $\boxed{\text{2nd}}$ $\boxed{\text{MATH}}$ $\boxed{\text{F3}}$ $\boxed{\text{F3}}$ 4 2 $\boxed{\text{F3}}$ 3 0 $\boxed{\text{F3}}$ $\boxed{\text{ENTER}}$. The grapher returns 5.70833333333, so 5°42′30″ ≈ 5.71°.

Section 5.3, Example 3 Convert 72.18° to D°M′S″ notation.

Press 7 2 $\boxed{\cdot}$ 1 8 $\boxed{\text{2nd}}$ $\boxed{\text{MATH}}$ $\boxed{\text{F3}}$ to select ANGLE. Then press $\boxed{\text{F4}}$ to select ▷DMS followed by $\boxed{\text{ENTER}}$. The grapher returns 72°10′48″.

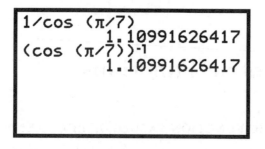

CONVERTING BETWEEN DEGREE AND RADIAN MEASURE

We can use the grapher to convert from degree to radian measure and vice versa. The grapher should be set in Radian mode when converting from degree to radian measure and in Degree mode when converting from radian to degree measure.

Section 5.3, Example 5 Convert each of the following to radians.

a) 120°   b) −297.25°

a) Set the grapher in Radian mode. Press 1 2 0 $\boxed{\text{2nd}}$ $\boxed{\text{MATH}}$ $\boxed{\text{F3}}$ $\boxed{\text{F1}}$ $\boxed{\text{ENTER}}$ to enter 120°. The grapher returns a decimal approximation of the radian measure. We see that 120° ≈ 2.09 radians.

b) With the grapher set in Radian mode and with the ANGLE menu displayed, press $\boxed{(-)}$ 2 9 7 $\boxed{\cdot}$ 2 5 $\boxed{\text{F1}}$ $\boxed{\text{ENTER}}$. We see that −297.25° ≈ −5.19 radians.

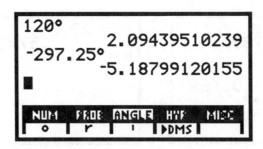

Section 5.3, Example 6 Convert each of the following to degrees.

a) $\frac{3\pi}{4}$ radians   b) 8.5 radians

a) Set the grapher in Degree mode. Then press $\boxed{(}$ 3 $\boxed{\text{2nd}}$ $\boxed{\pi}$ $\boxed{\div}$ 4 $\boxed{)}$ $\boxed{\text{2nd}}$ $\boxed{\text{MATH}}$ $\boxed{\text{F3}}$ $\boxed{\text{F2}}$ $\boxed{\text{ENTER}}$ to enter $\frac{3\pi}{4}$

radians. (π is the second operation associated with the $\boxed{\wedge}$ key). The grapher returns 135, so $\frac{3\pi}{4}$ radians = 135°. Note

that the parentheses are necessary in order to enter the entire expression in radian measure. Without the parentheses, the

grapher reads only the denominator, 4, in radian measure and an incorrect result occurs.

b) With the grapher set in Degree mode and with the ANGLE menu displayed, press 8 $\boxed{\cdot}$ 5 $\boxed{\text{F2}}$ $\boxed{\text{ENTER}}$. The grapher

returns 487.014125861, so 8.5 radians $\approx$ 487.01°.

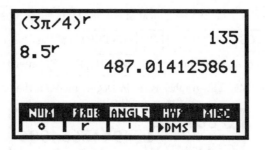

FINDING TRIGONOMETRIC FUNCTION VALUES OF ANGLES

The grapher's SIN, COS, and TAN operations can be used to find the values of trigonometric functions of angles measured

in degrees.

Section 5.5, Example 5 Find the trigonometric function value, rounded to four decimal places, of each of the following.

a) tan 29.7°   b) sec 48°   c) sin 84°10'39"

a) If the grapher is set in Degree mode, press $\boxed{\text{TAN}}$ 2 9 $\boxed{\cdot}$ 7 $\boxed{\text{ENTER}}$. If the grapher is set in Radian mode, press $\boxed{\text{2nd}}$

$\boxed{\text{MATH}}$ $\boxed{\text{F3}}$ $\boxed{\text{F1}}$ after the 7 to copy the degree symbol after the angle. This indicates to the grapher that the angle is

given in degrees. We find that tan 29.7° $\approx$ 0.5704.

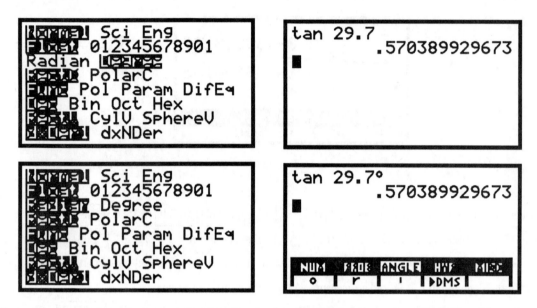

b) The secant, cosecant, and cotangent functions can be found by taking the reciprocals of the cosine, sine, and tangent functions, respectively. This can be done either by entering the reciprocal or by using the $\boxed{x^{-1}}$ key. To find sec 48° with the grapher set in Degree mode we can enter the reciprocal of cos 48° by pressing 1 $\boxed{\div}$ $\boxed{\text{COS}}$ 4 8 $\boxed{\text{ENTER}}$. To find sec 48° using the $\boxed{x^{-1}}$ key press $\boxed{(}$ $\boxed{\text{COS}}$ 4 8 $\boxed{)}$ $\boxed{\text{2nd}}$ $\boxed{x^{-1}}$ $\boxed{\text{ENTER}}$. (x^{-1} is the second operation associated with the $\boxed{\text{EE}}$ key.) If the grapher is set in Radian mode, press $\boxed{\text{2nd}}$ $\boxed{\text{MATH}}$ $\boxed{\text{F3}}$ $\boxed{\text{F1}}$ after the 8 to copy the degree symbol after the angle. The result is sec 48° ≈ 1.4945. The grapher is set in Degree mode in the figure below.

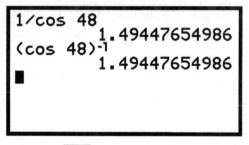

c) With the grapher set in Degree mode, press $\boxed{\text{SIN}}$ followed by 84°10′39″ entered as described above in Converting Between D°M′S″ and Decimal Degree Measure. Then press $\boxed{\text{ENTER}}$. We find that sin 84°10′39″ ≈ 0.9948.

FINDING ANGLES

The inverse trigonometric function keys provide a quick way to find an angle given a trigonometric function value for that angle.

Section 5.5, Example 6 Find the acute angle, to the nearest tenth of a degree, whose sine value is approximately 0.20113.

With the grapher set in Degree mode press $\boxed{\text{2nd}}$ $\boxed{\text{SIN}^{-1}}$ $\boxed{\cdot}$ 2 0 1 1 3 $\boxed{\text{ENTER}}$. (SIN^{-1} is the second operation associated with the $\boxed{\text{SIN}}$ key.) We find that the desired acute angle is approximately 11.6°.

Section 5.5, Exercise 39 Find the acute angle, to the nearest tenth of a degree, whose cotangent value is 2.127.

Angles whose secant, cosecant, or cotangent values are known can be found using the reciprocals of the cosine, sine, and tangent functions, respectively. Since $\cot\theta = \dfrac{1}{\tan\theta} = 2.127$, we have $\tan\theta = \dfrac{1}{2.127}$, or $(2.127)^{-1}$. To find θ press $\boxed{\text{2nd}}$ $\boxed{\text{TAN}^{-1}}$ $\boxed{(}$ 1 $\boxed{\div}$ 2 $\boxed{\cdot}$ 1 2 7 $\boxed{)}$ $\boxed{\text{ENTER}}$ or $\boxed{\text{2nd}}$ $\boxed{\text{TAN}^{-1}}$ 2 $\boxed{\cdot}$ 1 2 7 $\boxed{\text{2nd}}$ $\boxed{x^{-1}}$ $\boxed{\text{ENTER}}$. (TAN^{-1} is the second operation associated with the $\boxed{\text{TAN}}$ key.) Note that the parentheses are necessary in the first set of keystrokes. Without parentheses we would be finding the angle whose tangent is 1 and then dividing that angle by 2.127. We find that $\theta \approx 25.2°$.

```
sin⁻¹ .20113
            11.6030461313
tan⁻¹ (1/2.127)
            25.1803638359
tan⁻¹ 2.127⁻¹
            25.1803638359
■
```

Chapter 6
Trigonometric Identities, Inverse Functions, and Equations

FINDING INVERSE FUNCTION VALUES

We can use a grapher to find inverse function values in both radians and degrees.

Section 6.4, Example 2 (a), (e) Approximate $\cos^{-1}(-0.2689)$ and $\csc^{-1} 8.205$ in both radians and degrees.

To find inverse function values in radians, first set the grapher in Radian mode. Then, to approximate $\cos^{-1}(-0.2689)$, press 2nd COS^{-1} (−) . 2 6 8 9 ENTER . The grapher returns 1.84304711148, so $\cos^{-1}(-0.2689) \approx 1.8430$ radians.

To find $\csc^{-1} 8.205$, recall the identity $\csc\theta = \dfrac{1}{\sin\theta}$. Then $\csc^{-1} 8.205 = \sin^{-1}\left(\dfrac{1}{8.205}\right)$. Press 2nd SIN^{-1} (1 ÷ 8 . 2 0 5) ENTER or 2nd SIN^{-1} 8 . 2 0 5 2nd x^{-1} ENTER . The readout is .122180665346, so $\csc^{-1} 8.205 \approx 0.1222$ radians.

```
cos-1 -.2689
             1.84304711148
sin-1 (1/8.205)
              .122180665346
sin-1 8.205-1
              .122180665346
```

To find inverse function values in degrees, set the grapher in degree mode. Then use the keystrokes above to find that $\cos^{-1}(-0.2689) \approx 105.6°$ and $\csc^{-1} 8.205 \approx 7.0°$.

```
cos-1 -.2689
             105.598820932
sin-1 (1/8.205)
               7.00043646242
sin-1 8.205-1
               7.00043646242
```

We also use reciprocal relationships to find function values for arcsecant and arccotangent.

Chapter 7
Applications of Trigonometry

FINDING TRIGONOMETRIC NOTATION FOR COMPLEX NUMBERS

The TI-85 can be used to find trigonometric notation for a complex number.

Section 7.4, Example 3 (a) Find trigonometric notation for $1 + i$.

On the TI-85 we express $1 + i$ as the pair $(1, 1)$ where the first number is the real part of $1 + i$ and the second number is the imaginary part. Trigonometric notation for a complex number has the form $r(\cos\theta + i\sin\theta)$. We can find r using the abs feature from the CPLX menu. Press $\boxed{\text{2nd}}$ $\boxed{\text{CPLX}}$ to display this menu. (CPLX is the second operation associated with the 9 numeric key.) Then press $\boxed{\text{F5}}$ to copy "abs" to the home screen. Press $\boxed{(}$ 1 $\boxed{,}$ 1 $\boxed{)}$ $\boxed{\text{ENTER}}$. The grapher returns $|1 + i|$, the value of r. It is approximately 1.414213562. This is a decimal approximation for $\sqrt{2}$.

Now use the CPLX menu again to find θ in degrees. First select Degree mode. Then press $\boxed{\text{2nd}}$ $\boxed{\text{CPLX}}$ to display the CPLX menu. Select $\boxed{\text{F5}}$, "angle." Then press $\boxed{(}$ 1 $\boxed{,}$ 1 $\boxed{)}$ $\boxed{\text{ENTER}}$. The grapher returns 45, so the angle θ is 45°. We can use the same procedure to find θ in radians after Radian mode has been selected.

```
abs (1,1)
           1.41421356237
angle (1,1)
                      45
■


 conj  real  imag  abs  angle ▶
```

Chapter 8
Systems of Equations and Matrices

SOLVING SYSTEMS OF EQUATIONS

We can solve systems of up to 30 equations with 30 variables on the TI-85 using the SIMULT menu.

Section 8.1, Example 2 (b) Solve the following system:

$$4x + 3y = 11,$$
$$-5x + 2y = 15.$$

Begin by pressing $\boxed{\text{2nd}}$ $\boxed{\text{SIMULT}}$ to display the SIMULT screen. (SIMULT is the second operation associated with the $\boxed{\text{STAT}}$ key.) The blinking cursor is positioned to the right of the notation "Number =." Because there are two equations, press 2 $\boxed{\text{ENTER}}$.

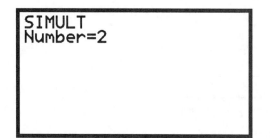

The coefficient entry screen for the first equation will appear. Enter the coefficients and the constant term of the first equation by pressing 4 $\boxed{\text{ENTER}}$ 3 $\boxed{\text{ENTER}}$ 1 1 $\boxed{\text{ENTER}}$. Now the coefficient entry screen for the second equation appears. Enter the coefficients and the constant term of the second equation by pressing $\boxed{(-)}$ 5 $\boxed{\text{ENTER}}$ 2 $\boxed{\text{ENTER}}$ 1 5. The second equation's coefficient screen could also have been accessed by pressing $\boxed{\text{F2}}$ to select NEXT rather than by pressing $\boxed{\text{ENTER}}$ after 11, the constant in the first equation.

To see the solution of the system of equations, press $\boxed{\text{F5}}$ to select SOLVE. The solution $(-1, 5)$ is displayed as "$x1 = -1$" and "$x2 = 5$."

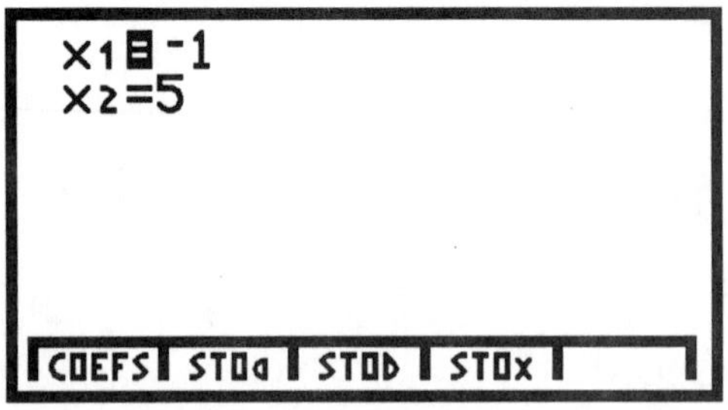

```
X1B-1
X2=5




 COEFS  STOa  STOb  STOx
```

MATRICES AND ROW-EQUIVALENT OPERATIONS

Matrices with up to 255 rows and 255 columns can be entered on the TI-85. The number of matrices that can be entered is limited only by the memory available. Row-equivalent operations can be performed on matrices using the grapher.

Section 8.3, Example 1 Solve the following system:

$$2x - y + 4z = -3,$$
$$x - 2y - 10z = -6,$$
$$3x \qquad + 4z = 7.$$

First we enter the augmented matrix

$$\begin{bmatrix} 2 & -1 & 4 & -3 \\ 1 & -2 & -10 & -6 \\ 3 & 0 & 4 & 7 \end{bmatrix}$$

on the grapher. Begin by pressing $\boxed{\text{2nd}}$ $\boxed{\text{MATRX}}$ to display the MATRX EDIT menu. (MATRX is the second operation associated with the $\boxed{7}$ key.) Then press $\boxed{\text{F2}}$ to select EDIT and name the matrix to be defined. We will name the matrix [**A**] by pressing $\boxed{\text{F1}}$ or by pressing A at the blinking cursor to the right of "Name =." Note that it is not necessary to press $\boxed{\text{ALPHA}}$ before pressing A in the MATRX EDIT screen. Now press $\boxed{\text{ENTER}}$.

The dimensions of the matrix are displayed on the top line of the next screen, with the cursor on the row dimension. Enter the dimensions of the augmented matrix, 3 x 4, by pressing 3 $\boxed{\text{ENTER}}$ 4 $\boxed{\text{ENTER}}$. Now the cursor moves to the element in the first row and first column of the matrix. Enter the elements of the first row by pressing 2 $\boxed{\text{ENTER}}$ $\boxed{(-)}$ 1 $\boxed{\text{ENTER}}$ 4 $\boxed{\text{ENTER}}$ $\boxed{(-)}$ 3 $\boxed{\text{ENTER}}$. The cursor moves to the element in the second row and first column of the matrix. Enter the elements of the second and third rows of the augmented matrix by typing each in turn followed by $\boxed{\text{ENTER}}$ as above. Note that the screen only displays the fourth column of the matrix at this point. The $\boxed{\triangle}$ and $\boxed{\triangledown}$ keys can be used to move the cursor to any element at any time.

Row-equivalent operations are performed by making selections from the MATRX OPS menu. To view this menu press $\boxed{\text{2nd}}$ $\boxed{\text{QUIT}}$ to leave the MATRX EDIT screen. Then press $\boxed{\text{2nd}}$ $\boxed{\text{MATRX}}$ $\boxed{\text{F4}}$. Now press $\boxed{\text{MORE}}$ to see the menu with the four row-equivalent operations: rSwap, rAdd, multR, and mRAdd in locations $\boxed{\text{F2}}$ through $\boxed{\text{F5}}$. These operations interchange two rows of a matrix, add two rows, multiply a row by a number, and multiply a row by a number and add it to a second row, respectively.

To view the matrix on the home screen press $\boxed{\text{ALPHA}}$ A $\boxed{\text{ENTER}}$. We will use the grapher to perform the row-equivalent operations that were done algebraically in the text. First, to interchange row 1 and row 2 of matrix [**A**], with the MATRX OPS menu displayed , press $\boxed{\text{F2}}$ to select rSwap. Then press $\boxed{\text{ALPHA}}$ A to select [**A**]. Follow this with a comma and the rows to be interchanged: $\boxed{,}$ 1 $\boxed{,}$ 2 $\boxed{)}$ $\boxed{\text{ENTER}}$.

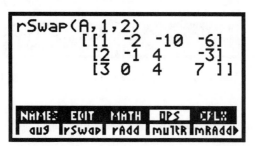

The grapher will not store the matrix produced using a row-equivalent operation, so when several operations are to be performed in succession it is helpful to store the result of each operation as it is produced. For example, to store the matrix resulting from interchanging the first and second rows of [**A**] as matrix [**B**] press $\boxed{\text{STO}\triangleright}$ B $\boxed{\text{ENTER}}$ immediately after interchanging the rows. Note that it is not necessary to press $\boxed{\text{ALPHA}}$ before pressing B in this situation.

Next we multiply the first row of [**B**] by -2, add it to the second row and store the result as [**B**] again by pressing $\boxed{\text{F5}}$ $\boxed{(-)}$ 2 $\boxed{,}$ $\boxed{\text{ALPHA}}$ B $\boxed{,}$ 1 $\boxed{,}$ 2 $\boxed{)}$ $\boxed{\text{STO}\triangleright}$ B $\boxed{\text{ENTER}}$. These keystrokes select mRAdd from the MATRX OPS menu; then they specify that the value of the multiplier is -2, the matrix being operated on is [**B**], and that a multiple of row 1 is being added to row 2; finally they store the result as [**B**].

To multiply row 1 by -3, add it to row 3, and store the result as [**B**] press $\boxed{\text{F5}}$ $\boxed{(-)}$ 3 $\boxed{,}$ $\boxed{\text{ALPHA}}$ B $\boxed{,}$ 1 $\boxed{,}$ 3 $\boxed{)}$ $\boxed{\text{STO}\triangleright}$ B $\boxed{\text{ENTER}}$.

```
mRAdd( -3,B,1,3)→B
       [[1  -2  -10  -6]
        [0  3   24   9 ]
        [0  6   34   25]]

NAMES  EDIT  MATH  OPS  CPLX
 aug  rSwap  rAdd  multR  mRAdd▶
```

Now multiply the second row by 1/3 and store the result as [**B**] again. Press $\boxed{\text{F4}}$ 1 $\boxed{(\div)}$ 3 $\boxed{,}$ $\boxed{\text{ALPHA}}$ B $\boxed{,}$ 2 $\boxed{)}$ $\boxed{\text{STO}\triangleright}$ B $\boxed{\text{ENTER}}$. These keystrokes select multR from the MATRX OPS menu; then they specify that the value of the multiplier is 1/3, the matrix being operated on is [**B**], and row 2 is being multiplied; finally they store the result as [**B**]. The keystrokes 1 $\boxed{(\div)}$ 3 could be replaced with 3 $\boxed{\text{2nd}}$ $\boxed{x^{-1}}$.

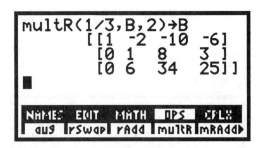

Multiply the second row by -6 and add it to the third row using mRAdd. Press $\boxed{\text{F5}}$ $\boxed{(-)}$ 6 $\boxed{\text{,}}$ $\boxed{\text{ALPHA}}$ B $\boxed{\text{,}}$ 2 $\boxed{\text{,}}$ 3 $\boxed{)}$ $\boxed{\text{STO}\triangleright}$ B $\boxed{\text{ENTER}}$.

The entry in the third row, second column is 1E$-$13. This is an approximation of 0 that occurs because of the manner in which the grapher performs calculations and should be treated as 0. In fact, it would be a good idea to return to the MATRX EDIT screen at this point to replace this entry of [**B**] with 0. Press $\boxed{\text{2nd}}$ $\boxed{\text{M2}}$ to select EDIT. Then press $\boxed{\text{F2}}$ $\boxed{\text{ENTER}}$ to display [**B**]. Move the cursor to the third row, second column and press 0 $\boxed{\text{ENTER}}$. Now press $\boxed{\text{2nd}}$ $\boxed{\text{QUIT}}$ to return to the home screen. Matrix **B** can be viewed by pressing $\boxed{\text{ALPHA}}$ B $\boxed{\text{ENTER}}$.

```
B
       [[1  -2 -10  -6]
        [0   1   8   3 ]
        [0   0 -14   7 ]]
■
```

Finally, multiply the third row by $-1/14$ by pressing $\boxed{\text{2nd}}$ $\boxed{\text{MATRX}}$ $\boxed{\text{F4}}$ $\boxed{\text{MORE}}$ to view the row operations under the OPS menu. Then press $\boxed{\text{F4}}$ $\boxed{(-)}$ 1 $\boxed{(\div)}$ $1\,4$ $\boxed{\text{,}}$ $\boxed{\text{ALPHA}}$ B $\boxed{\text{,}}$ 3 $\boxed{)}$ $\boxed{\text{ENTER}}$. The keystrokes $\boxed{(-)}$ 1 $\boxed{(\div)}$ $1\,4$ could be replaced with $\boxed{(-)}$ $1\,4$ $\boxed{\text{2nd}}$ $\boxed{x^{-1}}$.

```
multR( -1/14,B,3)
       [[1  -2 -10  -6 ]
        [0   1   8   3 ]
        [0   0   1   -.5]]

NAMES  EDIT  MATH  OPS  CPLX
 aug  rSwap  rAdd  multR mRAdd▶
```

Write the system of equations that corresponds to the final matrix. Then use back-substitution to solve for x, y, and z as illustrated in the text.

Instead of stopping with row-echelon form as we did above, we can continue to apply row-equivalent operations until the matrix is in reduced row-echelon form as in Example 3 in Section 8.3 of the text. Reduced row-echelon form of a matrix can be found directly by using the rref operation from the MATRX OPS menu. For example, to find reduced row-echelon form for matrix **A** in Example 1 above, after entering [**A**] and leaving the MATRX EDIT screen press 2nd MATRX F4 F5 ALPHA A ENTER. We can read the solution of the system of equations, $(3, 7, -0.5)$ directly from the resulting matrix.

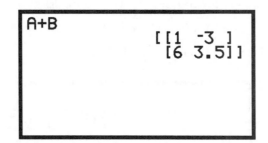

MATRIX OPERATIONS

We can use the grapher to add and subtract matrices, to multiply a matrix by a scalar, and to multiply matrices.

Section 8.4, Example 1 (a) Find $\mathbf{A} + \mathbf{B}$ for

a) $\mathbf{A} = \begin{bmatrix} -5 & 0 \\ 4 & \frac{1}{2} \end{bmatrix}$, $\mathbf{B} = \begin{bmatrix} 6 & -3 \\ 2 & 3 \end{bmatrix}$.

Enter **A** and **B** on the MATRX EDIT screen as [**A**] and [**B**] as described earlier in this chapter. Press 2nd QUIT to leave this screen. Then press ALPHA A + ALPHA B ENTER to display the sum.

```
A+B
              [[1  -3 ]
               [6  3.5]]
```

Section 8.4, Example 2 Find $\mathbf{C} - \mathbf{D}$ for each of the following.

a) $\mathbf{C} = \begin{bmatrix} 1 & 2 \\ -2 & 0 \\ -3 & -1 \end{bmatrix}$, $\mathbf{D} = \begin{bmatrix} 1 & -1 \\ 1 & 3 \\ 2 & 3 \end{bmatrix}$ b) $\mathbf{C} = \begin{bmatrix} 5 & -6 \\ -3 & 4 \end{bmatrix}$, $\mathbf{D} = \begin{bmatrix} -4 \\ 1 \end{bmatrix}$

a) Enter **C** and **D** on the MATRX EDIT screen as [**C**] and [**D**]. Press 2nd QUIT to leave this screen. Then press ALPHA C − ALPHA D ENTER to display the difference.

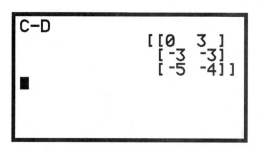

b) Enter **C** and **D** on the MATRX EDIT screen as [**C**] and [**D**]. Press $\boxed{\text{2nd}}$ $\boxed{\text{QUIT}}$ to leave this screen. Then press $\boxed{\text{ALPHA}}$ C $\boxed{-}$ $\boxed{\text{ALPHA}}$ D $\boxed{\text{ENTER}}$. The grapher returns the message ERROR 12 DIM MISMATCH, indicating that this subtraction is not possible. This is the case because the matrices have different orders.

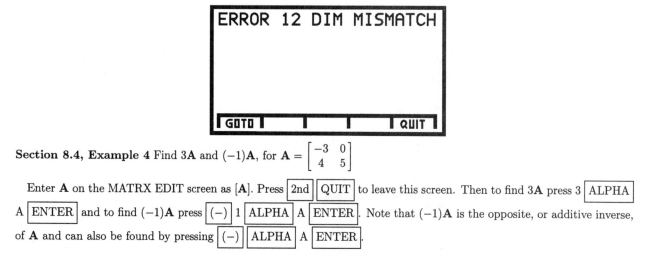

Section 8.4, Example 4 Find 3**A** and (-1)**A**, for $\mathbf{A} = \begin{bmatrix} -3 & 0 \\ 4 & 5 \end{bmatrix}$

Enter **A** on the MATRX EDIT screen as [**A**]. Press $\boxed{\text{2nd}}$ $\boxed{\text{QUIT}}$ to leave this screen. Then to find 3**A** press 3 $\boxed{\text{ALPHA}}$ A $\boxed{\text{ENTER}}$ and to find (-1)**A** press $\boxed{(-)}$ 1 $\boxed{\text{ALPHA}}$ A $\boxed{\text{ENTER}}$. Note that (-1)**A** is the opposite, or additive inverse, of **A** and can also be found by pressing $\boxed{(-)}$ $\boxed{\text{ALPHA}}$ A $\boxed{\text{ENTER}}$.

Section 8.4, Example 6 (a), (d) For

$$\mathbf{A} = \begin{bmatrix} 3 & 1 & -1 \\ 2 & 0 & 3 \end{bmatrix}, \mathbf{B} = \begin{bmatrix} 1 & 6 \\ 3 & -5 \\ -2 & 4 \end{bmatrix}, \text{ and } \mathbf{C} = \begin{bmatrix} 4 & -6 \\ 1 & 2 \end{bmatrix}$$

find each of the following.

a) **AB**   d) **AC**

First enter **A, B,**and **C** as [**A**], [**B**], and [**C**] on the MATRX EDIT screen. Press $\boxed{\text{2nd}}$ $\boxed{\text{QUIT}}$ to leave this screen.

a) To find **AB** press $\boxed{\text{ALPHA}}$ A $\boxed{\times}$ $\boxed{\text{ALPHA}}$ B $\boxed{\text{ENTER}}$.

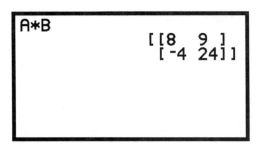

d) To find **AC** press ALPHA A × ALPHA C ENTER. The grapher returns the message ERROR 12 DIM MIS-MATCH, indicating that this multiplication is not possible. This is the case because the number of columns in **A** is not the same as the number of rows in **C**. Thus, the matrices cannot be multiplied in this order.

FINDING THE INVERSE OF A MATRIX

The inverse of a matrix can be found quickly on the grapher.

Section 8.5, Example 3 Find $\mathbf{A}^{-1}$, where

$$\mathbf{A} = \begin{bmatrix} -2 & 3 \\ -3 & 4 \end{bmatrix}.$$

Enter **A** as [**A**] on the MATRX EDIT screen. Then press 2nd QUIT to leave this screen. Now press ALPHA A 2nd x^{-1} ENTER.

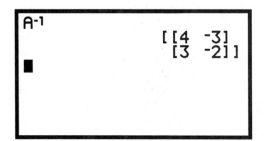

Section 8.5, Exercise 7 Find $\mathbf{A}^{-1}$, where

$$\mathbf{A} = \begin{bmatrix} 6 & 9 \\ 4 & 6 \end{bmatrix}.$$

Enter **A** as [**A**] on the MATRX EDIT screen and then press 2nd QUIT to leave this screen. Now press ALPHA A 2nd x^{-1} ENTER. The grapher returns the message ERROR 03 SINGULAR MAT, indicating that $\mathbf{A}^{-1}$ does not exist.

MATRIX SOLUTIONS OF SYSTEMS OF EQUATIONS

We can write a system of n linear equations in n variables as a matrix equation $\mathbf{AX} = \mathbf{B}$. If **A** has an inverse the solution of the system of equations is given by $\mathbf{X} = \mathbf{A}^{-1}\mathbf{B}$.

Section 8.5, Example 4 Use an inverse matrix to solve the following system of equations:

$$x + 2y - z = -2,$$
$$3x + 5y + 3z = 3,$$
$$2x + 4y + 3z = 1.$$

Enter $\mathbf{A} = \begin{bmatrix} 1 & 2 & -1 \\ 3 & 5 & 3 \\ 2 & 4 & 3 \end{bmatrix}$ and $\mathbf{B} = \begin{bmatrix} -2 \\ 3 \\ 1 \end{bmatrix}$ on the MATRX EDIT screen as [**A**] and [**B**]. Press $\boxed{\text{2nd}}$ $\boxed{\text{QUIT}}$ to leave

this screen. Then press $\boxed{\text{ALPHA}}$ A $\boxed{\text{2nd}}$ $\boxed{x^{-1}}$ $\boxed{\times}$ $\boxed{\text{ALPHA}}$ B $\boxed{\text{ENTER}}$. The result is the 3 x 1 matrix $\begin{bmatrix} 5 \\ -3 \\ 1 \end{bmatrix}$, so the

solution is $(5, -3, 1)$.

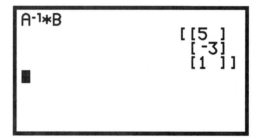

GRAPHS OF INEQUALITIES

We can graph linear inequalities on the grapher, shading the region of the solution set. The grapher should be set in Func mode at this point.

Section 8.6, Example 1 Graph: $y < x + 3$.

First we graph the related equation $y = x + 3$. We use the standard window $[-10, 10, -10, 10]$. Since the inequality symbol is $<$ we know that the line $y = x + 3$ is not part of the solution set. In a hand-drawn graph we would use a dashed line to indicate this. However, the only option here is to use a solid line, keeping in mind that it is not part of the solution set. After determining that the solution set of the inequality consists of all points below the line, we use the grapher's Shade operation to shade this region. Shade is accessed from the GRAPH screen by pressing $\boxed{\text{MORE}}$ $\boxed{\text{F2}}$ to select DRAW and then $\boxed{\text{F1}}$ to select Shade.

Now enter a lower function and an upper function and the region between them will be shaded. We want to shade the area between the bottom of the window, $y = -10$, and the line $y = x + 3$ so we enter $\boxed{(-)}$ 1 0 $\boxed{\text{,}}$ $\boxed{x\text{-VAR}}$ $\boxed{+}$ 3 $\boxed{)}$ $\boxed{\text{ENTER}}$. We can also enter $x + 3$ as y_1 by pressing $\boxed{\text{2nd}}$ $\boxed{\text{alpha}}$ $\boxed{\text{Y}}$ 1. The result is shown below.

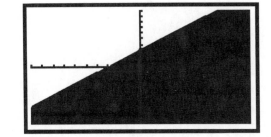

We can also use the Shade operation to graph a system of inequalities when the solution set lies between the graphs of two functions.

Section 8.6, Exercise 37 Graph:

$$y \leq x,$$

$$y \geq 3 - x.$$

First graph the related equations $y = x$ and $y = 3 - x$ and determine that the solution set consists of all the points on or above the graph of $y = 3 - x$ and on or below the graph of $y = x$. We will shade this region by starting on the GRAPH screen and pressing $\boxed{\text{MORE}}$ $\boxed{\text{F2}}$ $\boxed{\text{F1}}$ 3 $\boxed{-}$ $\boxed{x\text{-VAR}}$ $\boxed{,}$ $\boxed{x\text{-VAR}}$ $\boxed{)}$ $\boxed{\text{ENTER}}$. These keystrokes select the Shade operation from the DRAW menu and then enter $y = 3 - x$ as the lower function and $y = x$ as the upper function. We could also enter these functions as y_2 and y_1, respectively, by pressing $\boxed{\text{2nd}}$ $\boxed{\text{alpha}}$ $\boxed{\text{Y}}$ 2 $\boxed{,}$ $\boxed{\text{2nd}}$ $\boxed{\text{alpha}}$ $\boxed{\text{Y}}$ 1.

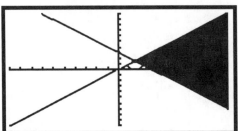

Chapter 9
Analytic Geometry Topics

Many conic sections are represented by equations that are not functions. Consequently, these equations must be entered on the TI-85 as two equations, each of which is a function.

GRAPHING PARABOLAS

To graph a parabola of the form $y^2 = 4px$ or $(y-k)^2 = 4p(x-h)$, we must first solve the equation for y.

Section 9.1, Example 4 Graph the parabola $y^2 - 2y - 8x - 31 = 0$.

In the text we used the quadratic formula to solve the equation for y:
$$y = \frac{2 \pm \sqrt{32x + 128}}{2}.$$

One way to produce the graph of the parabola is to enter $y_1 = \dfrac{2 + \sqrt{32x + 128}}{2}$ and $y_2 = \dfrac{2 - \sqrt{32x + 128}}{2}$, select a window, and press $\boxed{\text{F5}}$ to see the graph. Here we use $[-12, 12, -7, 7]$ since a square window gives the best representation of the shape of the parabola. The first equation produces the top half of the parabola and the second equation produces the lower half.

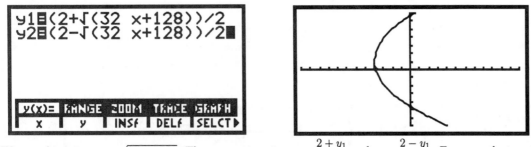

We can also enter $y_1 = \sqrt{32x + 128}$. Then use y_1 to enter $y_2 = \dfrac{2 + y_1}{2}$ and $y_3 = \dfrac{2 - y_1}{2}$. For example, to enter $y_2 = \dfrac{2 + y_1}{2}$ position the cursor beside "y2 =" and press $\boxed{(}$ $\boxed{2}$ $\boxed{+}$ $\boxed{\text{F2}}$ $\boxed{1}$ $\boxed{)}$ $\boxed{\div}$ 2. Enter $y_3 = \dfrac{2 - y_1}{2}$ in a similar manner. Finally, deselect y_1 by moving the cursor to the right of the equals sign following "y1 =" and pressing $\boxed{\text{F5}}$ to select SELCT. The top half of the graph is produced by y_2 and the lower half by y_3. The expression for y_1 was entered to avoid entering the square root more than once. By deselecting y_1 we prevent the graph of y_1 from appearing on the screen with the graph of the parabola.

```
y1=√(32x+128)
y2目(2+y1)/2
y3目(2-y1)/2




 y(x)目 RANGE ZOOM TRACE GRAPH
   x    y    INSf  DELf SELCT▶
```

We could also use the standard equation of the parabola found in the text:
$$(y - 1)^2 = 8(x + 4).$$

Solve this equation for y.
$$y - 1 = \pm\sqrt{8(x+4)}$$
$$y = 1 \pm \sqrt{8(x+4)}$$
Then enter $y_1 = 1 + \sqrt{8(x+4)}$ and $y_2 = 1 - \sqrt{8(x+4)}$, or enter $y_1 = \sqrt{8(x+4)}$, $y_2 = 1 + y_1$, and $y_3 = 1 - y_1$, and deselect y_1 as above.

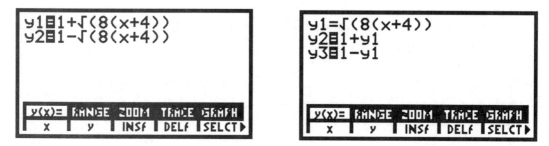

GRAPHING CIRCLES

The equation of a circle must be solved for y before it can be entered on a TI-85.

Section 9.2, Example 1 Graph the circle $x^2 + y^2 - 16x + 14y + 32 = 0$.

In the text we found the standard form for the equation of the circle and then solved for y:
$$y = -7 \pm \sqrt{81 - (x-8)^2}.$$
We could also have solved the original equation using the quadratic formula.

One way to produce the graph is to enter $y_1 = -7 + \sqrt{81 - (x-8)^2}$ and $y_2 = -7 - \sqrt{81 - (x-8)^2}$, select a square viewing rectangle, and press $\boxed{\text{F5}}$. Here we use $[-9, 31, -20, 4]$. The first equation produces the top half of the circle and the second equation produces the lower half.

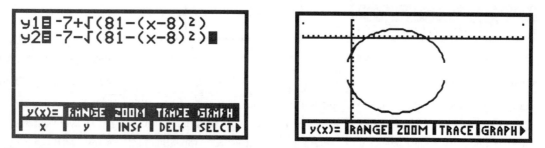

The software used to produce the graph above causes distortion. Nevertheless, when the circle is graphed on a grapher in a square viewing rectangle, there is no distortion.

We can also enter $y_1 = \sqrt{81 - (x-8)^2}$ and then enter $y_2 = -7 + y_1$ and $y_3 = -7 - y_1$. Then deselect y_1, select a square viewing rectangle, and press $\boxed{\text{F5}}$. We use y_1 to eliminate the need to enter the square root more than once. Deselecting it prevents the graph of y_1 from appearing on the screen with the graph of the circle. The top half of the graph is produced by y_2 and the lower half by y_3.

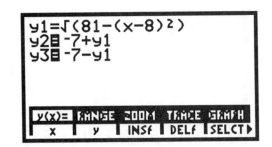

GRAPHING ELLIPSES

The equation of an ellipse must be solved for y before it can be entered on the TI-85. In Example 2 of Section 9.2 of the text the procedure for graphing an ellipse of the form $\dfrac{x^2}{a^2} + \dfrac{y^2}{b^2} = 1$ or $\dfrac{x^2}{b^2} + \dfrac{y^2}{a^2} = 1$ is described. Here we consider ellipses of the form $\dfrac{(x-h)^2}{a^2} + \dfrac{(y-k)^2}{b^2} = 1$ or $\dfrac{(x-h)^2}{b^2} + \dfrac{(y-k)^2}{a^2} = 1$

Section 9.2, Example 4 Graph the ellipse $4x^2 + y^2 + 24x - 2y + 21 = 0$.

Completing the square in the text, we found that the equation can be written as

$$\frac{(x+3)^2}{4} + \frac{(y-1)^2}{16} = 1.$$

Solve this equation for y.

$$\frac{(x+3)^2}{4} + \frac{(y-1)^2}{16} = 1$$

$$\frac{(y-1)^2}{16} = 1 - \frac{(x+3)^2}{4}$$

$$(y-1)^2 = 16 - 4(x+3)^2 \qquad \text{Multiplying by 16}$$

$$y - 1 = \pm\sqrt{16 - 4(x+3)^2}$$

$$y = 1 \pm \sqrt{16 - 4(x+3)^2}$$

Now we can produce the graph in either of two ways. One is to enter $y_1 = 1 + \sqrt{16 - 4(x+3)^2}$ and $y_2 = 1 - \sqrt{16 - 4(x+3)^2}$, select a square window, and press $\boxed{\text{F5}}$ to select GRAPH. Here we use $[-12, 12, -7, 7]$. The first equation produces the top half of the ellipse and the second equation produces the lower half.

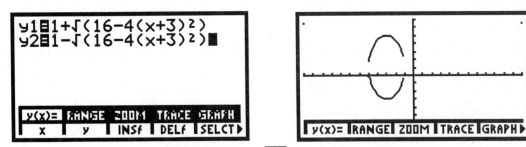

We can also enter $y_1 = \sqrt{16 - 4(x+3)^2}$ and use $\boxed{\text{F2}}$ to select y as described above in Graphing Parabolas to enter $y_2 = 1 + y_1$ and $y_3 = 1 - y_1$. Then deselect y_1, select a square window, and finally select GRAPH. As with parabolas, y_1 is used to eliminate the need to enter the square root more than once. Deselecting it prevents the graph of y_1 from appearing on the screen with the graph of the ellipse. The top half of the graph is produced by y_2 and the lower half by y_3.

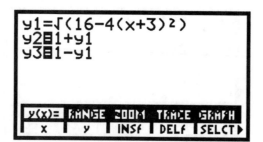

We could also begin by using the quadratic formula to solve the original equation for y.

$$4x^2 + y^2 + 24x - 2y + 21 = 0$$

$$y^2 - 2y + (4x^2 + 24x + 21) = 0$$

$$y = \frac{-(-2) \pm \sqrt{(-2)^2 - 4 \cdot 1 \cdot (4x^2 + 24x + 21)}}{2 \cdot 1}$$

$$y = \frac{2 \pm \sqrt{4 - 16x^2 - 96x - 84}}{2}$$

$$y = \frac{2 \pm \sqrt{-16x^2 - 96x - 80}}{2}$$

Then enter $y_1 = \dfrac{2 + \sqrt{-16x^2 - 96x - 80}}{2}$ and $y_2 = \dfrac{2 - \sqrt{-16x^2 - 96x - 80}}{2}$, or enter $y_1 = \sqrt{-16x^2 - 96x - 80}$, $y_2 = \dfrac{2 + y_1}{2}$, and $y_3 = \dfrac{2 - y_1}{2}$, and deselect y_1.

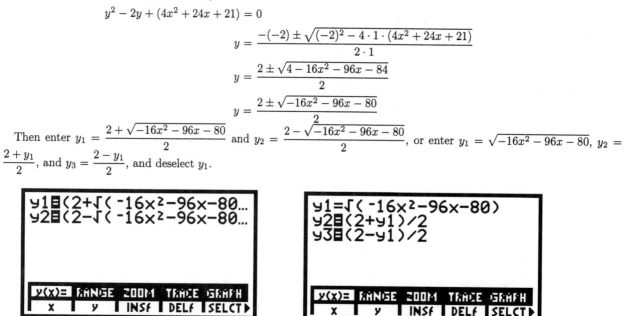

Select a square window and press $\boxed{\text{F5}}$ to display the graph.

GRAPHING HYPERBOLAS

As with equations of circles, parabolas, and ellipses, equations of hyperbolas must be solved for y before they can be entered on the TI-85.

Section 9.3, Example 2 Graph the hyperbola $9x^2 - 16y^2 = 144$.

First solve the equation for y.

$$9x^2 - 16y^2 = 144$$

$$-16y^2 = -9x^2 + 144$$

$$y^2 = \frac{-9x^2 + 144}{-16}$$

$$y = \pm\sqrt{\frac{-9x^2 + 144}{-16}}, \text{ or } \pm\sqrt{\frac{9x^2 - 144}{16}}$$

It is not necessary to simplify further.

Now enter $y_1 = \sqrt{\dfrac{9x^2 - 144}{16}}$ and either $y_2 = -\sqrt{\dfrac{9x^2 - 144}{16}}$ or $y_2 = -y_1$, select a square window, and press $\boxed{\text{F5}}$ to select GRAPH. Here we use $[-12, 12, -7, 7]$. The top half of the graph is produced by y_1 and the lower half by y_2.

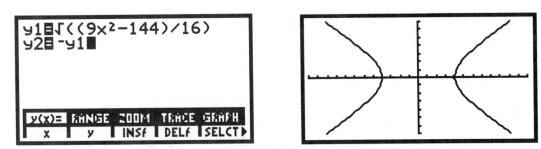

Section 9.3, Example 3 Graph the hyperbola $4y^2 - x^2 + 24y + 4x + 28 = 0$.

In the text we completed the square to get the standard form of the equation. Now solve the equation for y.

$$\frac{(y+3)^2}{1} - \frac{(x-2)^2}{4} = 1$$

$$(y+3)^2 = \frac{(x-2)^2}{4} + 1$$

$$y + 3 = \pm\sqrt{\frac{(x-2)^2}{4} + 1}$$

$$y = -3 \pm \sqrt{\frac{(x-2)^2}{4} + 1}$$

As with ellipses, the graph can be produced in either of two ways. One way is to enter $y_1 = -3 + \sqrt{\frac{(x-2)^2}{4} + 1}$ and $y_2 = -3 - \sqrt{\frac{(x-2)^2}{4} + 1}$, select a square window, and press $\boxed{\text{F5}}$ to select GRAPH. Here we use $[-12, 12, -7, 7]$. The first equation produces the top half of the hyperbola and the second the lower half.

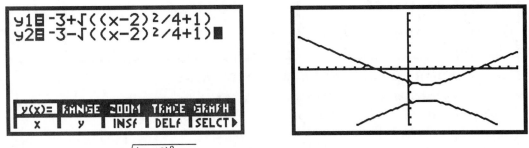

We can also enter $y_1 = \sqrt{\frac{(x-2)^2}{4} + 1}$, $y_2 = -3 + y_1$, and $y_3 = -3 - y_1$. Then deselect y_1, select a square window, and press $\boxed{\text{F5}}$ to select GRAPH. As with parabolas and ellipses, y_1 is used to eliminate the need to enter the square root more than once. Deselecting it prevents the graph of y_1 from appearing on the screen with the graph of the hyperbola. The top half of the graph is produced by y_2 and the lower half by y_3.

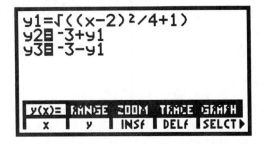

CONVERTING FROM RECTANGULAR TO POLAR COORDINATES

The grapher can be used to convert from rectangular to polar coordinates, expressing the result using either degrees or radians. The grapher will supply a positive value for r and an angle in the interval $(-180°, 180°]$, or $(-\pi, \pi]$.

Section 9.5, Example 2 (a) Convert $(3,3)$ to polar coordinates.

Set the grapher in Degree mode and PolarC mode. Then press $\boxed{(}\,\boxed{3}\,\boxed{,}\,\boxed{3}\,\boxed{)}$ $\boxed{\text{ENTER}}$. The readout is $(4.24264068712\angle 45)$, so $r \approx 4.2426$ (a decimal approximation for $3\sqrt{2}$) and $\theta = 45°$. Thus, polar notation for $(3,3)$ is $(4.2426, 45°)$.

   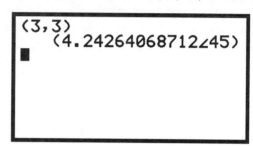

Set the grapher in Radian mode and PolarC mode to find θ in radians. Repeat the keystrokes for finding $(3,3)$ above to find that r is the same and $\theta \approx 0.7854$ (a decimal approximation for $\pi/4$). Thus polar notation for $(3,3)$ is $(4.2426, 0.7854)$.

CONVERTING FROM POLAR TO RECTANGULAR COORDINATES

The grapher can also be used to convert from polar to rectangular coordinates.

Section 9.5, Example 3 Convert each of the following to rectangular coordinates.

(a) $(10, \pi/3)$ (b) $(-5, 135°)$

(a) Set the grapher in RectC mode and, since the angle is given in radians, set it in Radian mode also. Press $\boxed{(}\,\boxed{1}\,\boxed{0}\,\boxed{\text{2nd}}$ $\boxed{\angle}\,\boxed{\text{2nd}}\,\boxed{\pi}\,\boxed{\div}\,\boxed{3}\,\boxed{)}$ $\boxed{\text{ENTER}}$. ($\angle$ is the second operation associated with the $\boxed{,}$ key.) The readout is $(5, 8.66025403784)$, where 8.66025403784 is a decimal approximation of $5\sqrt{3}$. Thus, rectangular notation for $(10, \pi/3)$ is $(5, 8.6603)$.

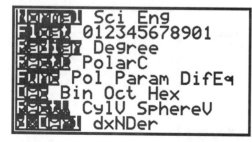

(b) Set the grapher in RectC mode and, since the angle is given in degrees, set it in Degree mode also. To find the x- and y-coordinates of rectangular notation, press $\boxed{(}\,\boxed{(-)}\,\boxed{5}\,\boxed{\text{2nd}}\,\boxed{\angle}\,\boxed{1}\,\boxed{3}\,\boxed{5}\,\boxed{)}$ $\boxed{\text{ENTER}}$. The readout is $(3.53553390593, -3.53553390593)$, where 3.53553390593 is a decimal approximation of $\dfrac{5\sqrt{2}}{2}$. Thus, rectangular notation for $(-5, 135°)$ is $(3.5355, -3.5355)$.

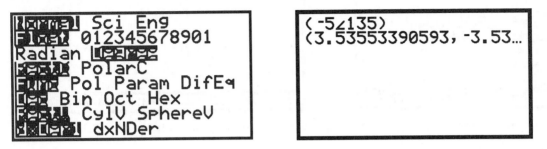

GRAPHING POLAR EQUATIONS

Polar equations can be graphed in either Radian mode or Degree mode. The equation must be written in the form $r = f(\theta)$ and the grapher must be set in polar (Pol) mode. Typically we begin with a range of $[0, 2\pi]$ or $[0°, 360°]$, but it might be necessary to increase the range to ensure that sufficient points are plotted to display the entire graph.

Section 9.5, Example 6 Graph: $r = 1 - \sin\theta$.

First set the grapher in Pol mode and in Radian mode.

The equation is given in $r = f(\theta)$ form. Press $\boxed{\text{GRAPH}}$ $\boxed{\text{F1}}$ to enter it on the "r(θ) =" screen. Clear any existing entries and, with the cursor beside "r1 =" press 1 $\boxed{-}$ $\boxed{\text{SIN}}$ $\boxed{\text{F1}}$. The keystroke $\boxed{\text{F1}}$ selects the variable θ. Now press $\boxed{\text{2nd}}$ $\boxed{\text{M2}}$ to select RANGE and enter the following settings:

θMin $= 0$	(Smallest value of θ to be evaluated)
θMax $= 2\pi$	(Largest value of θ to be evaluated)
θStep $= \pi/24$	(Increment in θ values)
xMin $= -6$	
xMax $= 6$	
xScl $= 1$	
yMin $= -3.5$	
yMax $= 3.5$	
yScl $= 1$	

With these settings the grapher evaluates the function from $\theta = 0$ to $\theta = 2\pi$ in increments of $\pi/24$ and displays the graph in the square window $[-6, 6, -3.5, 3.5]$. Values entered in terms of π appear on the screen as decimal approximations. Press $\boxed{\text{F5}}$ to display the graph.

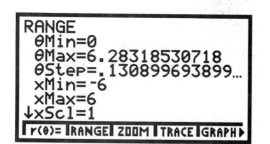 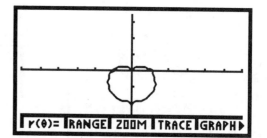

Although we have used a square window, the software used to produce the graph above causes some distortion. The graph produced on your grapher will not be distorted.

The curve can be traced with either rectangular or polar coordinates being displayed. The value of θ is also displayed when rectangular coordinates are selected. The choice of coordinates is made on the GRAPH FORMT screen. Press $\boxed{\text{GRAPH}}$ $\boxed{\text{MORE}}$ $\boxed{\text{F3}}$ to display this screen. Then position the blinking cursor over RectGC to select rectangular coordinates or over PolarGC to select polar coordinates.

GRAPHING PARAMETRIC EQUATIONS

Plane curves described with parametric equations can be graphed on a grapher.

Section 9.8, Example 1 (a) Using a grapher, graph the plane curve given by the set of parametric equations and the restriction for the parameter.

$$x = t^2, \ y = t - 1,; \ -1 \le t \le 4$$

First press $\boxed{\text{2nd}}$ $\boxed{\text{MODE}}$ and select Parametric (Param) mode.

Then press $\boxed{\text{GRAPH}}$ $\boxed{\text{F1}}$ to display the equation-editor screen. Enter $xt1 = t^2$ and $yt1 = t - 1$. Note that the keystroke $\boxed{\text{F1}}$ selects the variable t when the equation-editor screen is displayed in parametric mode. Now press $\boxed{\text{2nd}}$ $\boxed{\text{M2}}$ and enter the following range settings:

tMin $= -1$	(Smallest value of t to be evaluated)
tMax $= 4$	(Largest value of t to be evaluated)
tStep $= .1$	(Increment in t values)
xMin $= -2$	
xMax $= 18$	
xScl $= 1$	
yMin $= -4$	
yMax $= 4$	
yScl $= 1$	

Since $x = t^2$ and $-1 \le t \le 4$, we have $0 \le x \le 16$. Thus, we choose xMin and xMax to display this interval. Similarly, since $y = t - 1$, we have $-2 \le y \le 3$ and we choose yMin and yMax to show this interval. Press $\boxed{\text{F5}}$ to display the graph.

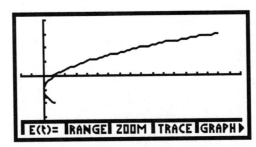

The curve can be traced as described in Example 6 from Section 9.5 above.

Chapter 10
Sequences, Series, and Combinatorics

Both the graphing capabilities and the computational capabilities of the grapher can be used when working with sequences, series, and combinatorics.

FINDING THE TERMS OF A SEQUENCE

Section 10.1, Example 2 Use a grapher to find the first 5 terms of the sequence whose general term is given by $a_n = n/(n+1)$.

We will use the "seq" feature from the LIST OPS menu. We will also use the ▷ Frac feature to express the terms as fractions. Press $\boxed{\text{2nd}}$ $\boxed{\text{LIST}}$ $\boxed{\text{F5}}$ to access this menu. (LIST is the second operation associated with the $\boxed{-}$ subtraction key.) Press $\boxed{\text{MORE}}$ $\boxed{\text{F3}}$ to paste "seq(" to the home screen. Then press $\boxed{\text{x-VAR}}$ $\boxed{\div}$ $\boxed{(}$ $\boxed{\text{x-VAR}}$ $\boxed{+}$ $\boxed{1}$ $\boxed{)}$ $\boxed{,}$ $\boxed{\text{x-VAR}}$ $\boxed{,}$ $\boxed{1}$ $\boxed{,}$ $\boxed{5}$ $\boxed{,}$ $\boxed{1}$ $\boxed{)}$ $\boxed{\text{2nd}}$ $\boxed{\text{MATH}}$ $\boxed{\text{F5}}$ $\boxed{\text{MORE}}$ $\boxed{\text{F1}}$ $\boxed{\text{ENTER}}$. If ▷ Frac has been entered in position F1 of your custom menu as described on page 85 of this manual, the keystrokes $\boxed{\text{2nd}}$ $\boxed{\text{MATH}}$ $\boxed{\text{F5}}$ $\boxed{\text{MORE}}$ can be replaced by $\boxed{\text{CUSTOM}}$.

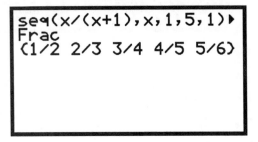

```
seq(x/(x+1),x,1,5,1)▶
Frac
(1/2 2/3 3/4 4/5 5/6)
```

GRAPHING SEQUENCES

The TI-85 does not have the capability to graph sequences.

FINDING PARTIAL SUMS

We can use a grapher to find partial sums of a sequence when a formula for the general term is known.

Section 10.1, Example 6 Use a grapher to find $S_1, S_2, S_3,$ and S_4 for the sequence whose general term is given by $a_n = n^2 - 3$.

Partial sums can be found by combining the sum and seq features. To find S_4, for example, we enter the general term, the variable, the numbers of the first and last terms in the sum, and the increment between the desired terms. Press $\boxed{\text{2nd}}$ $\boxed{\text{LIST}}$ $\boxed{\text{F5}}$ $\boxed{\text{MORE}}$ $\boxed{\text{F1}}$ $\boxed{\text{F3}}$ $\boxed{\text{x-VAR}}$ $\boxed{x^2}$ $\boxed{-}$ $\boxed{3}$ $\boxed{,}$ $\boxed{\text{x-VAR}}$ $\boxed{,}$ $\boxed{1}$ $\boxed{,}$ $\boxed{4}$ $\boxed{,}$ $\boxed{1}$ $\boxed{)}$ $\boxed{\text{ENTER}}$.

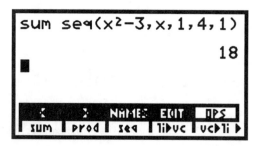

Replace 4 with 1, 2, and 3 to find S_1, S_2, and S_3, respectively.

Section 10.1, Example 7 (a) Evaluate $\displaystyle\sum_{k=1}^{5} k^3$.

We combine the sum and seq features as we did in Example 6 above. Press $\boxed{\text{2nd}}$ $\boxed{\text{LIST}}$ $\boxed{\text{F5}}$ $\boxed{\text{MORE}}$ $\boxed{\text{F1}}$ $\boxed{\text{F3}}$ $\boxed{\text{x-VAR}}$ $\boxed{\wedge}$ 3 $\boxed{,}$ $\boxed{\text{x-VAR}}$ $\boxed{,}$ 1 $\boxed{,}$ 5 $\boxed{,}$ 1 $\boxed{)}$ $\boxed{\text{ENTER}}$.

```
sum seq(x^3,x,1,5,1)
                 225
■




  ⟨      ⟩   NAMES  EDIT  OPS
 sum   prod   seq  li▶vc  vc▶li ▶
```

RECURSIVELY DEFINED SEQUENCES

Terms of recursively defined sequences can also be found on the TI-85.

Section 10.1, Example 7 Find the first 5 terms of the sequence defined by

$$a_1 = 5, \; a_{k+1} = 2a_k - 3, \text{ for } k \geq 1.$$

We will set up a counter that indicates which term of the sequence is displayed. First we will enter 1, indicating that the first term will follow, along with 5, the first term of the sequence. To do this press $\boxed{\text{2nd}}$ $\boxed{\text{LIST}}$ $\boxed{\text{F1}}$ 1 $\boxed{,}$ 5 $\boxed{\text{F2}}$ $\boxed{\text{ENTER}}$. These keystrokes enter 1 as Answer (1) and 5 as Answer (2) and display 5 as the first term of the sequence. We will add 1 to Answer (1) so that the counter increases by 1 each time a new term is displayed. We will also enter the general term of the sequence. Press $\boxed{\text{F1}}$ $\boxed{\text{2nd}}$ $\boxed{\text{ANS}}$ $\boxed{(}$ 1 $\boxed{)}$ $\boxed{+}$ 1 $\boxed{,}$ 2 $\boxed{\text{2nd}}$ $\boxed{\text{ANS}}$ $\boxed{(}$ 2 $\boxed{)}$ $\boxed{-}$ 3 $\boxed{\text{F2}}$ $\boxed{\text{ENTER}}$. Now we see the next term of the sequence, 7, along with the counter, 2, indicating that it is the second term. Press $\boxed{\text{ENTER}}$ again to see the a_3, 11. Press $\boxed{\text{ENTER}}$ once more to see a_4 and again to see a_5. Continue pressing $\boxed{\text{ENTER}}$ to see additional terms.

```
⟨1,5⟩
                ⟨1 5⟩
⟨Ans(1)+1,2 Ans(2)-3⟩

                ⟨2 7⟩
               ⟨3 11⟩
■
  ⟨   ⟩  NAMES  EDIT  OPS
```

```
⟨Ans(1)+1,2 Ans(2)-3⟩

                ⟨2 7⟩
               ⟨3 11⟩
               ⟨4 19⟩
               ⟨5 35⟩
■
  ⟨   ⟩  NAMES  EDIT  OPS
```

EVALUATING FACTORIALS, PERMUTATIONS, AND COMBINATIONS

Operations from the MATH PROB (probability) menu can be used to evaluate factorials, permutations, and combinations. Press $\boxed{\text{2nd}}$ $\boxed{\text{MATH}}$ $\boxed{\text{F2}}$ to display this menu.

Section 10.5, Exercise 6 Evaluate 7!.

With the MATH PROB menu displayed, press 7 $\boxed{\text{F1}}$ $\boxed{\text{ENTER}}$. These keystrokes enter 7, select ! from the MATH PROB menu, and then cause 7! to be evaluated. The result is 5040.

Section 10.5, Exercise 9 Evaluate $\frac{9!}{5!}$.

With the MATH PROB menu displayed, press 9 $\boxed{\text{F1}}$ $\boxed{\div}$ 5 $\boxed{\text{F1}}$ $\boxed{\text{ENTER}}$. The result is 3024.

```
7!
                      5040
9!/5!
                      3024
■

NUM  PROB  ANGLE  HYP   MISC
 !    nPr   nCr   rand
```

Section 10.5, Example 3 (a) Compute $_4P_4$.

With the MATH PROB menu displayed, press 4 $\boxed{\text{F2}}$ 4 $\boxed{\text{ENTER}}$.

Section 10.5, Example 6 Compute $_8P_4$.

With the MATH PROB menu displayed, press 8 $\boxed{\text{F2}}$ 4 $\boxed{\text{ENTER}}$. We could also edit the previous entry to find $_8P_4$. The result is 1680.

```
4 nPr 4
                        24
8 nPr 4
                      1680


NUM  PROB  ANGLE  HYP   MISC
 !    nPr   nCr   rand
```

Section 10.5, Example 3 Evaluate $\binom{7}{5}$.

With the MATH PROB menu displayed, press 7 $\boxed{\text{F3}}$ 5 $\boxed{\text{ENTER}}$. The result is 21.

```
7 nCr 5
                        21
■



NUM  PROB  ANGLE  HYP   MISC
 !    nPr   nCr   rand
```

The TI-86 Graphics Calculator

Introduction to Graphs and the Graphing Calculator

GETTING STARTED

Press $\boxed{\text{ON}}$ to turn on the TI-86 graphing calculator. ($\boxed{\text{ON}}$ is the key at the bottom left-hand corner of the keypad.) You should see a blinking rectangle, or cursor, on the screen. If you do not see the cursor, try adjusting the display contrast. To do this, first press $\boxed{\text{2nd}}$. ($\boxed{\text{2nd}}$ is the yellow key in the left column of the keypad.) Then press and hold $\boxed{\triangle}$ to increase the contrast or $\boxed{\triangledown}$ to decrease the contrast.

To turn the grapher off, press $\boxed{\text{2nd}}$ $\boxed{\text{OFF}}$. (OFF is the second operation associated with the $\boxed{\text{ON}}$ key.) The grapher will turn itself off automatically after about five minutes without any activity.

Press $\boxed{\text{2nd}}$ $\boxed{\text{MODE}}$ to display the MODE settings. (MODE is the second operation associated with the $\boxed{\text{MORE}}$ key.) Initially you should select the settings on the left side of the display.

To change a setting on the Mode screen use $\boxed{\triangledown}$ or $\boxed{\triangle}$ to move the cursor to the line of that setting. Then use $\boxed{\triangleright}$ or $\boxed{\triangleleft}$ to move the blinking cursor to the desired setting and press $\boxed{\text{ENTER}}$. Press $\boxed{\text{EXIT}}$, $\boxed{\text{CLEAR}}$, or $\boxed{\text{2nd}}$ $\boxed{\text{QUIT}}$ to leave the MODE screen. (QUIT is the second operation associated with the $\boxed{\text{EXIT}}$ key.) Pressing $\boxed{\text{EXIT}}$, $\boxed{\text{CLEAR}}$, or $\boxed{\text{2nd}}$ $\boxed{\text{QUIT}}$ will take you to the home screen where computations are performed.

It will be helpful to read the Quick Start section and Chapter 1: Operating the TI-86 in your TI-86 Guidebook before proceeding.

USING A MENU

A menu is a list of options that appears when a key is pressed. Thus, multiple options, and sometimes multiple menus, may be accessed by pressing one key. For example, the following screen appears when $\boxed{\text{2nd}}$ $\boxed{\text{MATH}}$ is pressed. (MATH is the second operation associated with the $\boxed{\times}$ multiplication key.) We see several submenus at the bottom of the screen. The $\boxed{\text{F1}}$ - $\boxed{\text{F5}}$ keys at the top of the keypad are used to select options from this menu. The arrow to the right of MISC indicates that there are more choices. They can be seen by pressing $\boxed{\text{MORE}}$.

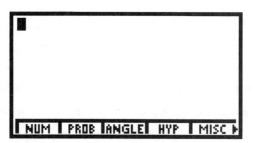

To choose the NUM submenu from the MATH menu press $\boxed{\text{F1}}$. (If you pressed $\boxed{\text{MORE}}$ to see the additional items on the MATH menu as described above, now press $\boxed{\text{MORE}}$ again to see the first five items on the menu. Then press $\boxed{\text{F1}}$ to choose NUM.) When NUM is chosen, the original submenus move up on the screen and the items on the NUM submenu appear at the bottom of the screen.

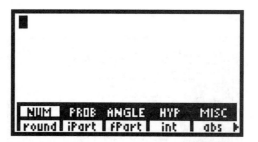

When two rows of options are displayed like this, the top row is accessed by pressing $\boxed{\text{2nd}}$ followed by one of the keys $\boxed{\text{F1}}$ - $\boxed{\text{F5}}$. These keystrokes access the second operations M1 - M5 associated with the $\boxed{\text{F1}}$ - $\boxed{\text{F5}}$ keys. The options on the bottom row are accessed by pressing one of the keys $\boxed{\text{F1}}$ - $\boxed{\text{F5}}$. Absolute value, denoted "abs," is selected from the NUM submenu and copied to the home screen, for instance, by pressing $\boxed{\text{F5}}$.

A menu can be removed from the screen by pressing $\boxed{\text{EXIT}}$. If both a menu and a submenu are displayed, press $\boxed{\text{EXIT}}$ once to remove the submenu and twice to remove both.

SETTING THE VIEWING WINDOW

The viewing window is the portion of the coordinate plane that appears on the grapher's screen. It is defined by the minimum and maximum values of x and y: xMin, xMax, yMin, and yMax. The notation [xMin, xMax, yMin, yMax] is used in the text to represent these window settings or dimensions. For example, $[-12, 12, -8, 8]$ denotes a window that displays the portion of the x-axis from -12 to 12 and the portion of the y-axis from -8 to 8. In addition, the distance between tick marks on the axes is defined by the settings xScl and yScl. In this manual xScl and yScl will be assumed to be 1 unless noted otherwise. The setting xRes sets the pixel resolution. We usually select xRes = 1. The window corresponding to the settings $[-20, 30, -12, 20]$, xScl = 5, yScl = 2, xRes = 1, is shown below.

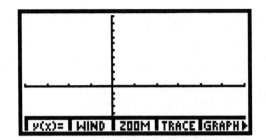

Press $\boxed{\text{GRAPH}}$ $\boxed{\text{F2}}$ to display the current window settings on your grapher. The standard settings $[-10, 10, -10, 10]$, xScl = 1, yScl = 1, are shown below.

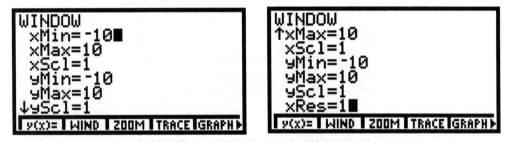

To change a setting, position the cursor beside the setting you wish to change and enter the new value. For example, to change from the standard settings to $[-20, 30, -12, 20]$, xScl = 5, yScl = 2, use the $\boxed{\triangle}$ and $\boxed{\triangledown}$ keys if necessary to position the cursor beside "xMax =" on the WINDOW screen. Then press $\boxed{(-)}$ 2 0 $\boxed{\text{ENTER}}$ 3 0 $\boxed{\text{ENTER}}$ 5 $\boxed{\text{ENTER}}$ $\boxed{(-)}$ 1 2 $\boxed{\text{ENTER}}$ 2 0 $\boxed{\text{ENTER}}$ 2 $\boxed{\text{ENTER}}$. You must use the $\boxed{(-)}$ key on the bottom of the keypad rather than the $\boxed{-}$ key in the right-hand column to enter a negative number. $\boxed{(-)}$ represents "the opposite of" or "the additive inverse of" whereas $\boxed{-}$ is the key for the subtraction operation. The $\boxed{\triangledown}$ key may be used instead of $\boxed{\text{ENTER}}$ after typing each window setting. To see the window shown above, press the $\boxed{\text{F5}}$ key on the top row of the keypad.

QUICK TIP: To return quickly to the standard window setting $[-10, 10, -10, 10]$, xScl = 1, yScl = 1, press $\boxed{\text{GRAPH}}$ $\boxed{\text{F3}}$ $\boxed{\text{F4}}$.

PLOTTING POINTS

We can plot points on a grapher by entering their coordinates in a list and choosing an appropriate viewing window.

Example 2, page 3 (Page numbers refer to pages in the text.) Use a grapher to graph the points $(-3, 5)$, $(4, 3)$, $(3, 4)$, $(-4, -2)$, $(3, -4)$, $(0, 4)$, $(-3, 0)$, and $(0, 0)$.

We choose a viewing window that will display all of the points, noting that the x-coordinates range from -4 to 4 and the y-coordinates range from -4 to 5. Thus, one good choice for a viewing window is the standard window $[-10, 10, -10, 10]$.

We will enter the coordinates of the ordered pairs on the STAT list editor screen. Press $\boxed{\text{2nd}}$ $\boxed{\text{QUIT}}$ to go to the home screen. Then, to clear any existing lists, first press $\boxed{\text{2nd}}$ $\boxed{\text{STAT}}$ $\boxed{\text{F2}}$ (for EDIT). (STAT is the second operation associated with the $\boxed{+}$ key.) Then use the arrow keys to move up to highlight "xStat" and press $\boxed{\text{CLEAR}}$ $\boxed{\text{ENTER}}$. Do the same for yStat.

Once the lists are cleared, we can enter the coordinates of the points. We will enter the first coordinates (x-coordinates) in xStat and the second coordinates (y-coordinates) in yStat. Position the cursor at the top of column xStat, below the xStat heading. To enter -3 press $\boxed{(-)}$ $\boxed{3}$ $\boxed{\text{ENTER}}$. Continue typing the x-values 4, 3, -4, 3, 0, -3, and 0, each followed by $\boxed{\text{ENTER}}$. The entries can be followed by $\boxed{\nabla}$ rather than $\boxed{\text{ENTER}}$ if desired. Press $\boxed{\triangleright}$ to move to the top of column yStat. Type the y-values 5, 3, 4, -2, -4, 4, 0, and 0 in succession, each followed by $\boxed{\text{ENTER}}$ or $\boxed{\nabla}$. Note that the coordinates of each point must be in the same position in both lists.

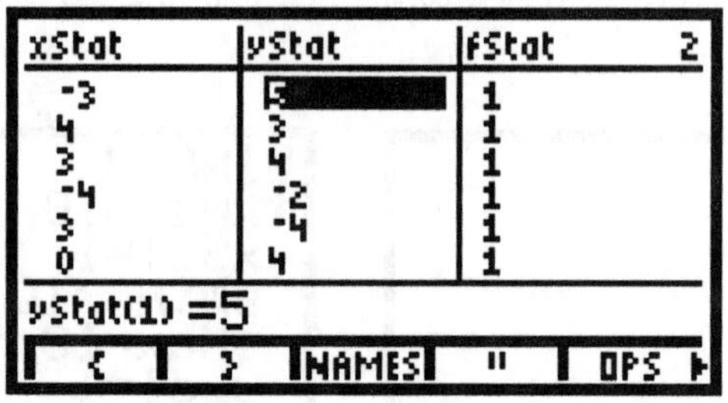

```
xStat      yStat      fStat         2
 -3         5          1
  4         3          1
  3         4          1
 -4        -2          1
  3        -4          1
  0         4          1
yStat(1)=5
   [  {  |  }  |NAMES|  "  |  OPS ▶
```

To plot the points, we turn on the STAT PLOT feature. To access the STAT PLOT screen, press $\boxed{\text{2nd}}$ $\boxed{\text{STAT}}$ $\boxed{\text{F3}}$.

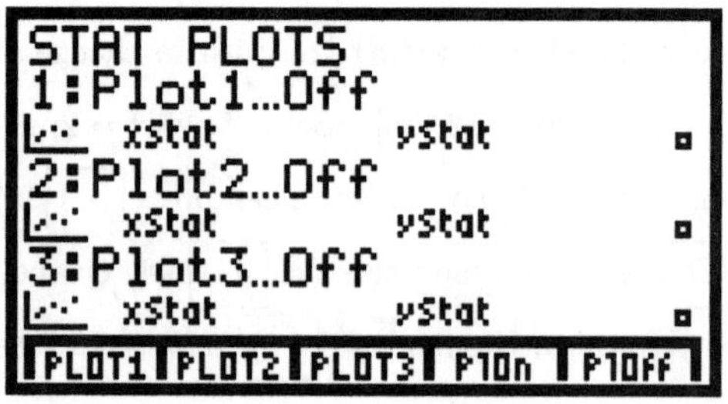

```
STAT PLOTS
1:Plot1…Off
  ⌐·· xStat      yStat            ▫
2:Plot2…Off
  ⌐·· xStat      yStat            ▫
3:Plot3…Off
  ⌐·· xStat      yStat            ▫
 |PLOT1|PLOT2|PLOT3| P1On | P1Off |
```

Choose Plot 1 by pressing $\boxed{\text{F1}}$. Now position the cursor over On and press $\boxed{\text{ENTER}}$ to turn on Plot 1. The entries Type, Xlist, and Ylist, and Mark should be as shown below. To select Type, use the $\boxed{\nabla}$ key to position the cursor beside Type $=$ and then press one the keys $\boxed{\text{F1}}$ - $\boxed{\text{F5}}$. Here we pressed $\boxed{\text{F1}}$ to select "SCAT" for a scatterplot. Use the $\boxed{\nabla}$ key again to position the cursor beside Xlist Name $=$ and press $\boxed{\text{F1}}$ to select xStat. Select yStat for Ylist similarly. The last item, Mark, allows us to choose a box, a cross, or a dot for each point. Here we have selected a box by positioning the cursor beside Mark $=$ and pressing $\boxed{\text{F1}}$.

```
On     Off
Type=⌐··

Xlist Name=xStat
Ylist Name=yStat▫
Mark=▫
 |PLOT1| PLOT2| PLOT3| P1On | P1Off |
 | xStat | yStat | fStat |     |      |
```

Note that there should be no equations entered on the "$y(x) =$" screen. Press $\boxed{\text{GRAPH}}$ $\boxed{\text{F1}}$ to go to this screen. If there are entries present clear them now. To clear an entry for $y1$, for example, position the cursor beside "$y1 =$" and press

CLEAR . Do this for each existing entry. If this is not done, the equations that are currently entered will be graphed along with the data points that are entered.

To see the plotted points, press GRAPH F5 or 2nd F5 .

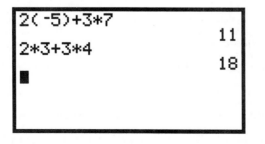

The menu at the bottom of the screen can be removed by pressing CLEAR and restored by pressing GRAPH .

QUICK TIP: Instead of entering the window dimensions directly, we can press GRAPH F3 MORE F5 . This activates the ZData operation which automatically defines a viewing window that displays all the points and also displays the graph.

The plot can be turned off in several ways. Press GRAPH F1 to go to the equation-editor screen. Notice that Plot 1 is highlighted at the top of the screen. Position the blinking cursor over Plot 1 and press ENTER . Plot 1 is no longer highlighted, indicating that it has been turned off. The plot can also be turned off by pressing 2nd STAT F3 F5 ENTER . In addition,it can be turned off by first pressing 2nd STAT F3 F1 to go to the Plot 1 screen. Then position the cursor over Off and press ENTER .

SOLUTIONS OF EQUATIONS

Example 3, page 4 Determine whether each ordered pair is a solution of $2x + 3y = 18$.

       a) $(-5, 7)$ **b)** $(3, 4)$

We can substitute each pair in the expression $2x + 3y$. If the resulting value is 18, the pair is a solution of the equation $2x + 3y = 18$. If not, the pair is not a solution. To perform the substitutions, first press 2nd QUIT or 2nd CLEAR to go to the home screen. To substitute -5 for x and 7 for y in $2x + 3y$, press 2 ((−) 5) + 3 × 7 ENTER . The result is 11, so $(-5, 7)$ is not a solution of the equation. To substitute 3 for x and 4 for y, press 2 × 3 + 3 × 4 ENTER . The result is 18, so $(3, 4)$ is a solution.

```
2( -5)+3*7
                    11
2*3+3*4
                    18
■
```

156   Introduction to Graphs and the Graphing Calculator

EDITING ENTRIES

You can recall and edit an entry if necessary. If, for instance, in entering the last expression in Example 3 above you pressed $\boxed{-}$ instead of $\boxed{+}$, first press $\boxed{\text{2nd}}$ $\boxed{\text{ENTRY}}$ to return to the last entry. (ENTRY is the second operation associated with the $\boxed{\text{ENTER}}$ key.) Then use the $\boxed{\triangleleft}$ key to move the cursor to $\boxed{-}$ and press $\boxed{+}$ to overwrite it. If you forgot to type the first 3, move the cursor to the $\boxed{+}$; then press $\boxed{\text{2nd}}$ $\boxed{\text{INS}}$ 3 to insert the 3 before the $\boxed{+}$. (INS is the second operation associated with the $\boxed{\text{DEL}}$ key.) You can continue to insert symbols immediately after the first insertion without pressing $\boxed{\text{2nd}}$ $\boxed{\text{INS}}$ again. If you typed 21 instead of 2, move the cursor to 1 and press $\boxed{\text{DEL}}$. This will delete the 1. If you notice that an entry needs to be edited before you press $\boxed{\text{ENTER}}$ to perform the computation, the editing can be done directly without recalling the entry.

The keystrokes $\boxed{\text{2nd}}$ $\boxed{\text{ENTRY}}$ can be used repeatedly to recall entries preceding the last one. Pressing $\boxed{\text{2nd}}$ $\boxed{\text{ENTRY}}$ twice, for example, will recall the next to last entry. Using these keystrokes a third time recalls the third to last entry and so on. The number of entries that can be recalled depends on the amount of storage they occupy in the calculator's memory.

THE CUSTOM MENU

The TI-86 allows you to create a custom menu containing up to 15 items selected from the Catalog. To display the custom menu, press $\boxed{\text{CUSTOM}}$.

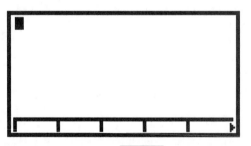

Press $\boxed{\text{MORE}}$ once to see the second menu group and press $\boxed{\text{MORE}}$ once again to see the third group.

To clear an item from the custom menu, press $\boxed{\text{2nd}}$ $\boxed{\text{CATLG-VARS}}$ $\boxed{\text{F1}}$ $\boxed{\text{F4}}$ to select BLANK from the Catalog menu. (CATLG-VARS is the second operation associated with the $\boxed{\text{CUSTOM}}$ key.) Then press one of the $\boxed{\text{F1}}$ - $\boxed{\text{F5}}$ keys corresponding to the location of the item to be cleared. To clear an item in the middle position of the first custom menu group, for instance, press $\boxed{\text{F3}}$. To clear an item in the second or third menu group, press $\boxed{\text{MORE}}$ once or twice before pressing one of the $\boxed{\text{F1}}$ - $\boxed{\text{F5}}$ keys. A new item added to a custom menu will replace the item currently in that location, so it is not necessary to clear an item before one is added in its place.

We will put "▷ Frac" in position F1 of the first menu group in a custom menu to illustrate the procedure for adding an item to the custom menu. First select Custom from the catalog menu be pressing $\boxed{\text{2nd}}$ $\boxed{\text{CATLG-VARS}}$ $\boxed{\text{F1}}$ $\boxed{\text{F3}}$. Now move the triangular selection cursor in the Catalog beside ▷ Frac. The fastest way to do this is to press $\boxed{\text{A}}$ to go to the first item in the Catalog that begins with A. Then use the $\boxed{\triangle}$ key to go to "▷ Frac." Copy this item to position F1 in the custom menu by pressing $\boxed{\text{F1}}$.

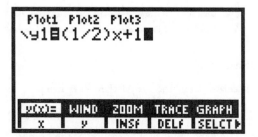

THE TABLE FEATURE

A table of x-and y-values representing ordered pairs that are solutions of an equation can be displayed. We must first enter the equation on the equation-editor screen before a table can be displayed.

Example 5, page 6 Create a table of ordered pairs that are solutions of the equation $y = \frac{1}{2}x + 1$.

First press $\boxed{\text{GRAPH}}$ $\boxed{\text{F1}}$ to access the equation-editor screen. Then clear any equations that are present. (See page 154 of this manual for the procedure to follow.) Also turn off any plots that are turned on. (See page 155 of this manual for the procedure to follow.) Next enter the equation by positioning the cursor beside "$y_1 =$" and pressing $\boxed{(}$ $\boxed{1}$ $\boxed{\div}$ $\boxed{2}$ $\boxed{)}$ $\boxed{\text{F1}}$ $\boxed{+}$ 1. The variable x could also be entered by pressing the $\boxed{\text{x-VAR}}$ key instead of $\boxed{\text{F1}}$. Although the parentheses are not necessary, the equation is more easily read when they are used.

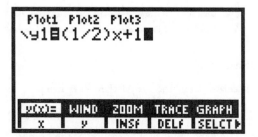

Once the equation in entered, press $\boxed{\text{TABLE}}$ $\boxed{\text{F2}}$ to display the table set-up screen. You can choose to supply the x-values yourself or you can set the grapher to supply them. To have the grapher supply the x-values, set "Indpnt" to "Auto" by positioning the cursor over "Auto" and pressing $\boxed{\text{ENTER}}$.

When "Indpnt" is set to "Auto," the grapher will supply values for x, beginning with the value specified as TblStart and continuing by adding the value of ΔTbl to the preceding value for x. We will display a table of values that starts with $x = -3$ and adds 1 to the preceding x-value. Press $\boxed{(-)}$ 3 $\boxed{\nabla}$ 1 or $\boxed{(-)}$ 3 $\boxed{\text{ENTER}}$ 1 to select a minimum x-value of -3 and an increment of 1. To display the table press $\boxed{\text{F1}}$.

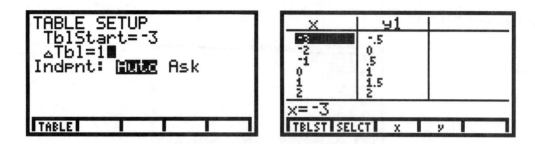

GRAPHING EQUATIONS

After entering an equation and setting a viewing window, you can view the graph of the equation.

Example 6, page 7   Graph using a grapher: $y = \frac{1}{2}x + 1$.

Enter the equation on the equation-editor screen as described in Example 5 above. The standard $[-10, 10, -10, 10]$ window is a good choice for this graph. Either enter these dimensions in the WINDOW screen and then press $\boxed{\text{F5}}$ to see the graph or, after entering the equation, simply press $\boxed{\text{2nd}}$ $\boxed{\text{F3}}$ $\boxed{\text{F4}}$ to select the standard window and see the graph.

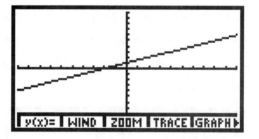

FINDING POINTS OF INTERSECTION

We can use the ISECT (Intersect) feature from the GRAPH MATH menu to find the point(s) of intersection of two graphs.

Example 9, page 9   Use a grapher to find the point of intersection of the graphs of $x - y = -5$ and $y = 4x + 10$.

We begin by entering the equations on the equation-editor screen. Since equations must be entered in the form "$y =$", we solve the first equation for y, obtaining $y = x + 5$. Then press $\boxed{\text{GRAPH}}$ $\boxed{\text{F1}}$ to go to the equation-editor screen. Clear any existing entries. Enter $y_1 = x + 5$ by positioning the cursor beside "$y_1 =$" and pressing $\boxed{\text{F1}}$ $\boxed{+}$ 5 or $\boxed{\text{x-VAR}}$ $\boxed{+}$ 5. Next position the cursor beside "$y_2 =$" and enter $y_2 = 4x + 10$ by pressing 4 $\boxed{\text{F1}}$ $\boxed{+}$ 1 0 or 4 $\boxed{\text{x-VAR}}$ $\boxed{+}$ 1 0. Now graph the equations. We begin by using the standard window and see that it is a good choice because it shows the point of intersection of the graphs.

We we will use the ISECT (Intersect) feature from the GRAPH MATH menu to find the coordinates of that point. To select this feature, from the GRAPH screen press $\boxed{\text{MORE}}$ $\boxed{\text{F1}}$ $\boxed{\text{MORE}}$ $\boxed{\text{F3}}$. The query "First curve?" appears at the bottom of the screen. The blinking cursor is positioned on the graph of y_1. This is indicated by a 1 in the upper right-hand corner of the screen. Press $\boxed{\text{ENTER}}$ to indicate that this is the first curve involved in the intersection. Next the query

"Second curve?" appears at the bottom of the screen. The blinking cursor is now positioned on the graph of y_2 and a 2 should appear in the top right-hand corner of the screen. Press ENTER to indicate that this is the second curve. We identify the curves for the grapher since we could have as many as ten graphs on the screen at once. After we identify the second curve, the query "Guess?" appears at the bottom of the screen. Use the right and left arrow keys to move the blinking cursor close to the point of intersection of the graphs. This provides the grapher with a guess as to the coordinates of this point. We do this since some pairs of curves can have more than one point of intersection. When the cursor is positioned, press ENTER a third time. Now the coordinates of the point of intersection appear at the bottom of the screen.

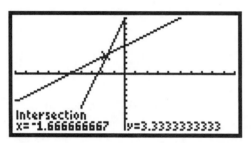

We see that the graphs intersect at the point $(-1.666666667, 3.3333333333)$. This is a decimal approximation for the point of intersection. If the coordinates are rational numbers, their exact values can be found using the " ▷ Frac" feature from the MATH MISC menu.

To do this first press 2nd QUIT to go to the home screen. The x- and y-coordinates of the point of intersection are stored in the calculator as x and y, respectively. To convert the decimal approximation to a rational number, press x-VAR 2nd MATH F5 MORE F1 ENTER. These keystrokes tell the grapher to use x, and then they access the MISC submenu of the MATH menu, copy " ▷ Frac" to the home screen, and display the conversion. If ▷ Frac has been placed in position 1 of your custom menu as described on page 156 of this manual, the keystrokes 2nd MATH F5 MORE can be replaced by CUSTOM. To convert y to a rational number press 2nd ALPHA Y F1 ENTER. (Y is the blue alphabetic operation associated with the 0 numeric key.) We see that the point of intersection is $\left(-\dfrac{5}{3}, \dfrac{10}{3}\right)$.

Chapter R
Basic Concepts of Algebra

ABSOLUTE VALUE

Section R.1, Example 3 Find the distance between -2 and 3.

The distance between -2 and 3 is $|-2-3|$, or $|3-(-2)|$. Absolute value notation is denoted "abs" on the TI-86 and is found on the MATH NUM menu. To enter $|-2-3|$, with the MATH NUM menu displayed, press 2nd MATH F1 F5 ((−) 2 − 3) ENTER. To enter $|3-(-2)|$ press 2nd MATH F1 F5 (3 − ((−) 2)) ENTER.

```
abs (-2-3)
                      5
abs (3-(-2))
                      5
■
```

Note that the expression inside the absolute value symbols must be enclosed in parentheses so that the absolute value of the entire expression will be found. The parentheses around -2 in the second expression are not necessary, but they allow the expression to be read more easily so we include them here.

SCIENTIFIC NOTATION

To enter a number in scientific notation, first type the decimal portion of the number; then press EE; finally type the exponent, which can be at most two digits. For example, to enter 1.789×10^{-11} in scientific notation, press 1 . 7 8 9 EE (−) 1 1 ENTER. To enter 6.084×10^{23} in scientific notation, press 6 . 0 8 4 2nd 2 3 ENTER. The decimal portion of each number appears before a small E while the exponent follows the E.

```
1.789e-11
                  1.789e-11
6.084e23
                  6.084e23
■
```

The grapher can be used to perform computations in scientific notation.

Section R.2, Example 7 *Distance to a Star.* Alpha Centauri is about 4.3 light-years from Earth. One light-year is the distance that light travels in one year and is about 5.88×10^{12} miles. How many miles is it from Earth to Alpha Centauri?

Express your answer in scientific notation.

To solve this problem we find the product $4.3 \times (5.88 \times 10^{12})$. Press 4 $.$ 3 $\times$ 5 $.$ $8\;8$ $\boxed{\text{EE}}$ $1\;2$ $\boxed{\text{ENTER}}$. The result is 2.5284×10^{13} miles.

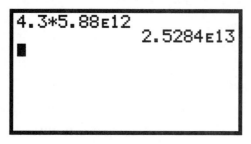

ORDER OF OPERATIONS

Section R.2, Example 8 (b) Calculate: $\dfrac{10 \div (8-6) + 9 \cdot 4}{2^5 + 3^2}$.

In order to divide the entire numerator by the entire denominator, we must enclose both the numerator and the denominator in parentheses. That is, we enter $(10 \div (8-6) + 9 \cdot 4) \div (2^5 + 3^2)$. Press $\boxed{(}$ $1\;0$ $\boxed{\div}$ $\boxed{(}$ 8 $\boxed{-}$ 6 $\boxed{)}$ $\boxed{+}$ 9 $\boxed{\times}$ 4 $\boxed{)}$ $\boxed{\div}$ $\boxed{(}$ 2 $\boxed{\wedge}$ 5 $\boxed{+}$ 3 $\boxed{x^2}$ $\boxed{)}$ $\boxed{\text{ENTER}}$. Note that 3^2 can be entered either as 3 $\boxed{x^2}$ or as 3 $\boxed{\wedge}$ 2.

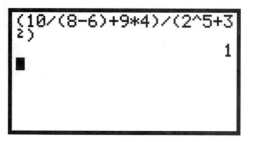

THE PATH GRAPH STYLE

Seven graph styles can be selected on the equation-editor screen of the TI-86. The path graph style can be used, along with the line style, to determine whether graphs coincide. This can be used to provide a partial check of certain algebraic procedures.

Section R.4, Example 2 Factor: $x^3 + 3x^2 - 5x - 15$.

Factoring by grouping, we find that $x^3 + 3x^2 - 5x - 15 = (x+3)(x^2-5)$. We can check this using two different graph styles on a grapher. First press $\boxed{\text{GRAPH}}$ $\boxed{\text{MORE}}$ $\boxed{\text{F3}}$ to determine whether Sequential graph format is selected. If it is not, position the blinking cursor over SeqG and then press $\boxed{\text{ENTER}}$.

Next, on the $y(x) =$ screen, enter $y_1 = x^3 + 3x^2 - 5x - 15$ and $y_2 = (x+3)(x^2 - 5)$. We will select the line graph style for y_1 and the path style for y_2. To select these graph styles, position the cursor anywhere in the equation and then press MORE . Now press F3 repeatedly until the desired style icon appears as shown below.

The grapher will graph y_1 first as a solid line. Then y_2 will be graphed as the circular cursor traces the leading edge of the graph, allowing us to determine visually whether the graphs coincide. In this case, the graphs appear to coincide, so the factorization is probably correct.

SELECTING THE DrawDot GRAPH FORMAT

When graphing an equation in which a variable appears in a denominator, the DrawDot graph format should be used. To select DrawDot press GRAPH MORE F3 and use ▽ and ▷ to position the blinking cursor over "DrawDot." Then press ENTER .

We can also select the DrawDot graph format by selecting the "dot" graph style on the equation-editor screen. Position the cursor anywhere in the equation to be graphed in DrawDot style and press MORE . Then press F3 repeatedly until the dotted icon appears.

RADICAL NOTATION

We can use the square-root and xth-root features to simplify radical expressions.

Section R.6, Example 1 Simplify each of the following.

a) $\sqrt{36}$ b) $-\sqrt{36}$ c) $\sqrt[5]{\dfrac{32}{243}}$ d) $\sqrt[3]{-8}$ e) $\sqrt[4]{-16}$

a) To find $\sqrt{36}$ press $\boxed{\text{2nd}}$ $\boxed{\sqrt{}}$ 3 6 $\boxed{\text{ENTER}}$. ($\sqrt{}$ is the second operation associated with the $\boxed{x^2}$ key.)

b) To find $-\sqrt{36}$ press $\boxed{(-)}$ $\boxed{\text{2nd}}$ $\boxed{\sqrt{}}$ 3 6 $\boxed{\text{ENTER}}$.

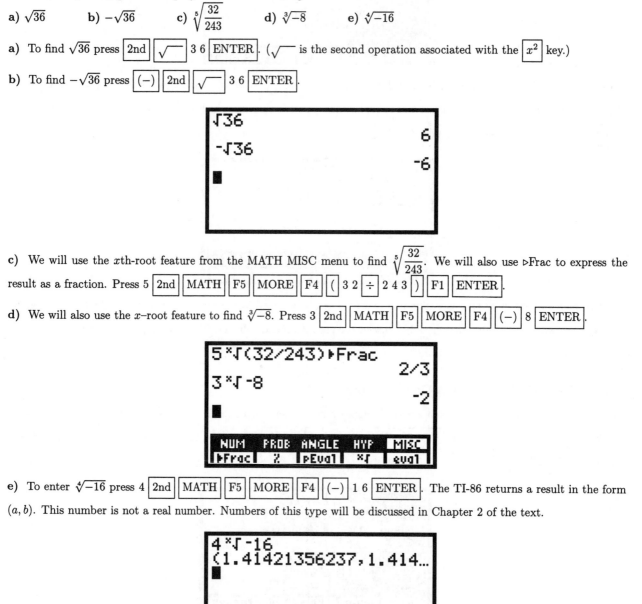

c) We will use the xth-root feature from the MATH MISC menu to find $\sqrt[5]{\dfrac{32}{243}}$. We will also use ▷Frac to express the result as a fraction. Press 5 $\boxed{\text{2nd}}$ $\boxed{\text{MATH}}$ $\boxed{\text{F5}}$ $\boxed{\text{MORE}}$ $\boxed{\text{F4}}$ $\boxed{(}$ 3 2 $\boxed{\div}$ 2 4 3 $\boxed{)}$ $\boxed{\text{F1}}$ $\boxed{\text{ENTER}}$.

d) We will also use the x–root feature to find $\sqrt[3]{-8}$. Press 3 $\boxed{\text{2nd}}$ $\boxed{\text{MATH}}$ $\boxed{\text{F5}}$ $\boxed{\text{MORE}}$ $\boxed{\text{F4}}$ $\boxed{(-)}$ 8 $\boxed{\text{ENTER}}$.

e) To enter $\sqrt[4]{-16}$ press 4 $\boxed{\text{2nd}}$ $\boxed{\text{MATH}}$ $\boxed{\text{F5}}$ $\boxed{\text{MORE}}$ $\boxed{\text{F4}}$ $\boxed{(-)}$ 1 6 $\boxed{\text{ENTER}}$. The TI-86 returns a result in the form (a, b). This number is not a real number. Numbers of this type will be discussed in Chapter 2 of the text.

SOLVING EQUATIONS GRAPHICALLY

We can use the ISECT (Intersect) feature from the GRAPH MATH menu to solve equations.

Section R.7, Example 1 Solve: $2(5 - 3x) = 8 - 3(x + 2)$.

On the equation-editor screen clear any existing entries and then enter $y_1 = 2(5 - 3x)$ and $y_2 = 8 - 3(x + 2)$. The solution of the original equation is the first coordinate of the point of intersection of the graphs of y_1 and y_2. Find the point of intersection as described on page 158 of this manual.

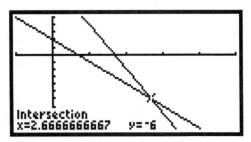

The first coordinate of the point of intersection is 2.6666666667. This is a decimal approximation of the solution. This number is stored in the calculator as X. If it is a rational number we can find fractional notation for the exact solution using the ▷Frac feature. Press $\boxed{\text{2nd}}$ $\boxed{\text{QUIT}}$ to go to the home screen. Then press $\boxed{\text{x-VAR}}$ $\boxed{\text{2nd}}$ $\boxed{\text{MATH}}$ $\boxed{\text{F5}}$ $\boxed{\text{MORE}}$ $\boxed{\text{F1}}$ $\boxed{\text{ENTER}}$. If you have put ▷ Frac in position F1 of your custom menu as described on page 156 of this manual, press $\boxed{\text{x-VAR}}$ $\boxed{\text{CUSTOM}}$ $\boxed{\text{F1}}$ $\boxed{\text{ENTER}}$. We see that the solution is 8/3.

Chapter 1
Graphs, Functions, and Models

FINDING FUNCTION VALUES

When a formula for a function is given, function values can be found in several ways.

Section 1.1, Example 4 (b) For $f(x) = 2x^2 - x + 3$, find $f(-7)$.

Method 1: Substitute the inputs directly in the formula. Press 2 $\boxed{(}$ $\boxed{(-)}$ 7 $\boxed{)}$ $\boxed{x^2}$ $\boxed{-}$ $\boxed{(}$ $\boxed{(-)}$ 7 $\boxed{)}$ $\boxed{+}$ 3 $\boxed{\text{ENTER}}$. Although it is not necessary to use the second set of parentheses, they allow the expression to be read more easily so we include them here.

```
2(-7)²-(-7)+3
                    108
■
```

Method 2: Enter $y_1 = 2x^2 - x + 3$ on the "y(x) =" screen. Then press $\boxed{\text{2nd}}$ $\boxed{\text{QUIT}}$ to go to the home screen. To find $f(-7)$, the value of y_1 when $x = -7$, press $\boxed{(-)}$ 7 $\boxed{\text{STO} \triangleright}$ $\boxed{\text{x-VAR}}$ $\boxed{\text{2nd}}$ $\boxed{:}$ $\boxed{\text{2nd}}$ $\boxed{\text{alpha}}$ $\boxed{\text{Y}}$ $\boxed{\text{ALPHA}}$ $\boxed{\text{ALPHA}}$ 1 $\boxed{\text{ENTER}}$. (: is the second operation associated with the $\boxed{.}$ key. alpha is the second operation associated with the $\boxed{\text{ALPHA}}$ key.) This series of keystrokes stores -7 as the value of x and then substitutes it in the function y_1.

```
-7→x:y1
                    108
■
```

Method 3: Enter $y_1 = 2x^2 - x + 3$ on the "y(x) =" screen and press $\boxed{\text{2nd}}$ $\boxed{\text{QUIT}}$ to go to the home screen. To find $f(-7)$ press $\boxed{\text{2nd}}$ $\boxed{\text{alpha}}$ $\boxed{\text{Y}}$ 1 $\boxed{(}$ $\boxed{(-)}$ 7 $\boxed{)}$ $\boxed{\text{ENTER}}$. Note that this entry closely resembles function notation.

Method 4: The TABLE feature can also be used to find function values. Enter $y_1 = 2x^2 - x + 3$ on the "$y(x) =$" screen. Then set up a table Ask mode, by pressing $\boxed{\text{TABLE}}$ $\boxed{\text{F2}}$, moving the cursor over "Indpnt: Ask," and pressing $\boxed{\text{ENTER}}$. In ASK mode, you supply x-values and the grapher returns the corresponding y-values. The settings for TblStart and ΔTbl are irrelevant in this mode. Press $\boxed{\text{F1}}$ to display the TABLE screen. Then press $\boxed{(-)}$ 7 $\boxed{\text{ENTER}}$ to find $f(-7)$.

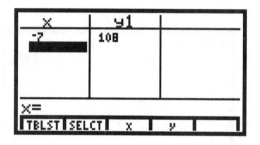

Method 5: We can also use the Eval feature from the GRAPH menu to find $f(-7)$. To do this, graph $y_1 = 2x^2 - x + 3$ in a window that includes the x-value -7. We will use the standard window. Then press $\boxed{\text{MORE}}$ $\boxed{\text{MORE}}$ $\boxed{\text{F1}}$ $\boxed{\text{ENTER}}$ to select Eval from the GRAPH menu. Now supply the desired x-value by pressing $\boxed{(-)}$ 7. Press $\boxed{\text{ENTER}}$ to see X $= -7$, Y $= 108$ at the bottom of the screen, Thus, $f(-7) = 108$.

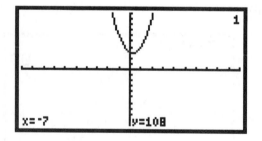

GRAPHS OF FUNCTIONS

The TI-86 does not use function notation. To graph a function, first replace the function notation with y. For example, to graph $f(x) = x^2 - 5$ replace $f(x)$ with y. Then enter the equation $y = x^2 - 5$ on the equation-editor screen and graph it as described on page 157 of this manual.

LINEAR REGRESSION

We can use the Linear Regression feature in the STAT CALC menu to fit a linear equation to a set of data.

Section 1.3, Example 1 The following table shows the number of apartment households in the United States, in millions, for years since 1970.

Years, x	Number of Apartment Households (in millions)
1970, 0	8.5
1975, 5	9.9
1980, 10	10.8
1985, 15	12.9
1990, 20	14.2
1997, 27	14.5

(a) Fit a regression line to the data using the linear regression feature on a grapher.

(b) Use the linear model to predict the number of apartment households in 2003.

(a) We will enter the data as ordered pairs on the STAT list editor screen as described on pages 153 and 154 of this manual.

The grapher's linear regression feature can be used to fit a linear equation to the data. Once the data have been entered in the lists, press $\boxed{\text{2nd}}$ $\boxed{\text{QUIT}}$ to go to the home screen. Then press $\boxed{\text{2nd}}$ $\boxed{\text{STAT}}$ $\boxed{\text{F1}}$ $\boxed{\text{F3}}$ $\boxed{\text{2nd}}$ $\boxed{\text{LIST}}$ $\boxed{\text{F3}}$ $\boxed{\text{F2}}$ $\boxed{,}$ $\boxed{\text{F3}}$ $\boxed{\text{ENTER}}$. (LIST is the second operation associated with the $\boxed{-}$ subtraction key.) These keystrokes select LinR (linear regression) from the STAT CALC menu and display the coefficients a and b of the regression equation $y = a + bx$ along with "corr," the coefficient of correlation and n, the number of data points.

```
LinReg
  y=a+bx
  a=8.7173854
  b=.240203735
↓corr=.975506836
■
    <    >   NAMES  EDIT   OPS
  PRegC  fStat  xStat  yStat
```

Immediately after the regression equation is found it can be copied to the equation-editor screen as y_1. Note that any previous entry in y_1 should be cleared first. Press $\boxed{\text{GRAPH}}$ $\boxed{\text{F1}}$ and position the cursor beside y_1. Then press $\boxed{\text{2nd}}$ $\boxed{\text{STAT}}$ $\boxed{\text{F5}}$ $\boxed{\text{MORE}}$ $\boxed{\text{MORE}}$ $\boxed{\text{F2}}$. These keystrokes select Variables from the STAT menu and then select the RegEq (Regression Equation) from this submenu and copy it to the equation-editor screen.

Before the regression equation is found, it is possible to select a y-variable to which it will be stored on the equation editor screen. After the data have been stored in the lists and the equation previously entered as y_1 has been cleared, press 2nd STAT F1 F3 2nd LIST F3 F2 , F3 , 2nd alpha Y 1 ENTER . The coefficients of the regression equation will be displayed on the home screen, and the regression equation will also be stored as y_1 on the equation-editor screen.

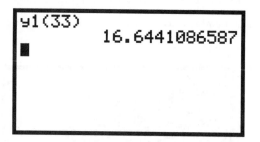

(b) To predict the number of apartment households in 2003, evaluate the regression equation for $x = 33$. (2003 is 33 years after 1970.) Use any of the methods for evaluating a function presented earlier in this chapter. (See pages 167 and 168 of this manual.) We will use function notation on the home screen.

```
y1(33)
            16.6441086587
■
```

When $x = 33, y \approx 16.6$, so we predict that there will be about 16.6 million apartment households in the United States in 2003.

We can also plot the data points along with the graph of the regression equation. To do this we first turn on the STAT PLOT feature as described on page 154 of this manual. Now select a viewing window. We will press GRAPH F3 MORE F5 to activate the ZData operation which automatically defines a viewing window that displays all of the points and also displays the graph.

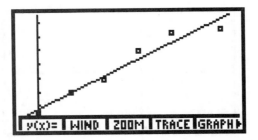

Turn off the STAT PLOT as described on page 155 of this manual before graphing other functions.

THE FMAX AND FMIN FEATURES

Section 1.4, Example 2 Use a grapher to determine any relative maxima or minima of the function $f(x) = 0.1x^3 - 0.6x^2 - 0.1x + 2$.

First graph $y_1 = 0.1x^3 - 0.6x^2 - 0.1x + 2$ in a window that displays the relative extrema of the function. Trial and error reveals that one good choice is $[-4, 6, -3, 3]$. Observe that a relative maximum occurs near $x = 0$ and a relative minimum occurs near $x = 4$.

To find the relative maximum, first press $\boxed{\text{MORE}}$ $\boxed{\text{F1}}$ $\boxed{\text{F5}}$ to select the FMAX feature from the GRAPH MATH menu. We are prompted to select a left bound for the relative maximum. This means that we must choose an x-value that is to the left of the x-value of the point where the relative maximum occurs. This can be done by using the left- and right-arrow keys to move the cursor to a point to the left of the relative maximum or by keying in an appropriate value.

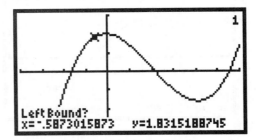

Once this is done, press $\boxed{\text{ENTER}}$. Now we are prompted to select a right bound. We move the cursor to a point to the right of the relative maximum or we key in an appropriate value.

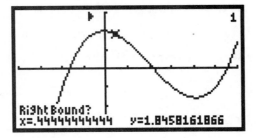

Press $\boxed{\text{ENTER}}$ again. Finally we are prompted to guess the x-value at which the relative maximum occurs. Move the cursor close to the relative maximum point or key in an x-value.

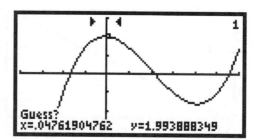

Press ENTER a third time. We see that a relative maximum function value of approximately 2.004 occurs when $x \approx -0.0817$.

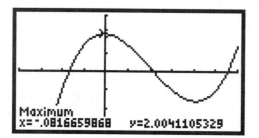

To find the relative minimum, select the FMIN feature from the GRAPH MATH menu by pressing GRAPH MORE F1 F4. Select left and right bounds for the relative minimum and guess the x-value at which it occurs as described above. We see that a relative minimum function value of approximately -1.604 occurs when $x \approx 4.082$.

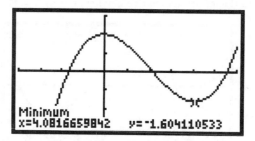

GRAPHING FUNCTIONS DEFINED PIECEWISE

Operations from the TEST menu are used to enter functions that are defined piecewise. (TEST is the second operation associated with the 2 numeric key.) Select the DrawDot graph format from the GRAPH FORMAT menu or use the graph style feature to select Dot style on the equation-editor screen when graphing such functions. (See page 163 of this manual.) Any style selected on the equation-editor screen overrides a GRAPH FORMAT selection.

Section 1.4, Example 5 Graph

$$f(x) = \begin{cases} 4, & \text{for } x \le 0, \\ 4 - x^2, & \text{for } 0 < x \le 2, \\ 2x - 6, & \text{for } x > 2. \end{cases}$$

Press GRAPH F1 and clear any functions that have previously been entered. With the cursor beside "$y_1 =$" enter the function as described on page 111 of the text by pressing (4) (x-VAR 2nd TEST F4 0) + (4 −

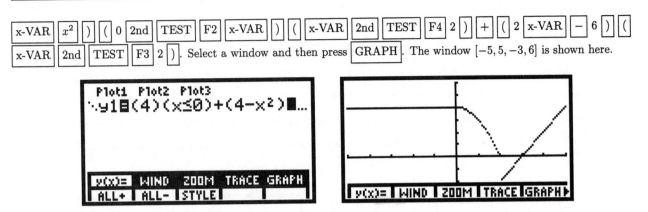

x-VAR x^2) (0 2nd TEST F2 x-VAR) (x-VAR 2nd TEST F4 2) + (2 x-VAR − 6) (
x-VAR 2nd TEST F3 2). Select a window and then press GRAPH. The window $[-5, 5, -3, 6]$ is shown here.

THE GREATEST INTEGER FUNCTION

The greatest integer function is found in the MATH NUM menu and is denoted "int." To find int(1.9) press 2nd
MATH F1 F4 1 . 9 ENTER.

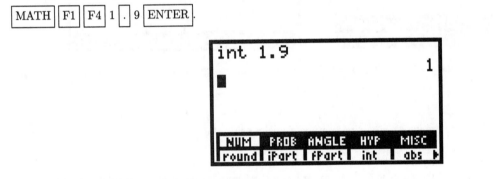

We can also graph the greatest integer function.

Section 1.4, Example 7 Graph $f(x) = \text{int}(x)$.

With the grapher set in the Dot graph style, press GRAPH F1 and clear any previously entered functions. Position
the cursor beside "$y_1 =$" and select the greatest integer function from the MATH NUM menu as follows. Press 2nd
MATH F1 F4 x-VAR. Select a window and press F5 to see the graph. The window $[-6, 6, -6, 6]$ is shown here.

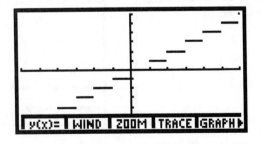

THE ALGEBRA OF FUNCTIONS

The grapher can be used to evaluate and graph combinations of functions.

Section 1.4, Example 8 (b) Given that $f(x) = x + 1$ and $g(x) = \sqrt{x + 3}$, find $(f + g)(6)$.

Press GRAPH F1 and enter $y_1 = x + 1$, $y_2 = \sqrt{x + 3}$, and $y_3 = y_1 + y_2$. To enter $y_3 = y_1 + y_2$ press F1 1 + F2

2. Note that $y_3 = f(x) + g(x)$, or $(f + g)(x)$. Use y_3 to find $(f + g)(6)$ employing one of the methods for finding function values described on pages 167 and 168 of this manual. We find that $(f + g)(6) = 10$.

To view the graphs of $f(x)$, $g(x)$, and $(f + g)(x)$ enter y_1, y_2, and y_3 as above, select a window, and press $\boxed{\text{F5}}$. These graphs appear on page 115 of the text. It is possible to deselect one or two of these functions and display the graph(s) of the remaining function(s). For example, to display only the graph of y_3 without deleting the equations of y_1 and y_2, press $\boxed{\text{GRAPH}}$ $\boxed{\text{F1}}$. Then move the cursor to y_1, position it anywhere in the equation, and press $\boxed{\text{F5}}$. This deselects or turns off y_1. Do the same for y_2. Now press $\boxed{\text{GRAPH}}$ $\boxed{\text{F5}}$ and see only the graph of y_3.

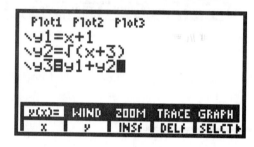 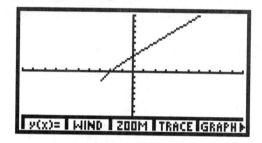

To select or turn on a function again, repeat this process. Note that the equals sign on a selected function is highlighted.

GRAPHING CIRCLES

If the center and radius of a circle are known, the circle can be graphed using the Circle feature from the DRAW menu.

Section 1.7, Exercise 37 Graph $(x - 1)^2 + (y - 5)^2 = 36$.

The center of this circle is $(1,5)$ and its radius is 6. To graph it using the Circle feature from the DRAW menu first press $\boxed{\text{GRAPH}}$ $\boxed{\text{F1}}$ and clear all previously entered equations. Then select a square window. (See page 150 of the text for a discussion on squaring the viewing window.) We will use $[-15, 15, -5, 13]$. Press $\boxed{\text{2nd}}$ $\boxed{\text{QUIT}}$ to go to the home screen. Then press $\boxed{\text{2nd}}$ $\boxed{\text{CATLG-VARS}}$ $\boxed{\text{F1}}$ $\boxed{\text{C}}$ $\boxed{\text{ENTER}}$ to copy "Circl(" to the home screen. Enter the coordinates of the center and the radius, separating the entries by commas, and close the parentheses: 1 $\boxed{,}$ 5 $\boxed{,}$ 6 $\boxed{)}$ $\boxed{\text{ENTER}}$.

 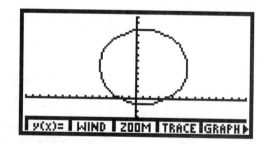

The software used to produce the graph above causes distortion. Nevertheless, when the circle is graphed on a grapher in a square window, there is no distortion.

Chapter 2
Functions and Equations: Zeros and Solutions

THE ROOT FEATURE

The Root feature on the TI-86 can be used to find the zeros of a function or to solve an equation in the form $f(x) = 0$.

Section 2.1, Example 1 Find the zero of $f(x) = 5x - 9$.

On the equation-editor screen, clear any existing entries and then enter $y_1 = 5x - 9$. Now graph the function in a viewing window that shows the x-intercept clearly. The standard window is a good choice.

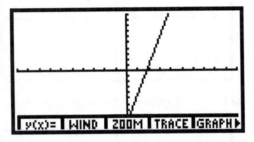

Press $\boxed{\text{MORE}}$ $\boxed{\text{F1}}$ to display the GRAPH MATH menu. Then press $\boxed{\text{F1}}$ to select the Root feature. We are first prompted to select a left bound. This means that we must choose an x-value that is to the left of the x-intercept. This can be done by using the left- and right-arrow keys to move the cursor to a point on the curve to the left of the x-intercept or by keying in a value less than the first coordinate of the intercept.

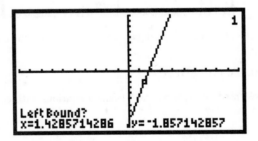

Once this is done press $\boxed{\text{ENTER}}$. Now we are prompted to select a right bound that is to the right of the x-intercept. Again, this can be done by using the arrow keys to move the cursor to a point on the curve to the right of the x-intercept or by keying in a value greater than the first coordinate of the intercept.

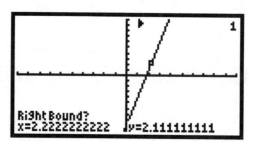

Press $\boxed{\text{ENTER}}$ again. Finally we are prompted to make a guess as to the value of the zero. Move the cursor to a point close to the zero or key in a value.

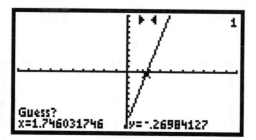

Press $\boxed{\text{ENTER}}$ a third time. We see that $y = 0$ when $x = 1.8$, so 1.8 is the zero of the function.

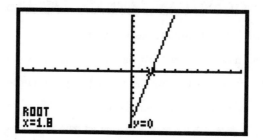

If a function has more than one zero, the Root feature can be used as many times as necessary to find all of them.

OPERATIONS WITH COMPLEX NUMBERS

A complex number $a + bi$ is represented as (a, b) on the TI-86. Operations with complex numbers can be performed on the grapher.

Section 2.1, Example 4

(a) Add: $(8 + 6i) + (3 + 2i)$.

To find this sum press $\boxed{\text{2nd}}$ $\boxed{\text{QUIT}}$ to go to the home screen and then press $\boxed{(}$ 8 $\boxed{,}$ 6 $\boxed{)}$ $\boxed{+}$ $\boxed{(}$ 3 $\boxed{,}$ 2 $\boxed{)}$ $\boxed{\text{ENTER}}$. The grapher returns $(11, 8)$, indicating that the sum is $11 + 8i$.

(b) Subtract: $(4 + 5i) - (6 - 3i)$.

Press $\boxed{(}\ 4\ \boxed{,}\ 5\ \boxed{)}\ \boxed{-}\ \boxed{(}\ 6\ \boxed{,}\ \boxed{-}\ 3\ \boxed{)}\ \boxed{\text{ENTER}}$. The grapher returns $(-2, 8)$, indicating that the difference is $-2 + 8i$.

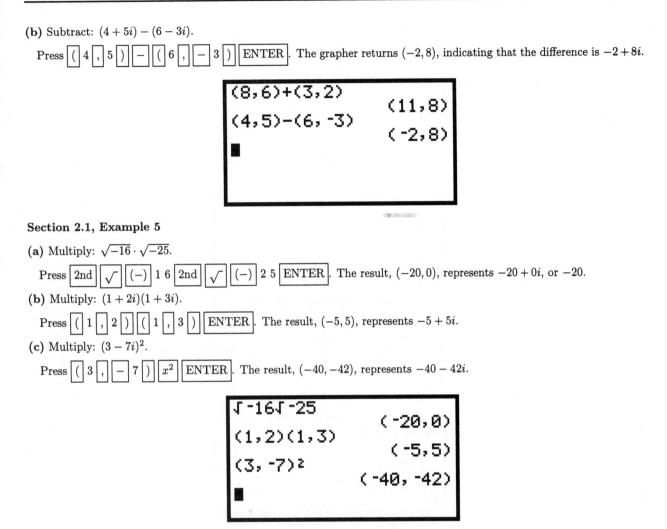

Section 2.1, Example 5

(a) Multiply: $\sqrt{-16} \cdot \sqrt{-25}$.

Press $\boxed{\text{2nd}}\ \boxed{\sqrt{}}\ \boxed{(-)}\ 1\ 6\ \boxed{\text{2nd}}\ \boxed{\sqrt{}}\ \boxed{(-)}\ 2\ 5\ \boxed{\text{ENTER}}$. The result, $(-20, 0)$, represents $-20 + 0i$, or -20.

(b) Multiply: $(1 + 2i)(1 + 3i)$.

Press $\boxed{(}\ 1\ \boxed{,}\ 2\ \boxed{)}\ \boxed{(}\ 1\ \boxed{,}\ 3\ \boxed{)}\ \boxed{\text{ENTER}}$. The result, $(-5, 5)$, represents $-5 + 5i$.

(c) Multiply: $(3 - 7i)^2$.

Press $\boxed{(}\ 3\ \boxed{,}\ \boxed{-}\ 7\ \boxed{)}\ \boxed{x^2}\ \boxed{\text{ENTER}}$. The result, $(-40, -42)$, represents $-40 - 42i$.

QUADRATIC REGRESSION

Quadratic functions can be fit to data using the quadratic regression operation from the STAT CALC menu. The operations of entering data, making scatterplots, and graphing and evaluating quadratic regression functions are the same as for linear regression functions.

Section 2.5, Example 1 *Leisure Time* The following table shows the median number of hours of leisure time that Americans had each week in various years.

Year	Median Number of Leisure Hours per Week
0, 1973	26.2
7, 1980	19.2
14, 1987	16.6
20, 1993	18.8
24, 1997	19.5

(a) Make a scatterplot of the data, letting x represent the number of years since 1973, and determine whether a linear function, a quadratic function, or neither seems to fit the data.

(b) Use a grapher to fit the type of function determined in part (a) to the data.

(c) Graph the equation with the scatterplot.

(d) Use the function found in part (c) to estimate the number of leisure hours per week in 1978; in 1990; in 2005.

(a) Clear any existing entries on the equation-editor screen. Then enter the data and make a scatterplot as described on pages 153 and 154 of this manual. We have used a ZData window here. It appears that a quadratic function fits the data.

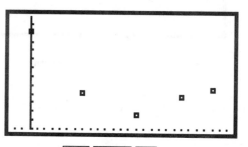

(b) To fit a quadratic function to the data, press $\boxed{\text{2nd}}$ $\boxed{\text{STAT}}$ $\boxed{\text{F1}}$ to view the STAT CALC menu. Then select P2Reg (quadratic regression) by pressing $\boxed{\text{MORE}}$ $\boxed{\text{F4}}$ $\boxed{\text{2nd}}$ $\boxed{\text{LIST}}$ $\boxed{\text{F3}}$ and select xStat. Then press $\boxed{,}$ and select yStat. Now press $\boxed{\text{ENTER}}$ to see the coefficients of a quadratic equation $y = ax^2 + bx + c$. Note that at least three data points are required for quadratic regression.

(c) The regression equation can be copied to the "$y(x) =$" screen as described on pages 169 and 170 of this manual. Once the regression equation is entered in the "$y(x) =$" screen, it can be graphed with the scatterplot.

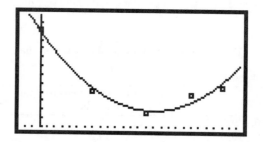

Be sure to turn off the STAT PLOT as described on page 154 of this manual before graphing future equations.

(d) To estimate the number of leisure hours per week in 1978, 1990, and 2005, we evaluate the regression function for 5, 17, and 32, respectively. We can use any of the methods for evaluating a function found on pages 167 and 168 of this manual.

Here we show a table set in Ask mode.

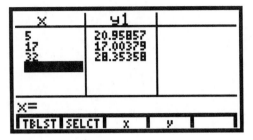

CHECKING SOLUTIONS OF INEQUALITIES

We can perform a partial check of the solution of an inequality using operations from the TEST menu.

Section 2.7, Example 2 Solve: $-3 < 2x + 5 \leq 7$.

The solution set is found algebraically in the text. It is $\{x| -4 < x \leq 1\}$, or $(-4, 1]$. We can perform a partial check of this solution by graphing $y = (-3 < 2x + 5)$ *and* $(2x + 5 \leq 7)$ using the DrawDot graph format. The value of y will be 1 for those x-values which make y a true statement. It will be 0 for those x-values for which y is false. To enter the expression for y, position the cursor beside y_1 on the $y(x) =$ screen. Then press $\boxed{(}$ $\boxed{(-)}$ 3 $\boxed{\text{2nd}}$ $\boxed{\text{TEST}}$ $\boxed{\text{F2}}$ 2 $\boxed{\text{x-VAR}}$ $\boxed{+}$ 5 $\boxed{)}$ $\boxed{\text{2nd}}$ $\boxed{\text{CATLG-VARS}}$ $\boxed{\text{F1}}$ $\boxed{\text{A}}$. Use the $\boxed{\triangledown}$ key to position the triangular selection cursor beside "and" and then press $\boxed{\text{ENTER}}$ to paste it into the expression on the $y(x) =$ screen. Then press $\boxed{(}$ 2 $\boxed{\text{x-VAR}}$ $\boxed{+}$ 5 $\boxed{\text{2nd}}$ $\boxed{\text{TEST}}$ $\boxed{\text{F4}}$ 7 $\boxed{)}$. (TEST is the second operation associated with the 2 numeric key.) The keystrokes $\boxed{\text{2nd}}$ $\boxed{\text{TEST}}$ $\boxed{\text{F2}}$ display the TEST menu and paste the symbol "<" from that menu to the equation-editor screen. The keystrokes $\boxed{\text{2nd}}$ $\boxed{\text{TEST}}$ $\boxed{\text{F4}}$ display the TEST menu again and paste the symbol "$\leq$" into the equation-editor screen.

Now select a window and press $\boxed{\text{F5}}$. We use the window $[-10, 10, -1, 2]$.

We see that $y = 1$ for x-values from -4 to 1, confirming that all x-values from -4 to 1 are in the solution set. The algebraic solution indicates that the endpoint 1 is also in the solution set.

Chapter 3
Polynomial and Rational Functions

POWER MODELS

A power model $y = ax^b$ can be fit to data using the power regression feature from the STAT CALC menu.

Section 3.1, Example 4 (a) *Cholesterol Level and the Risk of Heart Attack.* The data in the following table show the relationship of cholesterol level in men to the risk of a heart attack.

Cholesterol Level, x	Men Per 10,000 Who Suffer a Heart Attack
100	30
200	65
250	100
275	130
300	180

(a) Use a grapher to fit a power function to the data.

Enter the data as described on pages 153 and 154 of this manual. Then go to the home screen and select PwrReg (power regression) from the STAT CALC menu by pressing $\boxed{\text{2nd}}$ $\boxed{\text{STAT}}$ $\boxed{\text{F1}}$ $\boxed{\text{MORE}}$ $\boxed{\text{F1}}$ $\boxed{\text{2nd}}$ $\boxed{\text{LIST}}$ $\boxed{\text{F3}}$ $\boxed{\text{F3}}$ $\boxed{,}$ $\boxed{\text{F4}}$ $\boxed{\text{ENTER}}$. The grapher displays the coefficient a and the exponent b for the power function $y = ax^b$.

```
PwrReg
 y=a*x^b
 a=.024178957
 b=1.52745717
↓corr=.973936134
■
   ‹     ›    NAMES  EDIT    OPS
 fStat  xStat  yStat
```

This function can be saved or copied to the equation-editor screen using one of the methods described on pages 169 and 170 of this manual. Then it can be graphed. It can also be evaluated using one of the methods on pages 167 and 168.

CUBIC AND QUARTIC REGRESSION

We can fit third-degree, or cubic, functions and fourth-degree, or quartic, functions to data on a grapher.

Section 3.1, Example 5 (a) The table below shows the number of farms, in millions, for years after 1900. Model the data with both cubic and quartic functions. Let the first coordinate of each data point be the number of years after 1900.

Years after 1900	Number of Farms, in millions
10, 1910	6.4
20, 1920	6.5
30, 1930	6.3
40, 1940	6.1
50, 1950	5.4
59, 1959	3.7
69, 1969	2.7
78, 1978	2.3
87, 1987	2.1
97, 1997	1.9

Enter the data as described on pages 153 and 154 of this manual. To select cubic regression from the STAT CALC menu go to the home screen and press $\boxed{\text{2nd}}$ $\boxed{\text{STAT}}$ $\boxed{\text{F1}}$ $\boxed{\text{MORE}}$ $\boxed{\text{F5}}$ $\boxed{\text{2nd}}$ $\boxed{\text{LIST}}$ $\boxed{\text{F3}}$ $\boxed{\text{F2}}$ $\boxed{,}$ $\boxed{\text{F4}}$ $\boxed{\text{ENTER}}$. The grapher displays the coefficients of a cubic function $y = ax^3 + bx^2 + cx + d$. Use the $\boxed{\triangleright}$ key to see all of the coefficients.

```
CubicReg
 y=ax³+bx²+cx+d
 n=10
 PRegC=
 {2.95665152662E-5  -.…
 ■
```

To model the data with a quartic function select quartic regression from the STAT CALC menu. Press $\boxed{\text{2nd}}$ $\boxed{\text{STAT}}$ $\boxed{\text{F1}}$ $\boxed{\text{MORE}}$ $\boxed{\text{MORE}}$ $\boxed{\text{F1}}$ $\boxed{\text{2nd}}$ $\boxed{\text{LIST}}$ $\boxed{\text{F3}}$ $\boxed{\text{F3}}$ $\boxed{,}$ $\boxed{\text{F4}}$ $\boxed{\text{ENTER}}$ to see the coefficients of a quartic function $y = ax^4 + bx^3 + cx^2 + dx + e$. Use the $\boxed{\triangleright}$ key to see all of the coefficients.

```
QuarticReg
 y=ax⁴+bx³+cx²+dx+e
 n=10
 PRegC=
 {1.52292972626E-7  -3.…
 ■
    {    }   NAMES  EDIT   OPS
  PRegC  fStat  xStat  yStat
```

A scatterplot of the data can be graphed as described on page 154 of this manual. This function can be copied to the $y(x) =$ screen using one of the methods described on pages 169 and 170 of this manual. Then it can be graphed along with the scatterplot. It can also be evaluated using one of the methods on pages 167 and 168.

GRAPHING RATIONAL FUNCTIONS

Section 3.4, Example 1 Consider $f(x) = \dfrac{1}{x - 3}$ and graph f.

In the text the domain is found to be $\{x | x \neq 3\}$, or $(-\infty, 3) \cup (3, \infty)$. Thus, there is not a point on the graph with an x-coordinate of 3. Graphing the function in the DrawLine graph format can lead to an incorrect graph in which a line connects he last point plotted to the left of $x = 3$ with the last point plotted to the right of $x = 3$. This line can be eliminated by using the DrawDot format as described on page 163 of this manual. Selecting a ZDECM window from the ZOOM menu will also produce a graph in which this line does not appear. To do this, first enter $y = \dfrac{1}{x - 3}$ on the equation-editor screen and then press $\boxed{\text{2nd}}$ $\boxed{\text{F3}}$ $\boxed{\text{MORE}}$ $\boxed{\text{F4}}$. The resulting window dimensions and graph are shown below.

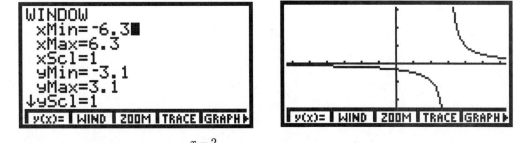

Section 3.4, Example 10 Graph: $g(x) = \dfrac{x - 2}{x^2 - x - 2}$.

As explained in the text, the graph of $g(x)$ is the graph of $y = \dfrac{1}{x + 1}$ with the point $\left(2, \dfrac{1}{3}\right)$ missing. The window used in the text to produce the graph with a "hole" at $\left(2, \dfrac{1}{3}\right)$ is obtained using the ZDECM feature from the ZOOM menu. After entering $y = \dfrac{x - 2}{x^2 - x - 2}$ on the equation-editor screen, press $\boxed{\text{GRAPH}}$ $\boxed{\text{F3}}$ $\boxed{\text{MORE}}$ $\boxed{\text{F4}}$ to select this window and display the graph.

Chapter 4
Exponential and Logarithmic Functions

THE COMPOSITION OF FUNCTIONS

We can evaluate composite functions on a grapher.

Section 4.1, Example 1 (a) Given that $f(x) = 2x - 5$ and $g(x) = x^2 - 3x + 8$, find $(f \circ g)(7)$ and $(g \circ f)(7)$.

On the equation-editor screen enter $y_1 = 2x - 5$ and $y_2 = x^2 - 3x + 8$. Then $(f \circ g)(7) = (y_1 \circ y_2)(7)$, or $y_1(y_2(7))$ and $(g \circ f)(7) = (y_2 \circ y_1)(7)$, or $y_2(y_1(7))$. To find these function values press $\boxed{\text{2nd}}$ $\boxed{\text{QUIT}}$ to go to the home screen. Then enter $y_1(y_2(7))$ by pressing $\boxed{\text{2nd}}$ $\boxed{\text{alpha}}$ $\boxed{\text{Y}}$ 1 $\boxed{(}$ $\boxed{\text{2nd}}$ $\boxed{\text{alpha}}$ $\boxed{\text{Y}}$ 2 $\boxed{(}$ 7 $\boxed{)}$ $\boxed{)}$ $\boxed{\text{ENTER}}$. Now enter $y_2(y_1(7))$ by pressing $\boxed{\text{2nd}}$ $\boxed{\text{ENTRY}}$ to recall the previous entry. Then edit the entry to interchange the 1 and the 2 and press $\boxed{\text{ENTER}}$. We can also enter $y_2(y_1(7))$ directly by pressing $\boxed{\text{2nd}}$ $\boxed{\text{alpha}}$ $\boxed{\text{Y}}$ 2 $\boxed{(}$ $\boxed{\text{2nd}}$ $\boxed{\text{alpha}}$ $\boxed{\text{Y}}$ 1 $\boxed{(}$ 7 $\boxed{)}$ $\boxed{)}$ $\boxed{\text{ENTER}}$.

```
y1(y2(7))
                         67
y2(y1(7))
                         62
■
```

GRAPHING AN INVERSE FUNCTION

The DrawInv operation can be used to graph a function and its inverse on the same screen. A formula for the inverse function need not be found in order to do this.

Section 4.1, Example 7 Graph $f(x) = 2x - 3$ and $f^{-1}(x)$ using the same set of axes.

Enter $y_1 = 2x - 3$ and either clear or deselect all other functions on the "$y(x) =$" screen. Also select a viewing window. The standard window is a good choice. Then press $\boxed{\text{2nd}}$ $\boxed{\text{QUIT}}$ $\boxed{\text{MORE}}$ $\boxed{\text{F2}}$ $\boxed{\text{MORE}}$ $\boxed{\text{MORE}}$ $\boxed{\text{MORE}}$ $\boxed{\text{F3}}$ $\boxed{\text{2nd}}$ $\boxed{\text{alpha}}$ $\boxed{\text{Y}}$ 1 to select the DrawInv operation. Press $\boxed{\text{ENTER}}$ to see the graph of the function and its inverse. The graphs are shown here in the standard window.

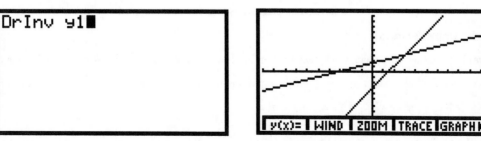

EVALUATING e^x, **Log** x, **and Ln** x

Use the grapher's scientific keys to evaluate e^x, $\log x$, and $\ln x$ for specific values of x.

Section 4.2, Example 6 (a), (b) Find the value of e^3 and $e^{-0.23}$. Round to four decimal places.

To find e^3 press $\boxed{\text{2nd}}$ $\boxed{e^x}$ $\boxed{3}$ $\boxed{)}$ $\boxed{\text{ENTER}}$. (e^x is the second operation associated with the $\boxed{\text{LN}}$ key.) The grapher returns 20.0855369232. Thus, $e^3 \approx 20.0855$. To find $e^{-0.23}$ press $\boxed{\text{2nd}}$ $\boxed{e^x}$ $\boxed{(-)}$ $\boxed{\cdot}$ $\boxed{2}$ $\boxed{3}$ $\boxed{)}$ $\boxed{\text{ENTER}}$. The grapher returns .794533602503, so $e^{-0.23} \approx 0.7945$.

Section 4.3, Example 4 Find the values of log 645,778, log 0.0000239, and log (-3). Round to four decimal places.

To find log 645,778 press $\boxed{\text{LOG}}$ $\boxed{6}$ $\boxed{4}$ $\boxed{5}$ $\boxed{7}$ $\boxed{7}$ $\boxed{8}$ $\boxed{)}$ $\boxed{\text{ENTER}}$ and read 5.8100832463. Thus, log $645,778 \approx 5.8101$. To find log 0.0000239 press $\boxed{\text{LOG}}$ $\boxed{\cdot}$ $\boxed{0}$ $\boxed{0}$ $\boxed{0}$ $\boxed{0}$ $\boxed{2}$ $\boxed{3}$ $\boxed{9}$ $\boxed{)}$ $\boxed{\text{ENTER}}$. The grapher returns -4.62160209905, so log $0.0000239 \approx -4.6216$. When we press $\boxed{\text{LOG}}$ $\boxed{(-)}$ $\boxed{3}$ $\boxed{)}$ $\boxed{\text{ENTER}}$ the result is a non-real complex number. This indicates that -3 is not in the domain of the function $\log x$.

Section 4.3, Example 5 (a), (b), (c) Find the values of ln 645,778, ln 0.0000239, and ln (-5). Round to four decimal places.

To find ln 645,778 and ln 0.0000239 repeat the keystrokes used above to find log 645,778 and log 0.0000239 but press $\boxed{\text{LN}}$ rather than $\boxed{\text{LOG}}$. We find that ln $645,778 \approx 13.3782$ and ln $0.0000239 \approx -10.6416$. When we press $\boxed{\text{LN}}$ $\boxed{(-)}$ $\boxed{5}$ $\boxed{\text{ENTER}}$ the result is a non-real complex number, indicating that -5 is not in the domain of the function $\ln x$.

USING THE CHANGE OF BASE FORMULA

To find a logarithm with a base other than 10 or e we use the change-of-base formula, $\log_b M = \dfrac{\log_a M}{\log_a b}$, where a and b are any logarithmic bases and M is any positive number.

Section 4.3, Example 6 Find $\log_5 8$ using common logarithms.

We let $a = 10$, $b = 5$, and $M = 8$ and substitute in the change-of-base formula. Press $\boxed{\text{LOG}}$ $\boxed{8}$ $\boxed{\div}$ $\boxed{\text{LOG}}$ $\boxed{5}$ $\boxed{\text{ENTER}}$. The result is about 1.2920. We could have let $a = e$ and used natural logarithms to find $\log_5 8$ as well.

```
log 8 /log 5
              1.29202967422
ln 8/ln 5
              1.29202967422
█
```

Section 4.3, Example 9 Graph $y = \log_5 x$.

To use a grapher we must first change the base to e or 10. Here we use e. Let $a = e$, $b = 5$, and $M = x$ and substitute in the change-of-base formula. Enter $y_1 = \dfrac{\ln x}{\ln 5}$ on the equation-editor screen, select a window, and press $\boxed{\text{F5}}$.

EXPONENTIAL AND LOGARITHMIC REGRESSION

In addition to the types of polynomial regression discussed earlier, exponential and logarithmic functions can be fit to data. The operations of entering data, making scatterplots, and graphing and evaluating these functions are the same as for linear regression functions. So are the procedures for copying a regression equation to the $y(x) =$ screen, graphing it, and using it to find function values.

Section 4.6, Example 6 (a) *Credit Card Volume.* The total credit card volume for Visa, MasterCard, American Express, and Discover has increased dramatically in recent years.

Year, x	Credit Card Volume (in billions)
1988, 0	$261.0
1989, 1	296.3
1990, 2	338.4
1991, 3	361.0
1992, 4	403.1
1993, 5	476.7
1994, 6	584.8
1995, 7	701.2
1996, 8	798.3
1997, 9	885.2

(a) Use a grapher to fit an exponential function to the data.

Enter the data as described on pages 153 and 154 of this manual. Then go to the home screen and select ExpR (exponential regression) from the STAT CALC menu by pressing $\boxed{\text{2nd}}$ $\boxed{\text{STAT}}$ $\boxed{\text{F1}}$ $\boxed{\text{F5}}$ $\boxed{\text{2nd}}$ $\boxed{\text{LIST}}$ $\boxed{\text{F3}}$ $\boxed{\text{F2}}$ $\boxed{,}$ $\boxed{\text{F3}}$ $\boxed{\text{ENTER}}$. The grapher displays the coefficient a and the base b for the exponential function $y = a \cdot b^x$.

A scatterplot of the data can be graphed as described on page 154 of this manual. This function can be copied to the equation-editor screen using one of the methods described on pages 169 and 170 of this manual. Then it can be graphed along with the scatterplot. It can also be evaluated using one of the methods on pages 167 and 168.

Section 4.6, Exercise 26 (a) *Forgetting.* In an art class, students were tested at the end of the course on a final exam. Then they were retested with an equivalent test at subsequent time intervals. Their scores after time t, in months, are given in the following table.

Time, t (in months)	Score, y
1	84.9%
2	84.6%
3	84.4%
4	84.2%
5	84.1%
6	83.9%

(a) Use a grapher to fit a logarithmic function $y = a + b \ln x$ to the data.

After entering the data as described on pages 153 and 154 of this manual, go to the home screen and press 2nd STAT F1 F4 2nd LIST F2 , F3 ENTER EXIT . The values of a and b for the logarithmic function $y = a + b \ln x$ are displayed.

```
LnReg
 y=a+blnx
 a=84.9435399
 b=-.54128341
↓corr=-.99098939
■
    <     >   NAMES EDIT   OPS
 fStat  xStat  yStat
```

LOGISTIC REGRESSION

A logistic function can be fit to data using the TI-86.

Section 4.6, Exercise 28 (a) *Effect of Advertising.* A company introduces a new software product on a trial run in a city. They advertised the product on television and found the following data relating the percent P of people who bought the product after x ads were run.

Number of Ads, x	Percent Who Bought, P
0	0.2
10	0.7
20	2.7
30	9.2
40	27
50	57.6
60	83.3
70	94.8
80	98.5
90	99.6

(a) Use a grapher to fit a logistic function $P(x) = \dfrac{a}{1 + be^{-kx}}$ to the data.

After entering the data as described on pages 153 and 154 of this manual, press $\boxed{\text{2nd}}$ $\boxed{\text{STAT}}$ $\boxed{\text{F1}}$ $\boxed{\text{MORE}}$ $\boxed{\text{F3}}$ $\boxed{\text{2nd}}$ $\boxed{\text{LIST}}$ $\boxed{\text{F3}}$ $\boxed{\text{F2}}$ $\boxed{,}$ $\boxed{\text{F3}}$ $\boxed{\text{ENTER}}$. The values of a, b, and c for the logistic function $y = \dfrac{a}{1 + be^{cx}} + d$ are displayed. Use the $\boxed{\triangledown}$ and $\boxed{\triangleright}$ keys to see all of the coefficients.

Chapter 5
The Trigonometric Functions

FINDING TRIGONOMETRIC FUNCTION VALUES OF REAL NUMBERS

The grapher's SIN, COS, and TAN operations can be used to find trigonometric function values of any real number. The grapher must be set in Radian mode when this is done.

Section 5.2, Example 5 Find each of the following function values using a grapher. Round the answers to four decimal places.

a) $\cos\dfrac{2\pi}{5}$ b) $\tan(-3)$ c) $\sin 24.9$ d) $\sin\dfrac{\pi}{7}$

a) With the grapher set in Radian mode, press $\boxed{\text{COS}}$ $\boxed{(}$ 2 $\boxed{\text{2nd}}$ $\boxed{\pi}$ $\boxed{\div}$ 5 $\boxed{)}$ $\boxed{\text{ENTER}}$. (π is the second operation associated with the $\boxed{\wedge}$ key.) We find that $\cos\dfrac{2\pi}{5} \approx 0.3090$.

```
Normal Sci Eng
Float 012345678901
Radian Degree
RectC PolarC
Func Pol Param DifEq
Dec Bin Oct Hex
RectV CylV SphereV
      dxNDer
```

```
cos (2π/5)
            .309016994375
■
```

b) To find $\tan(-3)$ press $\boxed{\text{TAN}}$ $\boxed{(-)}$ 3 $\boxed{\text{ENTER}}$. We find that $\tan(-3) \approx 0.1425$.

c) To find $\sin 24.9$ press $\boxed{\text{SIN}}$ 2 4 $\boxed{.}$ 9 $\boxed{\text{ENTER}}$. We find that $\sin 24.9 \approx -0.2306$.

```
tan -3
        .142546543074
sin 24.9
       -.230645705927
■
```

d) The secant, cosecant, and cotangent functions can be found by taking the reciprocals of the cosine, sine, and tangent functions, respectively. This can be done either by entering the reciprocal or by using the x^{-1} operation. To find $\sec\dfrac{\pi}{7}$ we can enter the reciprocal of $\cos\dfrac{\pi}{7}$ by pressing 1 $\boxed{\div}$ $\boxed{\text{COS}}$ $\boxed{(}$ $\boxed{\text{2nd}}$ $\boxed{\pi}$ $\boxed{\div}$ 7 $\boxed{)}$ $\boxed{\text{ENTER}}$. To find $\sec\dfrac{\pi}{7}$ using the x^{-1} operation press $\boxed{(}$ $\boxed{\text{COS}}$ $\boxed{(}$ $\boxed{\text{2nd}}$ $\boxed{\pi}$ $\boxed{\div}$ 7 $\boxed{)}$ $\boxed{)}$ $\boxed{\text{2nd}}$ $\boxed{x^{-1}}$ $\boxed{\text{ENTER}}$. (x^{-1} is the second operation associated with the $\boxed{\text{EE}}$ key.) The result is $\sec\dfrac{\pi}{7} \approx 1.1099$.

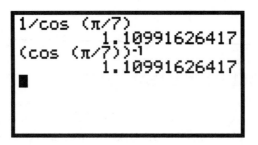

CONVERTING BETWEEN D°M′S″ AND DECIMAL DEGREE MEASURE

We can convert D°M′S″ notation to decimal notation and vice versa using features on the MATH ANGLE menu on the TI-86. This menu is accessed by pressing $\boxed{\text{2nd}}$ $\boxed{\text{MATH}}$ $\boxed{\text{F3}}$.

Section 5.3, Example 2 Convert 5°42′30″ to decimal degree notation.

Enter 5°42′30″ as 5′42′30′ by pressing 5 $\boxed{\text{2nd}}$ $\boxed{\text{MATH}}$ $\boxed{\text{F3}}$ $\boxed{\text{F3}}$ 4 2 $\boxed{\text{F3}}$ 3 0 $\boxed{\text{F3}}$ $\boxed{\text{ENTER}}$. The grapher returns 5.70833333333, so 5°42′30″ ≈ 5.71°.

Section 5.3, Example 3 Convert 72.18° to D°M′S″ notation.

We use the ▷DMS feature from the MATH ANGLE menu to do this conversion. Press 7 2 $\boxed{\cdot}$ 1 8 $\boxed{\text{2nd}}$ $\boxed{\text{MATH}}$ $\boxed{\text{F3}}$ $\boxed{\text{F4}}$ $\boxed{\text{ENTER}}$. The grapher returns 72°10′48″.

```
5'42'30'
            5.70833333333
72.18▸DMS
              72°10'48"
■

 NUM  PROB ANGLE  HYP  MISC
   °    r     '   ▸DMS
```

CONVERTING BETWEEN DEGREE AND RADIAN MEASURE

We can use the grapher to convert from degree to radian measure and vice versa. The grapher should be set in Radian mode when converting from degree to radian measure and in Degree mode when converting from radian to degree measure.

Section 5.3, Example 5 Convert each of the following to radians.

a) 120°   b) −297.25°

a) Set the grapher in Radian mode. Press 1 2 0 $\boxed{\text{2nd}}$ $\boxed{\text{MATH}}$ $\boxed{\text{F3}}$ $\boxed{\text{F1}}$ $\boxed{\text{ENTER}}$ to enter 120°. The grapher returns a decimal approximation of the radian measure. We see that 120° ≈ 2.09 radians.

b) With the grapher set in Radian mode press $\boxed{(-)}$ 2 9 7 $\boxed{\cdot}$ 2 5 $\boxed{\text{2nd}}$ $\boxed{\text{MATH}}$ $\boxed{\text{F3}}$ $\boxed{\text{F1}}$ $\boxed{\text{ENTER}}$. We see that −297.25° ≈ −5.19 radians.

Section 5.3, Example 6 Convert each of the following to degrees.

a) $\dfrac{3\pi}{4}$ radians   b) 8.5 radians

a) Set the grapher in Degree mode. Then press $\boxed{(}$ 3 $\boxed{\text{2nd}}$ $\boxed{\pi}$ $\boxed{\div}$ 4 $\boxed{)}$ $\boxed{\text{2nd}}$ $\boxed{\text{MATH}}$ $\boxed{\text{F3}}$ $\boxed{\text{F2}}$ $\boxed{\text{ENTER}}$ to enter $\dfrac{3\pi}{4}$

radians. (π is the second operation associated with the $\boxed{\wedge}$ key). The grapher returns 135, so $3\pi/4$ radians $= 135°$. Note

that the parentheses are necessary in order to enter the entire expression in radian measure. Without the parentheses, the

grapher reads only the denominator, 4, in radian measure and an incorrect result occurs.

b) With the grapher set in Degree mode press 8 $\boxed{\cdot}$ 5 $\boxed{\text{2nd}}$ $\boxed{\text{MATH}}$ $\boxed{\text{F3}}$ $\boxed{\text{F2}}$ $\boxed{\text{ENTER}}$. The grapher returns 487.014125861,

so 8.5 radians $\approx 487.01°$.

FINDING TRIGONOMETRIC FUNCTION VALUES OF ANGLES

The grapher's SIN, COS, and TAN operations can be used to find the values of trigonometric functions of angles measured

in degrees.

Section 5.5, Example 5 Find the trigonometric function value, rounded to four decimal places, of each of the following.

a) tan 29.7°   b) sec 48°   c) sin 84°10′39″

a) If the grapher is set in Degree mode, press $\boxed{\text{TAN}}$ 2 9 $\boxed{\cdot}$ 7 $\boxed{\text{ENTER}}$. If the grapher is set in Radian mode, press $\boxed{\text{2nd}}$

$\boxed{\text{MATH}}$ $\boxed{\text{F3}}$ $\boxed{\text{F1}}$ after the 7 to copy the degree symbol after the angle. This indicates to the grapher that the angle is

given in degrees. We find that tan 29.7° ≈ 0.5704.

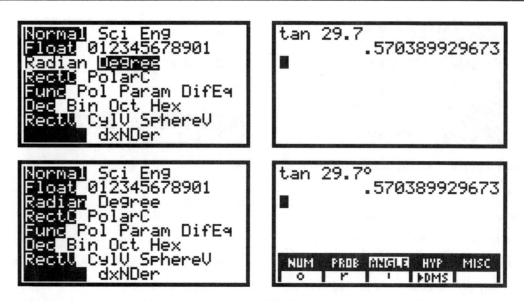

b) The secant, cosecant, and cotangent functions can be found by taking the reciprocals of the cosine, sine, and tangent functions, respectively. This can be done either by entering the reciprocal or by using the $\boxed{x^{-1}}$ key. To find sec 48° with the grapher set in Degree mode we can enter the reciprocal of cos 48° by pressing 1 $\boxed{\div}$ $\boxed{\text{COS}}$ 4 8 $\boxed{\text{ENTER}}$. To find sec 48° using the $\boxed{x^{-1}}$ key press $\boxed{(}$ $\boxed{\text{COS}}$ 4 8 $\boxed{)}$ $\boxed{\text{2nd}}$ $\boxed{x^{-1}}$ $\boxed{\text{ENTER}}$. (x^{-1} is the second operation associated with the $\boxed{\text{EE}}$ key.) If the grapher is set in Radian mode, press $\boxed{\text{2nd}}$ $\boxed{\text{MATH}}$ $\boxed{\text{F3}}$ $\boxed{\text{F1}}$ after the 8 to copy the degree symbol after the angle. The result is sec 48° ≈ 1.4945. In the figure below the grapher is set in Degree mode.

```
1/cos 48
          1.49447654986
(cos 48)⁻¹
          1.49447654986
■
```

c) With the grapher set in Degree mode, press $\boxed{\text{SIN}}$ followed by 84°10′39″ entered as described above in Converting Between D°M′S″ and Decimal Degree Measure for the grapher being used. Then press $\boxed{\text{ENTER}}$. We find that sin 84°10′39″ ≈ 0.9948.

FINDING ANGLES

The inverse trigonometric function keys provide a quick way to find an angle given a trigonometric function value for that angle.

Section 5.5, Example 6 Find the acute angle, to the nearest tenth of a degree, whose sine value is approximately 0.20113.

Although the TABLE feature can be used to approximate this angle, it is faster to use the inverse sine key. With the grapher set in Degree mode, press $\boxed{\text{2nd}}$ $\boxed{\text{SIN}^{-1}}$ $\boxed{\cdot}$ 2 0 1 1 3 $\boxed{\text{ENTER}}$. (SIN⁻¹ is the second operation associated with the $\boxed{\text{SIN}}$ key.) We find that the desired acute angle is approximately 11.6°.

```
sin⁻¹ .20113
           11.6030461313
■
```

Section 5.5, Exercise 39 Find the acute angle, to the nearest tenth of a degree, whose cotangent value is 2.127.

Angles whose secant, cosecant, or cotangent values are known can be found using the reciprocals of the cosine, sine, and tangent functions, respectively. Since $\cot\theta = \dfrac{1}{\tan\theta} = 2.127$, we have $\tan\theta = \dfrac{1}{2.127}$, or $(2.127)^{-1}$. To find θ press $\boxed{\text{2nd}}$ $\boxed{\text{TAN}^{-1}}$ $\boxed{(}$ 1 $\boxed{\div}$ 2 $\boxed{\cdot}$ 1 2 7 $\boxed{)}$ $\boxed{\text{ENTER}}$ or $\boxed{\text{2nd}}$ $\boxed{\text{TAN}^{-1}}$ 2 $\boxed{\cdot}$ 1 2 7 $\boxed{\text{2nd}}$ $\boxed{x^{-1}}$ $\boxed{\text{ENTER}}$. (TAN^{-1} is the second operation associated with the $\boxed{\text{TAN}}$ key.) Note that the parentheses are necessary in the first set of keystrokes. Without parentheses we would be finding the angle whose tangent is 1 and then dividing that angle by 2.127. We find that $\theta \approx 25.2°$.

```
tan⁻¹ (1/2.127)
           25.1803638359
tan⁻¹ 2.127⁻¹
           25.1803638359
■
```

Chapter 6
Trigonometric Identities, Inverse Functions, and Equations

FINDING INVERSE FUNCTION VALUES

We can use a grapher to find inverse function values in both radians and degrees.

Section 6.4, Example 2 (a), (e) Approximate $\cos^{-1}(-0.2689)$ and $\csc^{-1} 8.205$ in both radians and degrees.

To find inverse function values in radians, first set the grapher in Radian mode. Then to approximate $\cos^{-1}(-0.2689)$ press $\boxed{\text{2nd}}$ $\boxed{\text{COS}^{-1}}$ $\boxed{(-)}$ $\boxed{\cdot}$ 2 6 8 9 $\boxed{\text{ENTER}}$. The grapher returns 1.84304711148, so $\cos^{-1}(-0.2689) \approx 1.8430$ radians.

To find $\csc^{-1} 8.205$, recall the identity $\csc\theta = \dfrac{1}{\sin\theta}$. Then $\csc^{-1} 8.205 = \sin^{-1}\left(\dfrac{1}{8.205}\right)$. Press $\boxed{\text{2nd}}$ $\boxed{\text{SIN}^{-1}}$ $\boxed{(}$ 1 $\boxed{\div}$ 8 $\boxed{\cdot}$ 2 0 5 $\boxed{)}$ $\boxed{\text{ENTER}}$ or $\boxed{\text{2nd}}$ $\boxed{\text{SIN}^{-1}}$ 8 $\boxed{\cdot}$ 2 0 5 $\boxed{\text{2nd}}$ $\boxed{x^{-1}}$ $\boxed{\text{ENTER}}$. The readout is .122180665346, so $\csc^{-1} 8.205 \approx 0.1222$ radians.

To find inverse function values in degrees, set the grapher in degree mode. Then use the keystrokes above to find that $\cos^{-1}(-0.2689) \approx 105.6°$ and $\csc^{-1} 8.205 \approx 7.0°$.

SINE REGRESSION

The SinR operation can be used to fit a sine curve $y = a\sin(bx + c) + d$ to a set of data. At least four data points are required and there must be at least two data points per period. The output of SinR is always in radians, regardless of the Radian/Degree mode setting. To see the graph, however, we must set the grapher in Radian mode.

The operations of entering data, making scatterplots, and graphing and evaluating the regression function are the same as for linear regression functions. Reread the material on pages 153 - 145, 167, and 168 of this manual to review these procedures.

Section 6.5, Exercise 57 (a) Sales of certain products fluctuate in cycles. The data in the following table show the total sales of skis per month for a business in a northern climate.

Month, x	Total Sales, y (in thousands of dollars)
August, 8	0
November, 11	7
February, 2	14
May, 5	7
August, 8	0

Using the sine regression feature on a grapher, fit a sine function of the form $y = A\sin(Bx - C) + D$ to this set of data.

Enter the data in xStat and yStat as described in Chapter 1 of this manual. Then from the home screen press 2nd STAT F1 to view the STAT CALC menu. To select SinR press MORE F2 2nd LIST F3 , select xStat, press , , select yStat, and finally press , 2nd alpha Y 1. Here we used the usual option of specifying a $y =$ variable to which the regression equation can be stored. Now press ENTER to see the coefficients a, b, c, and d of the sine regression function

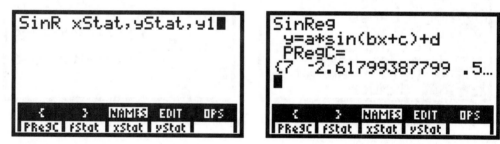

Chapter 7
Applications of Trigonometry

FINDING TRIGONOMETRIC NOTATION FOR COMPLEX NUMBERS

The TI-86 can be used to find trigonometric notation for a complex number.

Section 7.4, Example 3 (a) Find trigonometric notation for $1 + i$.

On the TI-86 we express $1 + i$ as the pair $(1, 1)$ where the first number is the real part of $1 + i$ and the second number is the imaginary part. Trigonometric notation for a complex number has the form $r(\cos\theta + i\sin\theta)$. We can find r using the abs feature from the CPLX menu. Press $\boxed{\text{2nd}}$ $\boxed{\text{CPLX}}$ to display this menu. (CPLX is the second operation associated with the 9 numeric key.) Then press $\boxed{\text{F4}}$ to copy "abs" to the home screen. Press $\boxed{(}$ 1 $\boxed{,}$ 1 $\boxed{)}$ $\boxed{\text{ENTER}}$. The grapher returns $|1 + i|$, the value of r. It is approximately 1.41421356237. This is a decimal approximation for $\sqrt{2}$.

Now use the CPLX menu again to find θ in degrees. First select Degree mode. Then press $\boxed{\text{2nd}}$ $\boxed{\text{CPLX}}$ to display the CPLX menu. Select $\boxed{\text{F5}}$, "angle." Then press $\boxed{(}$ 1 $\boxed{,}$ 1 $\boxed{)}$ $\boxed{\text{ENTER}}$. The grapher returns 45, so the angle θ is 45°. We can use the same procedure to find θ in radians after Radian mode has been selected.

```
abs (1,1)
          1.41421356237
angle (1,1)
                     45
■


 conj  real  imag   abs  angle ▶
```

Chapter 8
Systems of Equations and Matrices

SOLVING SYSTEMS OF EQUATIONS

We can solve systems of up to 30 equations with 30 variables on the TI-86 using the SIMULT menu.

Section 8.1, Example 2 (b) Solve the following system:

$$4x + 3y = 11,$$
$$-5x + 2y = 15.$$

Begin by pressing $\boxed{\text{2nd}}$ $\boxed{\text{SIMULT}}$ to display the SIMULT screen. (SIMULT is the second operation associated with the $\boxed{\text{TABLE}}$ key.) The blinking cursor is positioned to the right of the notation "Number =." Because there are two equations, press 2 $\boxed{\text{ENTER}}$.

The coefficient entry screen for the first equation will appear. Enter the coefficients and the constant term of the first equation by pressing 4 $\boxed{\text{ENTER}}$ 3 $\boxed{\text{ENTER}}$ 1 1 $\boxed{\text{ENTER}}$. Now the coefficient entry screen for the second equation appears. Enter the coefficients and the constant term of the second equation by pressing $\boxed{(-)}$ 5 $\boxed{\text{ENTER}}$ 2 $\boxed{\text{ENTER}}$ 1 5. The second equation's coefficient screen could also have been accessed by pressing $\boxed{\text{F2}}$ to select NEXT rather than by pressing $\boxed{\text{ENTER}}$ after 11, the constant in the first equation.

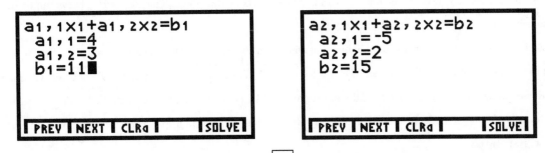

To see the solution of the system of equations, press $\boxed{\text{F5}}$ to select SOLVE. The solution $(-1, 5)$ is displayed as "$x1 = -1$" and "$x2 = 5$."

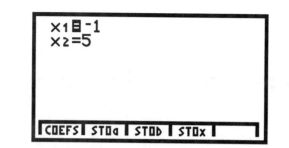

MATRICES AND ROW-EQUIVALENT OPERATIONS

Row-equivalent operations can be performed on matrices using the TI-86.

Section 8.3, Example 1 Solve the following system:

$$2x - y + 4z = -3,$$
$$x - 2y - 10z = -6,$$
$$3x + 4z = 7.$$

First we enter the augmented matrix

$$\begin{bmatrix} 2 & -1 & 4 & -3 \\ 1 & -2 & -10 & -6 \\ 3 & 0 & 4 & 7 \end{bmatrix}$$

on the grapher. Begin by pressing $\boxed{\text{2nd}}$ $\boxed{\text{MATRX}}$ to display the MATRX EDIT menu. (MATRX is the second operation associated with the $\boxed{7}$ key.) Then press $\boxed{\text{F2}}$ to select EDIT and name the matrix to be defined. We will name the matrix [A] by pressing A at the blinking cursor to the right of "Name =." Note that it is not necessary to press $\boxed{\text{ALPHA}}$ before pressing A in the MATRX EDIT screen. Now press $\boxed{\text{ENTER}}$.

The dimensions of the matrix are displayed on the top line of the next screen, with the cursor on the row dimension. Enter the dimensions of the augmented matrix, 3 x 4, by pressing 3 $\boxed{\text{ENTER}}$ 4 $\boxed{\text{ENTER}}$. Now the cursor moves to the element in the first row and first column of the matrix. Enter the elements of the first row by pressing 2 $\boxed{\text{ENTER}}$ $\boxed{(-)}$ 1 $\boxed{\text{ENTER}}$ 4 $\boxed{\text{ENTER}}$ $\boxed{(-)}$ 3 $\boxed{\text{ENTER}}$. The cursor moves to the element in the second row and first column of the matrix. Enter the elements of the second and third rows of the augmented matrix by typing each in turn followed by $\boxed{\text{ENTER}}$ as above. Note that the screen only displays the fourth column of the matrix at this point. The $\boxed{\triangle}$ and $\boxed{\triangledown}$ keys can be used to move the cursor to any element of the matrix at any time.

Row-equivalent operations are performed by making selections from the MATRX OPS menu. To view this menu press $\boxed{\text{2nd}}$ $\boxed{\text{QUIT}}$ to leave the MATRX EDIT screen. Then press $\boxed{\text{2nd}}$ $\boxed{\text{MATRX}}$ $\boxed{\text{F4}}$. Now press $\boxed{\text{MORE}}$ to see the menu with the four row-equivalent operations: rSwap, rAdd, multR, and mRAdd in locations $\boxed{\text{F2}}$ through $\boxed{\text{F5}}$. These operations interchange two rows of a matrix, add two rows, multiply a row by a number, and multiply a row by a number and add it to a second row, respectively.

To view the matrix on the home screen press $\boxed{\text{ALPHA}}$ A $\boxed{\text{ENTER}}$. We will use the grapher to perform the row-equivalent operations that were done algebraically in the text. First, to interchange row 1 and row 2 of matrix [A], with the MATRX OPS menu displayed , press $\boxed{\text{F2}}$ to select rSwap. Then press $\boxed{\text{ALPHA}}$ A to select [**A**]. Follow this with a comma and the rows to be interchanged: $\boxed{,}$ 1 $\boxed{,}$ 2 $\boxed{)}$ $\boxed{\text{ENTER}}$.

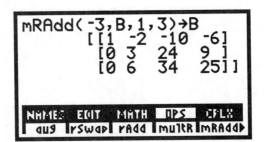

The grapher will not store the matrix produced using a row-equivalent operation, so when several operations are to be performed in succession it is helpful to store the result of each operation as it is produced. For example, to store the matrix resulting from interchanging the first and second rows of [**A**] as matrix [**B**] press $\boxed{\text{STO▷}}$ B $\boxed{\text{ENTER}}$ immediately after interchanging the rows. Note that it is not necessary to press $\boxed{\text{ALPHA}}$ before pressing B in this situation.

Next we multiply the first row of [**B**] by -2, add it to the second row and store the result as [**B**] again by pressing $\boxed{\text{F5}}$ $\boxed{(-)}$ 2 $\boxed{,}$ $\boxed{\text{ALPHA}}$ B $\boxed{,}$ 1 $\boxed{,}$ 2 $\boxed{)}$ $\boxed{\text{STO▷}}$ B $\boxed{\text{ENTER}}$. These keystrokes select mRAdd from the MATRX OPS menu; then they specify that the value of the multiplier is -2, the matrix being operated on is [**B**], and that a multiple of row 1 is being added to row 2; finally they store the result as [**B**].

To multiply row 1 by -3, add it to row 3, and store the result as [**B**] press $\boxed{\text{F5}}$ $\boxed{(-)}$ 3 $\boxed{,}$ $\boxed{\text{ALPHA}}$ B $\boxed{,}$ 1 $\boxed{,}$ 3 $\boxed{)}$ $\boxed{\text{STO▷}}$ B $\boxed{\text{ENTER}}$.

```
mRAdd( -3,B,1,3)→B
      [[1  -2  -10  -6]
       [0   3   24   9 ]
       [0   6   34  25]]

NAMES  EDIT  MATH   OPS   CPLX
 aug  rSwap  rAdd  multR  mRAdd▷
```

Now multiply the second row by 1/3 and store the result as [**B**] again. Press $\boxed{\text{F4}}$ 1 $\boxed{(÷)}$ 3 $\boxed{,}$ $\boxed{\text{ALPHA}}$ B $\boxed{,}$ 2 $\boxed{)}$ $\boxed{\text{STO▷}}$ B $\boxed{\text{ENTER}}$. These keystrokes select multR from the MATRX OPS menu; then they specify that the value of the multiplier is 1/3, the matrix being operated on is [**B**], and row 2 is being multiplied; finally they store the result as [**B**]. The keystrokes 1 $\boxed{(÷)}$ 3 could be replaced with 3 $\boxed{\text{2nd}}$ $\boxed{x^{-1}}$.

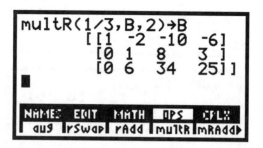

Multiply the second row by -6 and add it to the third row using mRAdd. Press F5 (−) 6 , ALPHA B , 2 , 3) STO▷ B ENTER.

The entry in the third row, second column is 1E−13. This is an approximation of 0 that occurs because of the manner in which the grapher performs calculations and should be treated as 0. In fact, it would be a good idea to return to the MATRX EDIT screen at this point to replace this entry of [**B**] with 0. Press 2nd M2 to select EDIT. Then press F2 ENTER to display [**B**]. Move the cursor to the third row, second column and press 0 ENTER. Now press 2nd QUIT to return to the home screen. Matrix **B** can be viewed by pressing ALPHA B ENTER.

B

$$\begin{bmatrix} 1 & -2 & -10 & -6 \\ 0 & 1 & 8 & 3 \\ 0 & 0 & -14 & 7 \end{bmatrix}$$

Finally, multiply the third row by $-1/14$ by pressing 2nd MATRX F4 MORE to view the row operations under the OPS menu. Then press F4 (−) 1 (÷) 1 4 , ALPHA B , 3) ENTER. The keystrokes (−) 1 (÷) 1 4 could be replaced with (−) 1 4 2nd x^{-1}.

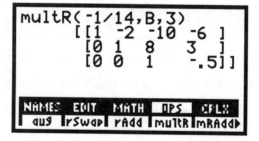

Write the system of equations that corresponds to the final matrix. Then use back-substitution to solve for x, y, and z as illustrated in the text.

Instead of stopping with row-echelon form as we did above, we can continue to apply row-equivalent operations until the matrix is in reduced row-echelon form as in Example 3 in Section 8.3 of the text. Reduced row-echelon form of a matrix can be found directly by using the rref operation from the MATRX OPS menu. For example, to find reduced row-echelon form for matrix **A** in Example 1 above, after entering [**A**] and leaving the MATRX EDIT screen press 2nd MATRX F4 F5 ALPHA A ENTER. We can read the solution of the system of equations, $(3, 7, -0.5)$ directly from the resulting matrix.

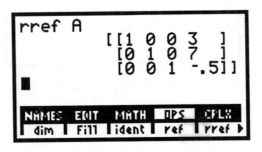

MATRIX OPERATIONS

We can use the grapher to add and subtract matrices, to multiply a matrix by a scalar, and to multiply matrices.

Section 8.4, Example 1 (a) Find **A** + **B** for

a) $\mathbf{A} = \begin{bmatrix} -5 & 0 \\ 4 & \frac{1}{2} \end{bmatrix}$, $\mathbf{B} = \begin{bmatrix} 6 & -3 \\ 2 & 3 \end{bmatrix}$.

Enter **A** and **B** on the MATRX EDIT screen as [**A**] and [**B**] as described earlier in this chapter. Press 2nd QUIT to leave this screen. Then press ALPHA A + ALPHA B ENTER to display the sum.

```
A+B
                [[1   -3 ]
                 [6   3.5]]
```

Section 8.4, Example 2 Find **C** − **D** for each of the following.

a) $\mathbf{C} = \begin{bmatrix} 1 & 2 \\ -2 & 0 \\ -3 & -1 \end{bmatrix}$, $\mathbf{D} = \begin{bmatrix} 1 & -1 \\ 1 & 3 \\ 2 & 3 \end{bmatrix}$ b) $\mathbf{C} = \begin{bmatrix} 5 & -6 \\ -3 & 4 \end{bmatrix}$, $\mathbf{D} = \begin{bmatrix} -4 \\ 1 \end{bmatrix}$

a) Enter **C** and **D** on the MATRX EDIT screen as [**C**] and [**D**]. Press 2nd QUIT to leave this screen. Then press ALPHA C − ALPHA D ENTER to display the difference.

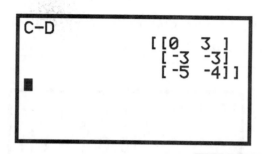

b) Enter **C** and **D** on the MATRX EDIT screen as [**C**] and [**D**]. Press $\boxed{\text{2nd}}$ $\boxed{\text{QUIT}}$ to leave this screen. Then press $\boxed{\text{ALPHA}}$ C $\boxed{-}$ $\boxed{\text{ALPHA}}$ D $\boxed{\text{ENTER}}$. The grapher returns the message ERROR 12 DIM MISMATCH, indicating that this subtraction is not possible. This is the case because the matrices have different orders.

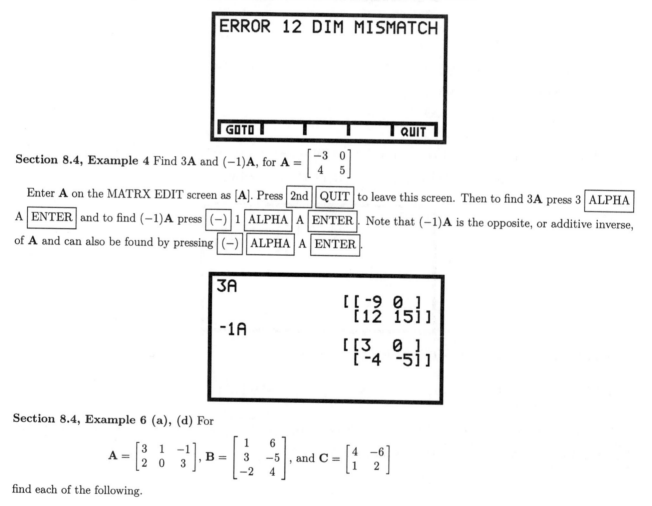

Section 8.4, Example 4 Find 3**A** and (-1)**A**, for $\mathbf{A} = \begin{bmatrix} -3 & 0 \\ 4 & 5 \end{bmatrix}$

Enter **A** on the MATRX EDIT screen as [**A**]. Press $\boxed{\text{2nd}}$ $\boxed{\text{QUIT}}$ to leave this screen. Then to find 3**A** press 3 $\boxed{\text{ALPHA}}$ A $\boxed{\text{ENTER}}$ and to find (-1)**A** press $\boxed{(-)}$ 1 $\boxed{\text{ALPHA}}$ A $\boxed{\text{ENTER}}$. Note that (-1)**A** is the opposite, or additive inverse, of **A** and can also be found by pressing $\boxed{(-)}$ $\boxed{\text{ALPHA}}$ A $\boxed{\text{ENTER}}$.

Section 8.4, Example 6 (a), (d) For

$$\mathbf{A} = \begin{bmatrix} 3 & 1 & -1 \\ 2 & 0 & 3 \end{bmatrix}, \mathbf{B} = \begin{bmatrix} 1 & 6 \\ 3 & -5 \\ -2 & 4 \end{bmatrix}, \text{ and } \mathbf{C} = \begin{bmatrix} 4 & -6 \\ 1 & 2 \end{bmatrix}$$

find each of the following.

a) **AB**   d) **AC**

First enter **A**, **B**, and **C** as [**A**], [**B**], and [**C**] on the MATRX EDIT screen. Press $\boxed{\text{2nd}}$ $\boxed{\text{QUIT}}$ to leave this screen.

a) To find **AB** press $\boxed{\text{ALPHA}}$ A $\boxed{\times}$ $\boxed{\text{ALPHA}}$ B $\boxed{\text{ENTER}}$.

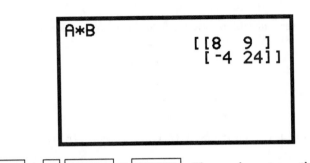

d) To find **AC** press ALPHA A × ALPHA C ENTER . The grapher returns the message ERROR 12 DIM MIS-MATCH, indicating that this multiplication is not possible. This is the case because the number of columns in **A** is not the same as the number of rows in **C**. Thus, the matrices cannot be multiplied in this order.

FINDING THE INVERSE OF A MATRIX

The inverse of a matrix can be found quickly on the grapher.

Section 8.5, Example 3 Find $\mathbf{A}^{-1}$, where

$$\mathbf{A} = \begin{bmatrix} -2 & 3 \\ -3 & 4 \end{bmatrix}.$$

Enter **A** as [**A**] on the MATRX EDIT screen. Then press 2nd QUIT to leave this screen. Now press ALPHA A 2nd x^{-1} ENTER .

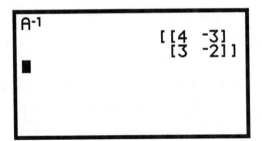

Section 8.5, Exercise 7 Find $\mathbf{A}^{-1}$, where

$$\mathbf{A} = \begin{bmatrix} 6 & 9 \\ 4 & 6 \end{bmatrix}.$$

Enter **A** as [**A**] on the MATRX EDIT screen and then press 2nd QUIT to leave this screen. Now press ALPHA A 2nd x^{-1} ENTER . The grapher returns the message ERROR 03 SINGULAR MAT, indicating that $\mathbf{A}^{-1}$ does not exist.

MATRIX SOLUTIONS OF SYSTEMS OF EQUATIONS

We can write a system of n linear equations in n variables as a matrix equation $\mathbf{AX} = \mathbf{B}$. If **A** has an inverse the solution of the system of equations is given by $\mathbf{X} = \mathbf{A}^{-1}\mathbf{B}$.

Section 8.5, Example 4 Use an inverse matrix to solve the following system of equations:

$$x + 2y - z = -2,$$
$$3x + 5y + 3z = 3,$$
$$2x + 4y + 3z = 1.$$

Enter $\mathbf{A} = \begin{bmatrix} 1 & 2 & -1 \\ 3 & 5 & 3 \\ 2 & 4 & 3 \end{bmatrix}$ and $\mathbf{B} = \begin{bmatrix} -2 \\ 3 \\ 1 \end{bmatrix}$ on the MATRX EDIT screen as [**A**] and [**B**]. Press 2nd QUIT to leave

this screen. Then press ALPHA A 2nd x^{-1} × ALPHA B ENTER. The result is the 3 x 1 matrix $\begin{bmatrix} 5 \\ -3 \\ 1 \end{bmatrix}$, so the

solution is $(5, -3, 1)$.

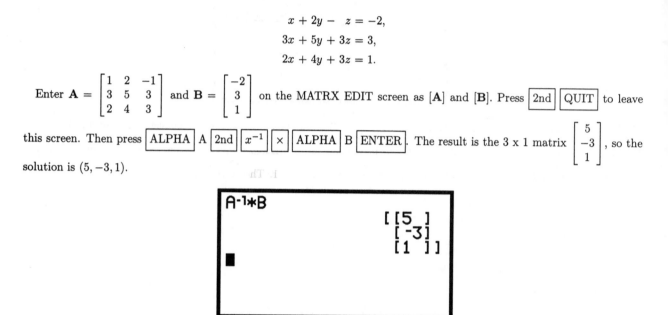

GRAPHS OF INEQUALITIES

We can graph linear inequalities on the grapher, shading the region of the solution set.

Section 8.6, Example 1 Graph: $y < x + 3$.

First enter the related equation $y_1 = x + 3$ on the equation-editor screen. Since the inequality states that y is *less than* $x+3$, we want to shade the half-plane below the graph of y_1. To do this, from the equation-editor screen first press MORE. The choice "Style" appears above F3. Press F3 until the "shade above" style icon appears to the left of "$y1 =$." If the "line" style was previously selected, the "Shade below" icon will appear after F3 is pressed three times. (To shade above a line we would press F3 until the "shade above" style symbol appears.) Then press 2nd F3 F4 to see the graph of the inequality in the standard viewing window.

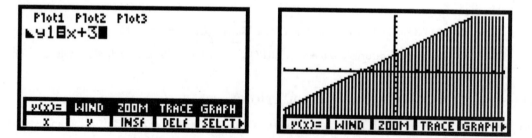

Note that when the "shade below" style is selected it is not also possible to select the dotted style so we must keep in mind the fact that the line $y = x + 3$ is not included in the graph of the inequality. If you graphed this inequality by hand, you would draw a dashed line.

We could also use the Shade operation to graph this inequality. First we graph the related equation $y = x + 3$. We use the standard window $[-10, 10, -10, 10]$. Since the inequality symbol is $<$ we know that the line $y = x + 3$ is not part of the solution set. In a hand-drawn graph we would use a dashed line to indicate this. However, the only option here is to use a solid line, keeping in mind that it is not part of the solution set. After determining that the solution set of the inequality consists of all points below the line, we use the grapher's Shade operation to shade this region. Shade is accessed from the GRAPH screen by pressing $\boxed{\text{MORE}}$ $\boxed{\text{F2}}$ to select DRAW and then $\boxed{\text{F1}}$ to select Shade.

Now enter a lower function and an upper function and the region between them will be shaded. We want to shade the area between the bottom of the window, $y = -10$, and the line $y = x + 3$ so we enter $\boxed{(-)}$ 1 0 $\boxed{,}$ $\boxed{x\text{-VAR}}$ $\boxed{+}$ 3 $\boxed{)}$ $\boxed{\text{ENTER}}$. We can also enter $x + 3$ as y_1 by pressing $\boxed{\text{2nd}}$ $\boxed{\text{alpha}}$ $\boxed{\text{Y}}$ 1. The result is shown below.

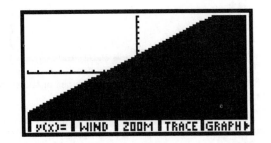

We can graph systems of inequalities by shading the solution set of each inequality in the system with a different pattern. When the "shade above" or "shade below" graph style options are selected the grapher rotates through four shading patterns. Vertical lines shade the first function, horizontal lines the second, negatively sloping diagonal lines the third, and positively sloping diagonal lines the fourth. These patterns repeat if more than four functions are graphed.

Section 8.6, Exercise 37 Graph:
$$y \le x,$$
$$y \ge 3 - x.$$

First enter the equation $y_1 = x$. We determine that the solution set of $y \le x$ consists of all points below the line $y_1 = x$, so we select the "shade below" graph style for this function. Next graph $y_2 = 3 - x$. The solution set of $y \ge 3 - x$ is all points above the line $y_2 = 3 - x$, so we choose the "shade above" graph style for this function. Now press $\boxed{\text{2nd}}$ $\boxed{\text{F3}}$ $\boxed{\text{F4}}$ to display the solution sets of each inequality in the system and the region where they overlap in the standard window. The region of overlap is the solution set of the system of inequalities.

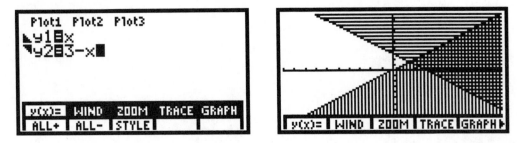

We can also use the Shade operation to graph a system of inequalities when the solution set lies between the graphs of two functions. We will do Exercise 37 above again using this procedure.

First graph the related equations $y_1 = x$ and $y_2 = 3 - x$ and determine that the solution set consists of all the points on or above the graph of $y_2 = 3 - x$ and on or below the graph of $y_1 = x$. We will shade this region by starting on the GRAPH screen and pressing $\boxed{\text{MORE}}\ \boxed{\text{F2}}\ \boxed{\text{F1}}\ \boxed{3}\ \boxed{-}\ \boxed{x\text{-VAR}}\ \boxed{,}\ \boxed{x\text{-VAR}}\ \boxed{)}\ \boxed{\text{ENTER}}$. These keystrokes select the Shade operation from the DRAW menu and then enter $y_2 = 3 - x$ as the lower function and $y_1 = x$ as the upper function. We could also enter these functions as y_2 and y_1, respectively, by pressing $\boxed{\text{2nd}}\ \boxed{\text{alpha}}\ \boxed{Y}\ \boxed{2}\ \boxed{,}\ \boxed{\text{2nd}}\ \boxed{\text{alpha}}\ \boxed{Y}\ \boxed{1}$.

 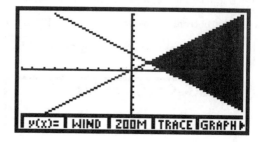

Section 8.6, Example 5 Graph the solution set of the system
$$x + y \le 4,$$
$$x - y \ge 2.$$

First enter the equation $x + y = 4$, entering it in the form $y_1 = -x + 4$. We determine that the solution set of $x + y \le 4$ consists of all points below the line $x + y = 4$, or $y_1 = -x + 4$, so we select the "shade below" graph style for this function. Next enter $x - y = 2$, entering it in the form $y_2 = x - 2$. The solution set of $x - y \ge 2$ is all points below the line $x - y = 2$, or $y_2 = x - 2$, so we also choose the "shade below" graph style for this function. Now, from the equation-editor screen, press $\boxed{\text{F5}}$ to display the solution sets of each inequality in the system and the region where they overlap. The region of overlap is the solution set of the system of inequalities.

 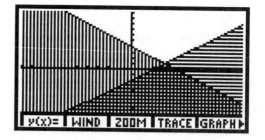

Chapter 9
Analytic Geometry Topics

Many conic sections are represented by equations that are not functions. Consequently, these equations must be entered

on the TI-86 as two equations, each of which is a function.

GRAPHING PARABOLAS

To graph a parabola of the form $y^2 = 4px$ or $(y - k)^2 = 4p(x - h)$, we must first solve the equation for y.

Section 9.1, Example 4 Graph the parabola $y^2 - 2y - 8x - 31 = 0$.

In the text we used the quadratic formula to solve the equation for y:
$$y = \frac{2 \pm \sqrt{32x + 128}}{2}.$$

One way to produce the graph of the parabola is to enter $y_1 = \dfrac{2 + \sqrt{32x + 128}}{2}$ and $y_2 = \dfrac{2 - \sqrt{32x + 128}}{2}$, select a

window, and press $\boxed{\text{F5}}$ to see the graph. Here we use $[-12, 12, -7, 7]$. The first equation produces the top half of the

parabola and the second equation produces the lower half.

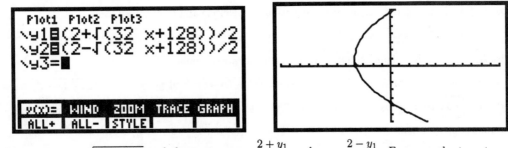

We can also enter $y_1 = \sqrt{32x + 128}$ and then enter $y_2 = \dfrac{2 + y_1}{2}$ and $y_3 = \dfrac{2 - y_1}{2}$. For example, to enter $y_2 = \dfrac{2 + y_1}{2}$

position the cursor beside "$y_2 =$" and press $\boxed{(}$ $\boxed{2}$ $\boxed{+}$ $\boxed{\text{F2}}$ $\boxed{1}$ $\boxed{)}$ $\boxed{\div}$ $\boxed{2}$. Enter $y_3 = \dfrac{2 - y_1}{2}$ in a similar manner. Finally,

deselect y_1 by positioning the cursor anywhere in y_1 and pressing $\boxed{\text{F5}}$. The top half of the graph is produced by y_2 and

the lower half by y_3. The expression for y_1 was entered to avoid entering the square root more than once. By deselecting

y_1 we prevent its graph from appearing on the screen with the graph of the parabola.

We could also use the standard equation of the parabola found in the text:
$$(y - 1)^2 = 8(x + 4).$$

Solve this equation for y.

$$y - 1 = \pm\sqrt{8(x+4)}$$
$$y = 1 \pm \sqrt{8(x+4)}$$

Then enter $y_1 = 1 + \sqrt{8(x+4)}$ and $y_2 = 1 - \sqrt{8(x+4)}$, or enter $y_1 = \sqrt{8(x+4)}$, $y_2 = 1 + y_1$, and $y_3 = 1 - y_1$, and deselect y_1 as described above.

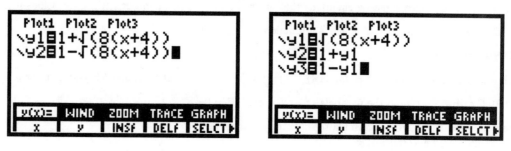

GRAPHING CIRCLES

The equation of a circle must be solved for y before it can be entered on the TI-86.

Section 9.2, Example 1 Graph the circle $x^2 + y^2 - 16x + 14y + 32 = 0$.

In the text we found the standard form for the equation of the circle and then solved for y:

$$y = -7 \pm \sqrt{81 - (x-8)^2}.$$

We could also have solved the original equation using the quadratic formula.

One way to produce the graph is to enter $y_1 = -7 + \sqrt{81 - (x-8)^2}$ and $y_2 = -7 - \sqrt{81 - (x-8)^2}$, select a square window, and press $\boxed{\text{F5}}$. Here we use $[-9, 31, -20, 4]$. The first equation produces the top half of the circle and the second equation produces the lower half.

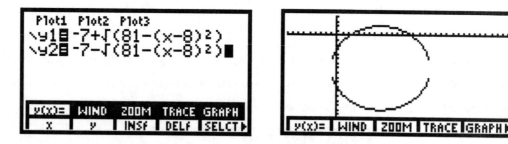

The software used to produce the graph above causes distortion. Nevertheless, when the circle is graphed on a grapher in a square viewing rectangle, there is no distortion.

We can also enter $y_1 = \sqrt{81 - (x-8)^2}$ and then enter $y_2 = -7 + y_1$ and $y_3 = -7 - y_1$. Then deselect y_1, select a square window, and press $\boxed{\text{F5}}$. We use y_1 to eliminate the need to enter the square root more than once. Deselecting it prevents the graph of y_1 from appearing on the screen with the graph of the circle. The top half of the graph is produced by y_2 and the lower half by y_3.

$$\begin{array}{l}\texttt{Plot1 Plot2 Plot3} \\ \texttt{\textbackslash y1}\blacksquare\sqrt{(81-(x-8)^2)} \\ \texttt{\textbackslash y2}\blacksquare\texttt{-7+y1} \\ \texttt{\textbackslash y3}\blacksquare\texttt{-7-y2}\blacksquare \\ \hline \boxed{\texttt{y(x)=}}\ \texttt{WIND}\ \ \texttt{ZOOM}\ \ \texttt{TRACE GRAPH} \\ \texttt{x}\quad \texttt{y}\quad \texttt{INSf}\ \ \texttt{DELf}\ \ \texttt{SELCT}\blacktriangleright \end{array}$$

GRAPHING ELLIPSES

The equation of an ellipse must be solved for y before it can be entered on the TI-86. In Example 2 of Section 9.2 of the text the procedure for graphing an ellipse of the form $\dfrac{x^2}{a^2} + \dfrac{y^2}{b^2} = 1$ or $\dfrac{x^2}{b^2} + \dfrac{y^2}{a^2} = 1$ is described. Here we consider ellipses of the form $\dfrac{(x-h)^2}{a^2} + \dfrac{(y-k)^2}{b^2} = 1$ or $\dfrac{(x-h)^2}{b^2} + \dfrac{(y-k)^2}{a^2} = 1$

Section 9.2, Example 4 Graph the ellipse $4x^2 + y^2 + 24x - 2y + 21 = 0$.

Completing the square in the text, we found that the equation can be written as
$$\frac{(x+3)^2}{4} + \frac{(y-1)^2}{16} = 1.$$

Solve this equation for y.

$$\begin{aligned} \frac{(x+3)^2}{4} + \frac{(y-1)^2}{16} &= 1 \\ \frac{(y-1)^2}{16} &= 1 - \frac{(x+3)^2}{4} \\ (y-1)^2 &= 16 - 4(x+3)^2 \qquad \text{Multiplying by 16} \\ y-1 &= \pm\sqrt{16 - 4(x+3)^2} \\ y &= 1 \pm \sqrt{16 - 4(x+3)^2} \end{aligned}$$

Now we can produce the graph in either of two ways. One is to enter $y_1 = 1 + \sqrt{16 - 4(x+3)^2}$ and $y_2 = 1 - \sqrt{16 - 4(x+3)^2}$, select a square window, and the press $\boxed{\text{F5}}$ to select GRAPH. Here we use $[-12, 12, -7, 7]$. The first equation produces the top half of the ellipse and the second equation produces the lower half.

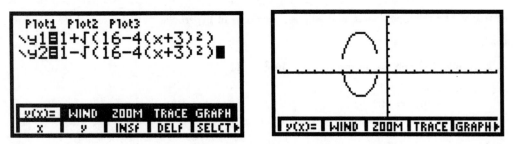

We can also enter $y_1 = \sqrt{16 - 4(x+3)^2}$ and then enter $y_2 = 1 + y_1$ and $y_3 = 1 - y_1$. Deselect y_1, select a square window, and press $\boxed{\text{F5}}$. We use y_1 to eliminate the need to enter the square root more than once. Deselecting it prevents the graph of y_1 from appearing on the screen with the graph of the ellipse. The top half of the graph is produced by y_2 and the lower half by y_3.

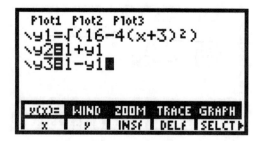

We could also begin by using the quadratic formula to solve the original equation for y.

$$4x^2 + y^2 + 24x - 2y + 21 = 0$$

$$y^2 - 2y + (4x^2 + 24x + 21) = 0$$

$$y = \frac{-(-2) \pm \sqrt{(-2)^2 - 4 \cdot 1 \cdot (4x^2 + 24x + 21)}}{2 \cdot 1}$$

$$y = \frac{2 \pm \sqrt{4 - 16x^2 - 96x - 84}}{2}$$

$$y = \frac{2 \pm \sqrt{-16x^2 - 96x - 80}}{2}$$

Then enter $y_1 = \dfrac{2 + \sqrt{-16x^2 - 96x - 80}}{2}$ and $y_2 = \dfrac{2 - \sqrt{-16x^2 - 96x - 80}}{2}$, or enter $y_1 = \sqrt{-16x^2 - 96x - 80}$, $y_2 = \dfrac{2 + y_1}{2}$, and $y_3 = \dfrac{2 - y_1}{2}$, and deselect y_1.

Select a square window and press $\boxed{\text{F5}}$ to display the graph.

GRAPHING HYPERBOLAS

As with equations of circles, parabolas, and ellipses, equations of hyperbolas must be solved for y before they can be entered on the TI-86.

Section 9.3, Example 2 Graph the hyperbola $9x^2 - 16y^2 = 144$.

First solve the equation for y.

$$9x^2 - 16y^2 = 144$$

$$-16y^2 = -9x^2 + 144$$

$$y^2 = \frac{-9x^2 + 144}{-16}$$

$$y = \pm\sqrt{\frac{-9x^2 + 144}{-16}}, \text{ or } \pm\sqrt{\frac{9x^2 - 144}{16}}$$

It is not necessary to simplify further.

Now enter $y_1 = \sqrt{\dfrac{9x^2 - 144}{16}}$ and either $y_2 = -\sqrt{\dfrac{9x^2 - 144}{16}}$ or $y_2 = -y_1$, select a square window, and press $\boxed{\text{F5}}$ to select GRAPH. Here we use $[-9, 9, -7, 7]$. The top half of the graph is produced by y_1 and the lower half by y_2.

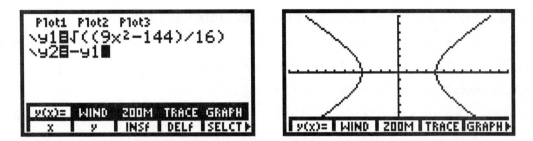

Section 9.3, Example 3 Graph the hyperbola $4y^2 - x^2 + 24y + 4x + 28 = 0$.

In the text we completed the square to get the standard form of the equation. Now solve the equation for y.

$$\frac{(y+3)^2}{1} - \frac{(x-2)^2}{4} = 1$$

$$(y+3)^2 = \frac{(x-2)^2}{4} + 1$$

$$y + 3 = \pm\sqrt{\frac{(x-2)^2}{4} + 1}$$

$$y = -3 \pm \sqrt{\frac{(x-2)^2}{4} + 1}$$

The graph can be produced in either of two ways. One is to enter $y_1 = -3 + \sqrt{\frac{(x-2)^2}{4} + 1}$ and $y_2 = -3 - \sqrt{\frac{(x-2)^2}{4} + 1}$, select a square window, and press $\boxed{\text{F5}}$ to select GRAPH. Here we use $[-12, 12, -7, 7]$. The first equation produces the top half of the hyperbola and the second the lower half.

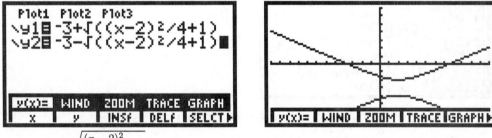

We can also enter $y_1 = \sqrt{\frac{(x-2)^2}{4} + 1}$, $y_2 = -3 + y_1$, and $y_3 = -3 - y_1$. Then deselect y_1, select a square window, and press $\boxed{\text{F5}}$ to select GRAPH. Again, y_1 is used to eliminate the need to enter the square root more than once. Deselecting it prevents the graph of y_1 from appearing on the screen with the graph of the hyperbola. The top half of the graph is produced by y_2 and the lower half by y_3.

CONVERTING FROM RECTANGULAR TO POLAR COORDINATES

The grapher can be used to convert from rectangular to polar coordinates, expressing the result using either degrees or radians. The grapher will supply a positive value for r and an angle in the interval $(-180°, 180°]$, or $(-\pi, \pi]$.

Section 9.5, Example 2 (a) Convert $(3,3)$ to polar coordinates.

Set the grapher in Degree and PolarC modes. Then press $(\boxed{(}\,\boxed{3}\,\boxed{,}\,\boxed{3}\,\boxed{)}$ $\boxed{\text{ENTER}}$. The readout is $(4.24264068712\angle45)$. The first number is a decimal approximation for r, $3\sqrt{2}$ and the second number indicates that $\theta = 45°$. Thus polar notation for $(3,3)$ is $(4.2426, 45°)$.

Set the grapher in Radian and PolarC modes to find θ in radians. Repeat the keystrokes above to find that $\theta \approx 0.7854$. This is a decimal approximation for $\pi/4$. Thus polar notation for $(3,3)$ is $(4.2426, 0.7854)$.

CONVERTING FROM POLAR TO RECTANGULAR COORDINATES

The grapher can also be used to convert from polar to rectangular coordinates.

Section 9.5, Example 3 Convert each of the following to rectangular coordinates.

(a) $(10, \pi/3)$ (b) $(-5, 135°)$

(a) Set the grapher in RectC mode. Since the angle is given in radians select Radian mode also. Press $\boxed{(}\,\boxed{1}\,\boxed{0}\,\boxed{\text{2nd}}\,\boxed{\angle}$ $\boxed{\text{2nd}}\,\boxed{\pi}\,\boxed{\div}\,\boxed{3}\,\boxed{)}$ $\boxed{\text{ENTER}}$. ($\angle$ is the second operation associated with the $\boxed{,}$ key). The readout is $(5, 8.66025403784)$, where 8.66025403784 is a decimal approximation for $5\sqrt{3}$. Thus, rectangular notation for $(10, \pi/3)$ is $(5, 8.6603)$.

(b) Set the grapher in RectC mode and, since the angle is given in degrees, select Degree mode also. To find the x- and y-coordinates of rectangular notation, press $\boxed{(}$ $\boxed{(-)}$ 5 $\boxed{\text{2nd}}$ $\boxed{\angle}$ 1 3 5 $\boxed{)}$ $\boxed{\text{ENTER}}$. The readout is (3.53553390593, -3.53553390593), where 3.533553390593 is a decimal approximation for $\dfrac{5\sqrt{2}}{2}$. Thus, rectangular notation for $(-5, 135°)$ is $(3.5355, -3.5355)$.

GRAPHING POLAR EQUATIONS

Polar equations can be graphed in either Radian mode or Degree mode. The equation must be written in the form $r = f(\theta)$ and the grapher must be set in Polar (Pol) mode. Typically we begin with a range of $[0, 2\pi]$ or $[0°, 360°]$, but it might be necessary to increase the range to ensure that sufficient points are plotted to display the entire graph.

Section 9.5, Example 6 Graph: $r = 1 - \sin\theta$.

First set the grapher in Polar and Radian modes.

```
Normal Sci Eng
Float 012345678901
Radian Degree
RectC PolarC
Func Pol Param DifE◀
Dec Bin Oct Hex
RectV CylV SphereV
       dxNDer
```

The equation is given in $r = f(\theta)$ form. Press $\boxed{\text{GRAPH}}$ $\boxed{\text{F1}}$ to enter it on the "$r(\theta) =$" screen. Clear any existing entries and, with the cursor beside "$r_1 =$," press 1 $\boxed{-}$ $\boxed{\text{SIN}}$ $\boxed{\text{F1}}$. The keystroke $\boxed{\text{F1}}$ selects the variable θ. Now press $\boxed{\text{2nd}}$ $\boxed{\text{F2}}$ and enter the following settings:

θmin $= 0$ (Smallest value of θ to be evaluated)
θmax $= 2\pi$ (Largest value of θ to be evaluated)
θstep $= \pi/24$ (Increment in θ values)
Xmin $= -6$
Xmax $= 6$
Xscl $= 1$
Ymin $= -3.5$
Ymax $= 3.5$
Yscl $= 1$

With these settings the grapher evaluates the function from $\theta = 0$ to $\theta = 2\pi$ in increments of $\pi/24$ and displays the graph in the square window $[-6, 6, -3.5, 3.5]$. Values entered in terms of π appear on the screen as decimal approximations. Press

F5 to display the graph.

 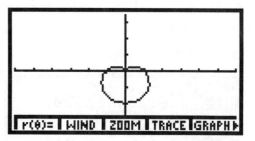

The curve can be traced with either rectangular or polar coordinates being displayed. The value of θ is also displayed when rectangular coordinates are selected. The choice of coordinates is made on the GRAPH FORMT screen. Press GRAPH MORE F3 to display this screen. Then position the blinking cursor over RectGC to select rectangular coordinates or over PolarGC to select polar coordinates and press ENTER .

GRAPHING PARAMETRIC EQUATIONS

Plane curves described with parametric equations can be graphed on a grapher.

Section 9.8, Example 1 (a) Using a grapher, graph the plane curve given by the set of parametric equations and the restriction for the parameter.

$$x = t^2, \ y = t - 1,; \ -1 \le t \le 4$$

First press 2nd MODE and select Parametric (Param) mode.

Then press GRAPH F1 to display the equation-editor screen. Enter xt1 $= t^2$ and yt1 $= t - 1$. Note that the keystroke F1 selects the variable t when the equation-editor screen is displayed in parametric mode. Now press 2nd F2 and enter the following settings:

tMin $= -1$	(Smallest value of t to be evaluated)
tMax $= 4$	(Largest value of t to be evaluated)
tStep $= .1$	(Increment in t values)
xMin $= -2$	
xMax $= 18$	
xScl $= 1$	
yMin $= -4$	
yMax $= 4$	
yScl $= 1$	

Since $x = t^2$ and $-1 \le t \le 4$, we have $0 \le x \le 16$. Thus, we choose xMin and xMax to display this interval. Similarly, since $y = t - 1$, we have $-2 \le y \le 3$ and we choose yMin and yMax to show this interval. Press $\boxed{\text{F5}}$ to display the graph.

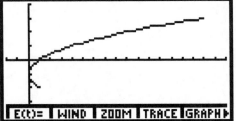

The curve can be traced as described in Example 6 from Section 9.5 above.

Chapter 10
Sequences, Series, and Combinatorics

Both the graphing capabilities and the computational capabilities of the grapher can be used when working with sequences, series, and combinatorics.

FINDING THE TERMS OF A SEQUENCE

Section 10.1, Example 2 Use a grapher to find the first 5 terms of the sequence whose general term is given by $a_n = n/(n+1)$.

Although we could use a table, we will use the Seq feature. Press $\boxed{\text{2nd}}$ $\boxed{\text{LIST}}$ $\boxed{\text{F5}}$ to display the LIST OPS menu. Then press $\boxed{\text{MORE}}$ $\boxed{\text{F3}}$ to paste "seq(" to the home screen. (LIST is the second operation associated with the $\boxed{-}$ subtraction key.) Then enter the general term of the sequence, the variable, the numbers of the first and last terms desired, and the increment between the terms to be displayed. We will also use the ▷Frac feature to express the terms as fractions. Press $\boxed{\text{x-VAR}}$ $\boxed{\div}$ $\boxed{(}$ $\boxed{\text{x-VAR}}$ $\boxed{+}$ 1 $\boxed{)}$ $\boxed{,}$ $\boxed{\text{x-VAR}}$ $\boxed{,}$ 1 $\boxed{,}$ 5 $\boxed{,}$ 1 $\boxed{)}$ $\boxed{\text{2nd}}$ $\boxed{\text{MATH}}$ $\boxed{\text{F5}}$ $\boxed{\text{MORE}}$ $\boxed{\text{F1}}$ $\boxed{\text{ENTER}}$. If ▷ Frac was entered in position F1 of the custom menu as described on page 156 of this manual, we can press $\boxed{\text{CUSTOM}}$ instead of $\boxed{\text{2nd}}$ $\boxed{\text{MATH}}$ $\boxed{\text{F5}}$ $\boxed{\text{MORE}}$.

```
seq(x/(x+1),x,1,5,1)▶
Frac
{1/2 2/3 3/4 4/5 5/6}
█



  NUM  PROB ANGLE  HYP  MISC
▶Frac   %  ▶Eval   ×√  eval
```

GRAPHING SEQUENCES

The TI-86 does not have the capability to graph sequences.

FINDING PARTIAL SUMS

We can use a grapher to find partial sums of a sequence when a formula for the general term is known.

Section 10.1, Example 6 Use a grapher to find S_1, S_2, S_3, and S_4 for the sequence whose general term is given by $a_n = n^2 - 3$.

We will use the cSum feature from the LIST OPS menu. The grapher will write the partial sums as a list. First press $\boxed{\text{2nd}}$ $\boxed{\text{LIST}}$ $\boxed{\text{F5}}$ $\boxed{\text{MORE}}$ $\boxed{\text{MORE}}$ $\boxed{\text{F3}}$ to paste "cSum(" to the home screen. Then press $\boxed{\text{2nd}}$ $\boxed{\text{LIST}}$ $\boxed{\text{F5}}$ $\boxed{\text{MORE}}$ $\boxed{\text{F3}}$ to paste "seq(" into the cSum expression. Finally press $\boxed{\text{x-VAR}}$ $\boxed{x^2}$ $\boxed{-}$ 3 $\boxed{,}$ $\boxed{\text{x-VAR}}$ $\boxed{,}$ 1 $\boxed{,}$ 4 $\boxed{)}$ $\boxed{)}$ $\boxed{\text{ENTER}}$.

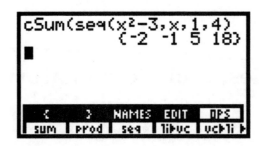

RECURSIVELY DEFINED SEQUENCES

Recursively defined sequences can also be entered on a grapher set in Seq mode.

Section 10.1, Example 7 Find the first 5 terms of the sequence defined by

$$a_1 = 5, \; a_{k+1} = 2a_k - 3, \text{ for } k \geq 1.$$

We will set up a counter that indicates which term of the sequence is displayed. First we will enter 1, indicating that the first term will follow, along with 5, the first term of the sequence. To do this press $\boxed{\text{2nd}}\boxed{\text{LIST}}\boxed{\text{F1}}\,1\,\boxed{,}\,5\,\boxed{\text{F2}}\boxed{\text{ENTER}}$. These keystrokes enter 1 as Answer (1) and 5 as Answer (2) and display 5 as the first term of the sequence. We will add 1 to Answer (1) so that the counter increases by 1 each time a new term is displayed. We will also enter the general term of the sequence. Press $\boxed{\text{F1}}\boxed{\text{2nd}}\boxed{\text{ANS}}\boxed{(}\,1\,\boxed{)}\boxed{+}\,1\,\boxed{,}\,2\,\boxed{\text{2nd}}\boxed{\text{ANS}}\boxed{(}\,2\,\boxed{)}\boxed{-}\,3\,\boxed{\text{F2}}\boxed{\text{ENTER}}$. Now we see the next term of the sequence, 7, along with the counter, 2, indicating that it is the second term. Press $\boxed{\text{ENTER}}$ again to see the a_3, 11. Press $\boxed{\text{ENTER}}$ once more to see a_4 and again to see a_5. Continue pressing $\boxed{\text{ENTER}}$ to see additional terms.

EVALUATING FACTORIALS, PERMUTATIONS, AND COMBINATIONS

Operations from the MATH PROB (probability) menu can be used to evaluate factorials, permutations, and combinations. Press $\boxed{\text{2nd}}\boxed{\text{MATH}}\boxed{\text{F2}}$ to display this menu.

Section 10.5, Exercise 6 Evaluate 7!.

With the MATH PROB menu displayed, press 7 $\boxed{\text{F1}}\boxed{\text{ENTER}}$. These keystrokes enter 7, select ! from the MATH PROB menu, and then cause 7! to be evaluated. The result is 5040.

Section 10.5, Exercise 9 Evaluate $\dfrac{9!}{5!}$.

With the MATH PROB menu displayed, press 9 $\boxed{\text{F1}}\boxed{\div}$ 5 $\boxed{\text{F1}}\boxed{\text{ENTER}}$. The result is 3024.

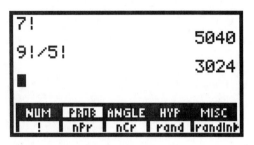

Section 10.5, Example 3 (a) Compute $_4P_4$.

With the MATH PROB menu displayed, press 4 | F2 | 4 | ENTER |.

Section 10.5, Example 6 Compute $_8P_4$.

With the MATH PROB menu displayed, press 8 | F2 | 4 | ENTER |. We could also edit the previous entry to find $_8P_4$. The result is 1680.

Section 10.5, Example 3 Evaluate $\binom{7}{5}$.

With the MATH PROB menu displayed, press 7 | F3 | 5 | ENTER |. The result is 21.

The TI-89 Graphics Calculator

Introduction to Graphs and the Graphing Calculator

GETTING STARTED

Press $\boxed{\text{ON}}$ to turn on the TI-89 graphing calculator. ($\boxed{\text{ON}}$ is the key at the bottom left-hand corner of the keypad.) The home screen is displayed. You should see a row of boxes at the top of the screen and two horizontal lines with lettering below them at the bottom of the screen. If you do not see anything, try adjusting the display contrast. To do this, first press and hold down the $\boxed{\diamond}$ key. ($\boxed{\diamond}$ is the key in the left column of the keypad with a green diamond inside a green border. All operations associated with the $\boxed{\diamond}$ key are printed on the keyboard in green, the same color as the $\boxed{\diamond}$ key.) Then press and hold $\boxed{+}$ to darken the display or $\boxed{-}$ to lighten the display. Be sure to use the black $\boxed{-}$ key in the right column of the keypad rather than the gray $\boxed{(-)}$ key on the bottom row.

One way to turn the grapher off is to press $\boxed{\text{2nd}}$ $\boxed{\text{OFF}}$. (OFF is the second operation associated with the $\boxed{\text{ON}}$ key. All operations accessed by using the $\boxed{\text{2nd}}$ key are printed on the keyboard in yellow, the same color as the $\boxed{\text{2nd}}$ key.) When you turn the TI-89 on again the home screen will be displayed regardless of the screen that was displayed when the grapher was turned off. $\boxed{\text{2nd}}$ $\boxed{\text{OFF}}$ cannot be used to turn off the grapher if an error message is displayed. The grapher can also be turned off by pressing $\boxed{\diamond}$ $\boxed{\text{OFF}}$. This will work even if an error message is displayed. When the TI-89 is turned on again the display will be exactly as it was when it was turned off. The grapher will turn itself off automatically after several minutes without any activity. When this happens the display will be just as you left it when you turn the grapher on again.

From top to bottom, the home screen consists of the tool bar, the large history area where entries and their corresponding results are displayed, the entry line where expressions or instructions are entered, and the status line which shows the current state of the calculator. These areas will be discussed in more detail as the need arises.

Press $\boxed{\text{MODE}}$ to display the MODE settings. Modes that are not currently valid, due to the existing choices of settings, are dimmed. Initially you should select the settings shown below.

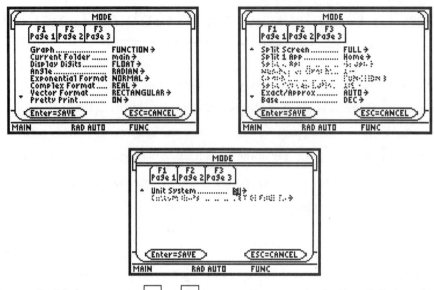

To change a setting on the Mode screen use $\triangledown$ or $\triangle$ to move the cursor to the line of that setting. Then use $\triangleright$ to display the options. Press the number of the desired option to copy it to the Mode screen. Then press ENTER to save it there. Instead of pressing the number of the desired setting, you can highlight it and then press ENTER ENTER to copy it to the Mode screen and save it there. Note that the cursor skips dimmed settings as you move through the options.

It will be helpful to read Chapter 1: Getting Started and Chapter 2: Operating the TI-89 in the TI-89 Guidebook before proceeding.

USING A MENU

A menu is a list of options that appear when a key is pressed. For example, press F1 to display the Tools menu. We can select an item from a menu by using $\triangledown$ to highlight it and then pressing ENTER or by simply pressing the number of the item. If we press 8 when the Tools menu is displayed, for instance, we select "Clear Home" and any previously entered computations will be cleared from the history area of the home screen. If an item is identified by a letter rather than a number, press the purple alpha key followed by the letter of the item to select it. The letters are printed in purple above the keys on the keypad. The down-arrow beside item 8 in the menu below indicates that there are additional items in the menu. Use $\triangledown$ to scroll down to them.

SETTING THE VIEWING WINDOW

The viewing window is the portion of the coordinate plane that appears on the grapher's screen. It is defined by the minimum and maximum values of x and y: xmin, xmax, ymin, and ymax. The notation [xmin, xmax, ymin, ymax] is used in the text to represent these window settings or dimensions. For example, $[-12,\ 12,\ -8,\ 8]$ denotes a window that displays the portion of the x-axis from -12 to 12 and the portion of the y-axis from -8 to 8. In addition, the distance between tick marks on the axes is defined by the settings xscl and yscl. In this manual xscl and yscl will be assumed to be 1 unless noted otherwise. The setting xres sets the pixel resolution. We usually select xres = 2. The window corresponding to the settings $[-20,\ 30,\ -12,\ 20]$, xscl = 5, yscl = 2, xres = 2, is shown below.

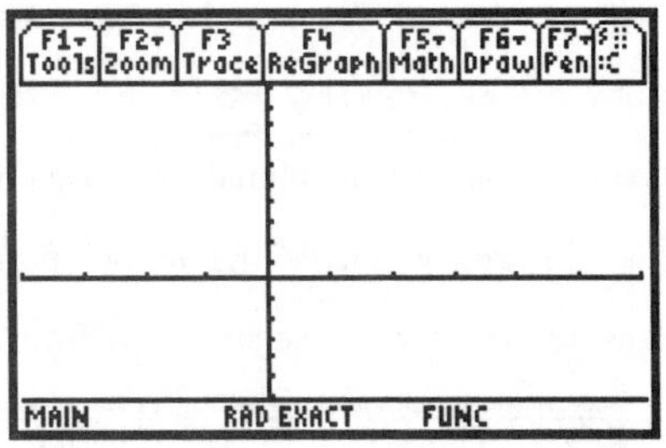

Press $\boxed{\diamond}$ $\boxed{\text{WINDOW}}$ to display the current window settings on your grapher. (WINDOW is the green $\diamond$ operation associated with the $\boxed{\text{F2}}$ key on the top row of the keypad.) The standard settings are shown below.

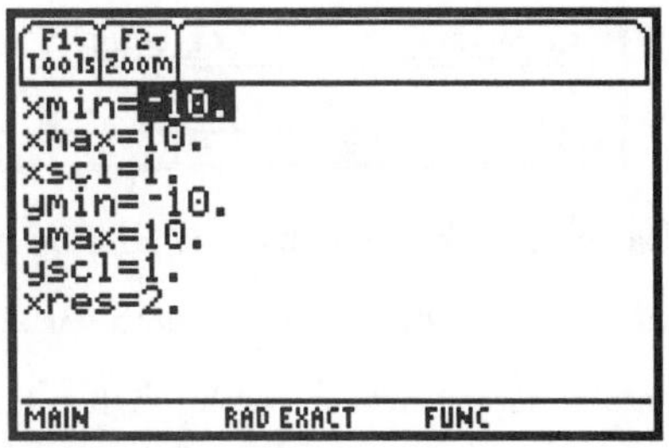

To change a setting, position the cursor beside the setting you wish to change and enter the new value. For example, to change from the standard settings to $[-20,\ 30,\ -12,\ 20]$, xscl = 5, yscl = 2, on the WINDOW screen, start with the setting beside "xmin =" highlighted and press $\boxed{(-)}$ 2 0 $\boxed{\text{ENTER}}$ 3 0 $\boxed{\text{ENTER}}$ 5 $\boxed{\text{ENTER}}$ $\boxed{(-)}$ 1 2 $\boxed{\text{ENTER}}$ 2 0 $\boxed{\text{ENTER}}$ 2 $\boxed{\text{ENTER}}$. You must use the $\boxed{(-)}$ key on the bottom row of the keypad rather than the $\boxed{-}$ key in the right-hand column to enter a negative number. $\boxed{(-)}$ represents "the opposite of" or "the additive inverse of" whereas $\boxed{-}$ is the key for the subtraction operation. The $\boxed{\triangledown}$ key may be used instead of $\boxed{\text{ENTER}}$ after typing each window setting. To see the window shown above, press $\boxed{\diamond}$ $\boxed{\text{GRAPH}}$. (GRAPH is the green $\diamond$ operation associated with the $\boxed{\text{F3}}$ key on the top row of the keypad.)

QUICK TIP: To return quickly to the standard window setting $[-10,\ 10,\ -10,\ 10]$, xscl = 1, yscl = 1, when either the Window screen or the Graph screen is displayed, press $\boxed{\text{F2}}$ to access the ZOOM menu and then press 6 to select item 6, ZoomStd (Zoom Standard).

PLOTTING POINTS

We can plot points on a grapher by entering their coordinates in a list and choosing an appropriate viewing window.

Example 2, page 3 (Page numbers refer to pages in the text.) Use a grapher to graph the points $(-3, 5)$, $(4, 3)$, $(3, 4)$, $(-4, -2)$, $(3, -4)$, $(0, 4)$, $(-3, 0)$, and $(0, 0)$.

We choose a viewing window that will display all of the points, noting that the x-coordinates range from -4 to 4 and the y-coordinates range from -4 to 5. Thus, one good choice for a viewing window is the standard window $[-10, 10, -10, 10]$.

We will enter the coordinates in the Data/Matrix editor. Press $\boxed{\text{APPS}}$ 6 3 to display a new data variable screen in the Data/Matrix editor. We must now enter a data variable name in the Variable box on this screen. The name can contain from 1 to 8 characters and cannot start with a numeral. Some names are preassigned to other uses on the TI-89. If you try to use one of these, you will get an error message. Press $\boxed{\triangledown}\,\boxed{\triangledown}$ to move the cursor to the Variable box. We will name our data variable "points." To enter this name, first lock the alphabetic keys on by pressing $\boxed{\text{2nd}}\,\boxed{\text{a-lock}}$. Then press $\boxed{\text{P}}$ $\boxed{\text{O}}\,\boxed{\text{I}}\,\boxed{\text{N}}\,\boxed{\text{T}}\,\boxed{\text{S}}$. Note that P, O, I, N, and S are the purple alphabetic operations associated with the $\boxed{\text{STO} \triangleright}$, $\boxed{-}$, 9, 6, and 3 keys, respectively. The letter T has its own key on the sixth row from the bottom of the keypad.

After typing the name of the data variable, unlock the alphabetic keys by pressing the purple $\boxed{\text{alpha}}$ key. Now press $\boxed{\text{ENTER}}\,\boxed{\text{ENTER}}$ to go to the data-entry screen. Assuming the data variable name "points" has not previously been used in your calculator, this screen will contain empty data lists with row 1, column 1 highlighted. If entries have previously been made in a data variable named "points," they can be cleared by pressing $\boxed{\text{F1}}$ 8 $\boxed{\text{ENTER}}$.

We will enter the first coordinates (x-coordinates) of the points in column c1 and the second coordinates (y-coordinates) in c2. To enter the first x-coordinate, -3, press $\boxed{(-)}$ 3 $\boxed{\text{ENTER}}$. Continue typing the x-values 4, 3, -4, 3, 0, -3, and 0, each followed by $\boxed{\text{ENTER}}$. The entries can be followed by $\boxed{\triangledown}$ rather than $\boxed{\text{ENTER}}$ if desired. Press $\boxed{\triangleright}\,\boxed{\triangle}\,\boxed{\triangle}\,\boxed{\triangle}$ $\boxed{\triangle}\,\boxed{\triangle}\,\boxed{\triangle}\,\boxed{\triangle}\,\boxed{\triangle}$ to move to the top of column c2. Type the y-values 5, 3, 4, -2, -4, 4, 0, and 0 in succession, each followed by $\boxed{\text{ENTER}}$ or $\boxed{\triangledown}$. Note that the coordinates of each point must be in the same position in both lists.

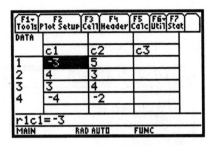

To plot the points we access the Plot Setup screen by pressing $\boxed{\text{F2}}$. We will use Plot 1, which is highlighted. If any plot settings are currently entered beside "Plot 1," clear them by pressing $\boxed{\text{F3}}$. Clear settings shown beside any other plots as well by using $\boxed{\triangledown}$ to highlight each plot in turn and then pressing $\boxed{\text{F3}}$.

Now we define Plot 1. Use $\boxed{\triangle}$ to highlight Plot 1 if necessary. Then press $\boxed{\text{F1}}$ to display the Plot Definition screen. The item on the first line, Plot Type, is highlighted. We will choose a scatterplot, by pressing $\boxed{\triangleright}$ 1. Now press $\boxed{\triangledown}$ to go to the next line, Mark. Here we select the type of mark or symbol that will be used to plot the points. We select a box by pressing $\boxed{\triangleright}$ 1. Now we must tell the grapher which columns of the data variable to use for the x- and y-coordinates of the points to be plotted. Press $\boxed{\triangledown}$ to move the cursor to the "x" line and enter c1 as the source of the x-coordinates by pressing $\boxed{\text{alpha}}$ $\boxed{\text{C}}$ 1. (C is the purple alphabetic operation associated with the $\boxed{)}$ key.) Press $\boxed{\triangledown}$ $\boxed{\text{alpha}}$ $\boxed{\text{C}}$ 2 to go the the "y" line and enter c2 as the source of the y-coordinates.

Save the plot definition and return to the Plot Setup screen by pressing $\boxed{\text{ENTER}}$ $\boxed{\text{ENTER}}$. Beside "Plot 1:" you will now see a shorthand notation for the definition of the plot. The check mark to the left of Plot 1 indicates that it is turned on.

In order to see only the graph of the points we have entered we must be certain that there are no equations entered in the equation-editor screen of the grapher. Access this screen by pressing $\boxed{\diamond}$ $\boxed{\text{Y} =}$. (Y = is the green operation associated with the $\boxed{\text{F1}}$ key.) If there are entries present clear them now. To clear an entry for y1, for example, position the cursor beside" y1 =" and press $\boxed{\text{CLEAR}}$. Do this for each existing entry. If this is not done, the equations that are currently entered will be graphed along with the data points that are entered.

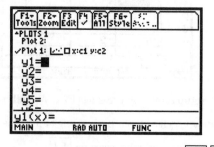

To see the points plotted in the window that was previously entered, press $\boxed{\diamond}$ $\boxed{\text{GRAPH}}$.

QUICK TIP: Instead of entering the window dimensions directly, we can press $\boxed{\text{F2}}$ 9 after entering the coordinates of the points in lists and defining Plot 1. This activates the ZoomData operation which automatically defines a viewing window that displays all the points and also displays the graph.

To turn off the plot, first press $\boxed{\text{APPS}}$ 6 1 $\boxed{\text{F2}}$ to return to the Plot Setup screen. Then highlight Plot 1 and press $\boxed{\text{F4}}$. Note that there is no check mark to the left of Plot 1 when it is turned off.

SOLUTIONS OF EQUATIONS

Example 3, page 4 Determine whether each ordered pair is a solution of $2x + 3y = 18$.

$\qquad$ **a)** $(-5, 7)$ $\qquad\qquad$ **b)** $(3, 4)$

We can substitute each pair in the expression $2x + 3y$. If the resulting value is 18, the pair is a solution of the equation $2x + 3y = 18$. If not, the pair is not a solution. To perform the substitutions, first press $\boxed{\text{HOME}}$ or $\boxed{\text{2nd}}$ $\boxed{\text{QUIT}}$ to go to the home screen. You might want to clear any previously entered computations from the history area of the home screen first. To do this, access Tools from the toolbar at the top of the screen by pressing $\boxed{\text{F1}}$, the blue key at the top left-hand corner of the keypad. Then select item 8, Clear Home, from this menu by pressing 8.

The entry line on the home screen can be cleared by pressing CLEAR . This is not necessary if the current entry is highlighted, since it will automatically be cleared when the first character of a new entry is entered.

Now, to substitute -5 for x and 7 for y in $2x + 3y$, press 2 ((−) 5) + 3 × 7 ENTER . The result is 11, so $(-5, 7)$ is not a solution of the equation. To substitute 3 for x and 4 for y, press 2 × 3 + 3 × 4 ENTER . The result is 18, so $(3, 4)$ is a solution.

```
 F1▾  F2▾  F3▾  F4▾  F5   F6▾
Tools Algebra Calc Other Prgmi0 Clean Up


■ 2· -5 + 3·7                        11
■ 2·3 + 3·4                          18
2*3+3*4
MAIN        RAD AUTO       FUNC      2/30
```

EDITING ENTRIES

You can edit your entry if necessary. After ENTER is pressed to evaluate an expression, the TI-89 leaves the expression on the entry line and highlights it. To edit the expression you must first remove the highlight to avoid the possibility of accidently typing over the entire expression. To do this, press ◁ or ▷ to move the cursor (a blinking vertical line) toward the side of the expression to be edited. If, for instance, in entering the last expression in Example 3 above you pressed − instead of + , first press ◁ to move the cursor to the beginning of the expression or ▷ to move it to the end of the expression. Now, to type a + over the −, first select overtype mode by pressing 2nd INS . (INS is the second operation associated with the ← key.) Now the cursor becomes a dark, blinking rectangle rather than a vertical line. Use ▷ to position the cursor over the − and then press + to write a + over the −. To leave overtype mode press 2nd INS again. The grapher is now in the insert mode, indicated by a vertical cursor, and will remain in that mode until overtype mode is once again selected.

If you forgot to type the first 3, move the insert cursor to the left of the + and press 3 to insert the 3 before the +. You can continue to insert symbols immediately after the first insertion. If you typed 21 instead of 2, move the cursor to the left of 1 and press ← . This will delete the 1. Instead of using overtype mode to overtype a character as described above, we can use ← to delete the character and then, in insert mode, insert a new character.

If you accidently press △ instead of ◁ or ▷ while editing an expression, the cursor will move up into the history area of the screen. Press $\boxed{\text{ESC}}$ to return immediately to the entry line. The $\boxed{\triangledown}$ key can also be used to return to the entry line. It must be pressed the same number of times the $\boxed{\triangle}$ key was pressed accidently.

If you notice that an entry needs to be edited before you press $\boxed{\text{ENTER}}$ to perform the computation, the editing can be done as described above without the necessity of first removing the highlight from the entry.

The keystrokes $\boxed{\text{2nd}}$ $\boxed{\text{ENTRY}}$ can be used repeatedly to recall entries preceding the last one. (ENTRY is the second function associated with the $\boxed{\text{ENTER}}$ key.) Pressing $\boxed{\text{2nd}}$ $\boxed{\text{ENTRY}}$ twice, for example, will recall the next to last entry. Using these keystrokes a third time recalls the third to last entry and so on. The number of entries that can be recalled depends on the amount of storage they occupy in the calculator's memory.

Previous entries and results of computations can also be copied to the entry line by first using the $\boxed{\triangle}$ key to move through the history area until the desired entry or result is highlighted. Then press $\boxed{\text{ENTER}}$ to copy it to the entry line.

THE TABLE FEATURE

A table of x-and y-values representing ordered pairs that are solutions of an equation can be displayed. We must first enter the equation on the equation-editor screen before a table can be displayed.

Example 5, page 6 Create a table of ordered pairs that are solutions of the equation $y = \frac{1}{2}x + 1$.

Press $\boxed{\diamond}$ $\boxed{\text{Y}=}$ to access the equation-editor screen. (Y = is the green $\diamond$ operation associated with the $\boxed{\text{F1}}$ key.) If any plots are turned on they should be turned off, or deselected, now. A check mark beside the name of a plot indicates that it is currently selected. To deselect it, move the cursor to the plot. Then press $\boxed{\text{F4}}$. There should now be no check mark beside the name of the plot, indicating that it has been deselected. If there is currently an expression displayed for y_1, clear it by positioning the cursor beside "y1 =" and then press $\boxed{\text{CLEAR}}$. Do the same for expressions that appear on all other "y =" lines by using $\boxed{\triangledown}$ to move to a line and then pressing $\boxed{\text{CLEAR}}$. Then use $\boxed{\triangle}$ or $\boxed{\triangledown}$ to move the cursor beside "y1 =." Now enter $y_1 = \frac{1}{2}x + 1$ on the entry line of the equation-editor screen and paste it beside "y1 =" by pressing $\boxed{(}$ $1 \boxed{\div} 2 \boxed{)} \boxed{\text{X}} \boxed{+} 1 \boxed{\text{ENTER}}$. Although the parentheses are not necessary, the equation is more easily read on the entry line when they are used.

Once the equation in entered, press $\boxed{\diamond}$ $\boxed{\text{TblSet}}$ or $\boxed{\diamond}$ $\boxed{\text{TABLE}}$ $\boxed{\text{F2}}$ to access the TABLE SETUP window. (TblSet is the green $\diamond$ operation associated with the $\boxed{\text{F4}}$ key.) If "Independent" is set to "Auto" on the Table Setup screen, the grapher will supply values for x, beginning with the value specified as tblStart and continuing by adding the value of Δtbl to the preceding value for x. If the table was previously set to Ask, the blinking cursor will be positioned over ASK. Change this setting to AUTO by pressing $\boxed{\triangleright}$ 1. Now use the $\boxed{\triangle}$ key to move the cursor to tblStart. Enter a minimum x-value of -3, an increment of 1, and a Graph $< - >$ Table setting of OFF by first positioning the cursor beside tblStart and then pressing $\boxed{(-)}$ 3 $\boxed{\triangledown}$ 1 $\boxed{\triangledown}$ $\boxed{\triangleright}$ 1 $\boxed{\text{ENTER}}$. Press $\boxed{\diamond}$ $\boxed{\text{TABLE}}$ to see the table. (TABLE is the green $\diamond$ operation associated with the $\boxed{\text{F5}}$ key.)

GRAPHING EQUATIONS

After entering an equation and setting a viewing window, you can view the graph of the equation.

Example 6, page 7 Graph using a grapher: $y = \frac{1}{2}x + 1$.

Enter the equation on the equation-editor screen as described in Example 5 above. The standard $[-10, 10, -10, 10]$ window is a good choice for this graph. Either enter these dimensions in the WINDOW screen and then press $\boxed{\diamond}$ $\boxed{\text{GRAPH}}$ to see the graph or, from the WINDOW screen, simply press $\boxed{\text{F2}}$ 6 to select the standard window and see the graph.

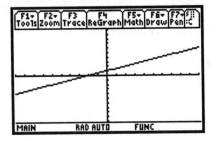

FINDING POINTS OF INTERSECTION

We can use the Intersection feature from the Math menu on the GRAPH screen to find the point(s) of intersection of two graphs.

Example 9, page 9 Use a grapher to find the point of intersection of the graphs of $x - y = -5$ and $y = 4x + 10$.

We begin by entering the equations on the equation-editor screen. Since equations must be entered in the form "$y =$", we solve the first equation for y, obtaining $y = x + 5$. Then press $\boxed{\diamond}$ $\boxed{\text{Y} =}$ to go to the equation-editor screen. Clear any existing entries. Enter $y_1 = x + 5$ by positioning the cursor beside "$y_1 =$" and pressing $\boxed{\text{X}}$ $\boxed{+}$ 5 $\boxed{\text{ENTER}}$. Next position the cursor beside "$y_2 =$" and enter $y_2 = 4x + 10$ by pressing 4 $\boxed{\text{X}}$ $\boxed{+}$ 1 0 $\boxed{\text{ENTER}}$. Now graph the equations. We begin by using the standard window and see that it is a good choice because it shows the point of intersection of the graphs.

We will use the Intersection feature to find the coordinates of the point of intersection. Press $\boxed{\text{F5}}$ 5 to select Intersection from the Math menu on the Graph screen. The query "1st curve?" appears at the bottom of the screen. The blinking cursor is positioned on the graph of y_1. This is indicated by the 1 in the upper right-hand corner of the screen. Press $\boxed{\text{ENTER}}$ to indicate that this is the first curve involved in the intersection. Next the query "2nd curve?" appears at the bottom of the screen. The blinking cursor is now positioned on the graph of y_2 and the notation 2 should appear in the top right-hand corner of the screen. Press $\boxed{\text{ENTER}}$ to indicate that this is the second curve. We identify the curves for the grapher since we could have more than two graphs on the screen at once. After we identify the second curve, the query "Lower bound?" appears at the bottom of the screen. Use the left or right arrow key to move the blinking cursor to a point to the left of the point of intersection of the lines or type an x-value less than the x-coordinate of the point of intersection. Then press $\boxed{\text{ENTER}}$. Next the query "Upper bound?" appears. Move the cursor to a point to the right of the point of intersection or type an x-value greater than the x-value of the point of intersection and press $\boxed{\text{ENTER}}$. We give a lower and an upper bound since some pairs of curves have more than one point of intersection. Now the coordinates of the point of intersection appear at the bottom of the screen.

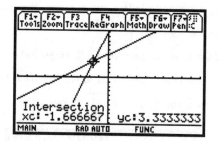

We see that the graphs intersect at the point $(-1.666667, 3.3333333)$.

Chapter R
Basic Concepts of Algebra

ABSOLUTE VALUE

Section R.1, Example 3 Find the distance between -2 and 3.

The distance between -2 and 3 is $|-2-3|$, or $|3-(-2)|$. Absolute value notation is denoted "abs" on the grapher. It is item 2 on the MATH Number menu.

To enter $|-2-3|$ press $\boxed{\text{2nd}}$ $\boxed{\text{MATH}}$ $\boxed{\triangleright}$ $\boxed{2}$ $\boxed{(-)}$ $\boxed{2}$ $\boxed{-}$ $\boxed{3}$ $\boxed{)}$ $\boxed{\text{ENTER}}$. (MATH is the second operation associated with the 5 numeric key.)To enter $|3-(-2)|$ press $\boxed{\text{2nd}}$ $\boxed{\text{MATH}}$ $\boxed{\triangleright}$ $\boxed{2}$ 3 $\boxed{-}$ $\boxed{(}$ $\boxed{(-)}$ $\boxed{2}$ $\boxed{)}$ $\boxed{)}$ $\boxed{\text{ENTER}}$. Note that the grapher supplies the left parenthesis in the absolute value notation. We close the expression with a right parenthesis. Although the parentheses around -2 in the second expression are not necessary, they allow the expression to be more easily read on the entry line so we include them here.

Instead of pressing $\boxed{\text{2nd}}$ $\boxed{\text{MATH}}$ $\boxed{\triangleright}$ 2 to access "abs(" and copy it to the home screen, we could have pressed $\boxed{\text{2nd}}$ $\boxed{\text{MATH}}$ $\boxed{\triangleright}$ $\boxed{\triangledown}$ $\boxed{\text{ENTER}}$. Absolute value notation can also be found as the first item in the Catalog and copied to the home screen. Access the Catalog by pressing $\boxed{\text{CATALOG}}$. Then use the $\boxed{\triangle}$ or $\boxed{\triangledown}$ key to position the triangular selection cursor beside "abs(." This cursor can be positioned quickly by pressing $\boxed{A}$ to move the cursor to the first item in the Catalog that begins with A 'abs(." (A is the purple alphabetic operation associated with the $\boxed{=}$ key.) Note that, when we are in the Catalog, it is not necessary to press $\boxed{\text{alpha}}$ before an alphabetic entry.

SCIENTIFIC NOTATION

To enter a number in scientific notation, first type the decimal portion of the number; then press the $\boxed{\text{EE}}$ key in the left column of the keypad; finally type the exponent, which can be at most three digits. For example, to enter 1.789×10^{-11} in scientific notation, go to the home screen and press 1 $\boxed{.}$ 7 8 9 $\boxed{\text{EE}}$ $\boxed{(-)}$ 1 1 $\boxed{\text{ENTER}}$. To enter 6.084×10^{23} in scientific notation, press 6 $\boxed{.}$ 0 8 4 $\boxed{\text{EE}}$ 2 3 $\boxed{\text{ENTER}}$. The decimal portion of each number appears before a small E while the exponent follows the E.

The grapher can be used to perform computations in scientific notation.

Section R.2, Example 7 *Distance to a Star*. Alpha Centauri is about 4.3 light-years from Earth. One light-year is the distance that light travels in one year and is about 5.88×10^{12} miles. How many miles is it from Earth to Alpha Centauri? Express your answer in scientific notation.

To solve this problem we find the product $4.3 \times (5.88 \times 10^{12})$. Press 4 $\boxed{.}$ 3 $\boxed{\times}$ 5 $\boxed{.}$ 8 8 $\boxed{\text{EE}}$ 1 2 $\boxed{\text{ENTER}}$. The result is 2.5284×10^{13} miles.

ORDER OF OPERATIONS

Section R.2, Example 8 (b) Calculate: $\dfrac{10 \div (8 - 6) + 9 \cdot 4}{2^5 + 3^2}$.

In order to divide the entire numerator by the entire denominator, we must enclose both the numerator and the denominator in parentheses. That is, we enter $(10 \div (8 - 6) + 9 \cdot 4) \div (2^5 + 3^2)$. On the home screen press $\boxed{(}$ 1 0 $\boxed{\div}$ $\boxed{(}$ 8 $\boxed{-}$ 6 $\boxed{)}$ $\boxed{+}$ 9 $\boxed{\times}$ 4 $\boxed{)}$ $\boxed{\div}$ $\boxed{(}$ 2 $\boxed{\wedge}$ 5 $\boxed{+}$ 3 $\boxed{\wedge}$ 2 $\boxed{)}$ $\boxed{\text{ENTER}}$.

THE PATH GRAPH STYLE

Graph styles can be selected from the Style menu on the equation-editor screen of the TI-89. The path graph style can be used, along with the line style, to determine whether graphs coincide. This can be used to provide a partial check of certain algebraic procedures.

Section R.4, Example 2 Factor: $x^3 + 3x^2 - 5x - 15$.

Factoring by grouping, we find that $x^3 + 3x^2 - 5x - 15 = (x + 3)(x^2 - 5)$. We can check this using two different graph styles on a grapher. First, on the Y = screen, enter $y_1 = x^3 + 3x^2 - 5x - 15$ and $y_2 = (x + 3)(x^2 - 5)$. For y_2 we will select the path graph style from the Style menu. To do this, highlight the expression for y_2 and then press $\boxed{\text{2nd}}$ $\boxed{\text{F6}}$ 6 or press $\boxed{\text{2nd}}$ $\boxed{\text{F6}}$ $\boxed{\triangledown}$ $\boxed{\triangledown}$ $\boxed{\triangledown}$ $\boxed{\triangledown}$ $\boxed{\triangledown}$ $\boxed{\text{ENTER}}$.

The grapher will graph y_1 first as a solid line. Then y_2 will be graphed as the circular cursor traces the leading edge of the graph, allowing us to determine visually whether the graphs coincide. In this case, the graphs appear to coincide, so the factorization is probably correct.

SELECTING THE DOT GRAPH STYLE

When graphing an equation in which a variable appears in a denominator, the Dot graph style should be used. If this is not done, a vertical line that is not part of the graph could appear. We will demonstrate selecting the Dot graph style with the equation $y = \dfrac{2}{x - 3}$. First enter this equation on the equation-editor screen. Then highlight it and press $\boxed{\text{2nd}}$ $\boxed{\text{F6}}$ 2 or $\boxed{\text{2nd}}$ $\boxed{\text{F6}}$ $\boxed{\triangledown}$ $\boxed{\text{ENTER}}$.

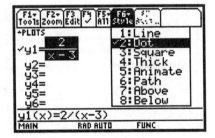

RADICAL NOTATION

We can use the square-root key and rational exponents to simplify radical expressions.

Section R.6, Example 1 Simplify each of the following.

a) $\sqrt{36}$ b) $-\sqrt{36}$ c) $\sqrt[5]{\dfrac{32}{243}}$ d) $\sqrt[3]{-8}$ e) $\sqrt[4]{-16}$

a) To find $\sqrt{36}$ go to the home screen and press $\boxed{\text{2nd}}$ $\boxed{\sqrt{}}$ 3 6 $\boxed{)}$ $\boxed{\text{ENTER}}$. ($\sqrt{}$ is the second operation associated with the $\boxed{\times}$ multiplication key.) Note that the grapher supplies a left parenthesis with the radical symbol and we must close the expression with a right parenthesis.

b) To find $-\sqrt{36}$ press $\boxed{(-)}$ $\boxed{\text{2nd}}$ $\boxed{\sqrt{}}$ $3\ 6\ \boxed{)}$ $\boxed{\text{ENTER}}$.

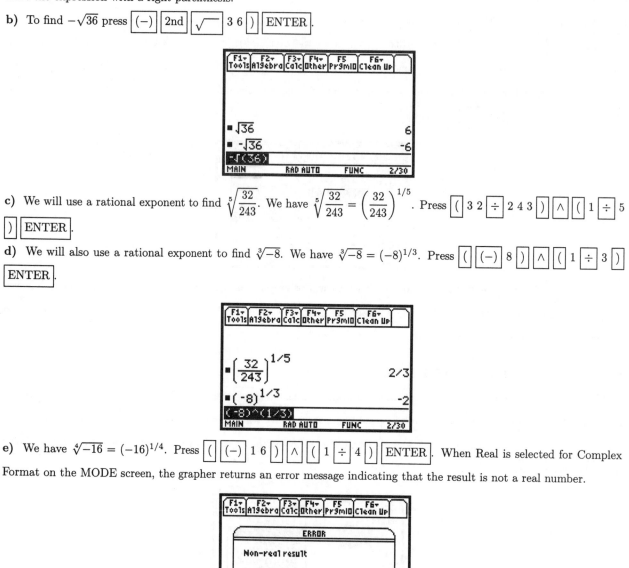

c) We will use a rational exponent to find $\sqrt[5]{\dfrac{32}{243}}$. We have $\sqrt[5]{\dfrac{32}{243}} = \left(\dfrac{32}{243}\right)^{1/5}$. Press $\boxed{(}\ 3\ 2\ \boxed{\div}\ 2\ 4\ 3\ \boxed{)}\ \boxed{\wedge}\ \boxed{(}\ 1\ \boxed{\div}\ 5$ $\boxed{)}$ $\boxed{\text{ENTER}}$.

d) We will also use a rational exponent to find $\sqrt[3]{-8}$. We have $\sqrt[3]{-8} = (-8)^{1/3}$. Press $\boxed{(}\ \boxed{(-)}\ 8\ \boxed{)}\ \boxed{\wedge}\ \boxed{(}\ 1\ \boxed{\div}\ 3\ \boxed{)}$ $\boxed{\text{ENTER}}$.

e) We have $\sqrt[4]{-16} = (-16)^{1/4}$. Press $\boxed{(}\ \boxed{(-)}\ 1\ 6\ \boxed{)}\ \boxed{\wedge}\ \boxed{(}\ 1\ \boxed{\div}\ 4\ \boxed{)}$ $\boxed{\text{ENTER}}$. When Real is selected for Complex Format on the MODE screen, the grapher returns an error message indicating that the result is not a real number.

SOLVING EQUATIONS GRAPHICALLY

We can use the Intersection feature from the Math menu on the GRAPH screen to solve equations.

Section R.7, Example 1 Solve: $2(5 - 3x) = 8 - 3(x + 2)$.

On the equation-editor screen clear any existing entries and then enter $y_1 = 2(5 - 3x)$ and $y_2 = 8 - 3(x + 2)$. The solution of the original equation is the first coordinate of the point of intersection of the graphs of y_1 and y_2. Find the point of intersection as described on page 235 of this manual.

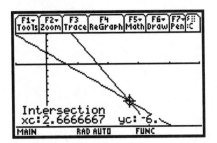

The first coordinate of the point of intersection is 2.6666667. This is a decimal approximation of the solution of the equation.

Chapter 1
Graphs, Functions, and Models

FINDING FUNCTION VALUES

When a formula for a function is given, function values can be found in several ways.

Section 1.1, Example 4 (b) For $f(x) = 2x^2 - x + 3$, find $f(-7)$.

Method 1: Substitute the inputs directly in the formula. On the home screen press 2 $\boxed{(}$ $\boxed{(-)}$ $\boxed{7}$ $\boxed{)}$ $\boxed{\wedge}$ 2 $\boxed{-}$ $\boxed{(}$ $\boxed{(-)}$ $\boxed{7}$ $\boxed{)}$ $\boxed{+}$ 3 $\boxed{\text{ENTER}}$.

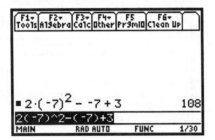

Method 2: Enter $y_1 = 2x^2 - x + 3$ on the "y =" screen. Then press $\boxed{\text{HOME}}$ or $\boxed{\text{2nd}}$ $\boxed{\text{QUIT}}$ to go to the home screen. To find $f(-7)$, the value of y_1 when $x = -7$, press $\boxed{(-)}$ 7 $\boxed{\text{STO} \triangleright}$ $\boxed{\text{X}}$ $\boxed{\text{2nd}}$ $\boxed{:}$ $\boxed{\text{Y}}$ 1 $\boxed{(}$ $\boxed{\text{X}}$ $\boxed{)}$ $\boxed{\text{ENTER}}$. (: is the second operation associated with the 4 numeric key.) This series of keystrokes stores -7 as the value of x and then substitutes it in the function y_1.

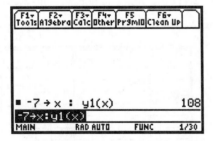

Method 3: Enter $y_1 = 2x^2 - x + 3$ on the "Y =" screen and press $\boxed{\text{HOME}}$ or $\boxed{\text{2nd}}$ $\boxed{\text{QUIT}}$ to go to the home screen. Then press $\boxed{\text{Y}}$ 1 $\boxed{(}$ $\boxed{(-)}$ 7 $\boxed{)}$ $\boxed{\text{ENTER}}$. Note that this entry closely resembles function notation.

Method 4: The TABLE feature can also be used to find function values. Enter $y_1 = 2x^2 - x + 3$ on the "Y =" screen. Then set up a table Ask mode. Press $\boxed{\diamond}$ $\boxed{\text{TblSet}}$ or $\boxed{\diamond}$ $\boxed{\text{TABLE}}$ $\boxed{\text{F2}}$ to access the TableSetup screen. Move the cursor to the "Independent" line. Then press $\boxed{\triangleright}$ $\boxed{2}$ $\boxed{\text{ENTER}}$ to select Ask mode. In Ask mode the grapher disregards the other settings on the Table Setup screen.

Now press $\boxed{\diamond}$ $\boxed{\text{TABLE}}$ to view the table. (TABLE is the second operation associated with the $\boxed{\text{F5}}$ key.) If you select Ask before a table is displayed for the first time on your grapher, a blank table is displayed. If a table has previously been displayed, the table you now see will continue to show the values in the previous table.

Values for x can be entered in the x-column of the table and the corresponding values for y_1 will be displayed in the $y1$-column. To enter -7, press $\boxed{(-)}$ $\boxed{7}$ $\boxed{\text{ENTER}}$. Any additional x-values that are displayed are from a table that was previously displayed on the Auto setting. We see that $y_1 = 108$ when $x = -7$, so $f(-7) = 108$.

Method 5: We can also use the Value feature from the Math menu on the GRAPH screen to find $f(-7)$. To do this, graph $y_1 = 2x^2 - x + 3$ in a window that includes the x-value -7. We will use the standard window. Then press $\boxed{\text{F5}}$ $\boxed{\text{ENTER}}$ to access the Math menu and select item 1, Value. Now supply the desired x-value by pressing $\boxed{(-)}$ 7. Press $\boxed{\text{ENTER}}$ to see $x = -7$, $y = 108$ at the bottom of the screen, Thus, $f(-7) = 108$.

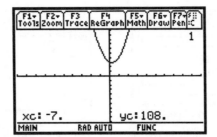

GRAPHS OF FUNCTIONS

The TI-89 does not use function notation. To graph a function, first replace the function notation with y. For example, to graph $f(x) = x^2 - 5$ replace $f(x)$ with y. Then enter the equation $y = x^2 - 5$ on the equation-editor screen and graph it as described on page 234 of this manual.

LINEAR REGRESSION

We can use the Linear Regression feature to fit a linear equation to a set of data.

Section 1.3, Example 1 The following table shows the number of apartment households in the United States, in millions, for years since 1970.

Years, x	Number of Apartment Households (in millions)
1970, 0	8.5
1975, 5	9.9
1980, 10	10.8
1985, 15	12.9
1990, 20	14.2
1997, 27	14.5

(a) Fit a regression line to the data using the linear regression feature on a grapher.

(b) Use the linear model to predict the number of apartment households in 2003.

(a) We will enter the data as ordered pairs in the Data/Matrix editor as described on page 230 of this manual.

Now press F5 to display the Calculate menu. Press ▷ 5 to select LinReg (linear regression). Then press ▽ alpha C 1 ▽ alpha C 2 to indicate that the data in c1 and c2 will be used for x and y, respectively. Press ▽ ▷ ▽ ENTER to indicate that the regression equation should be copied to the equation-editor screen as y_1. Finally press ENTER again to see the STAT VARS screen which displays the coefficients a and b of the regression equation $y = ax + b$.

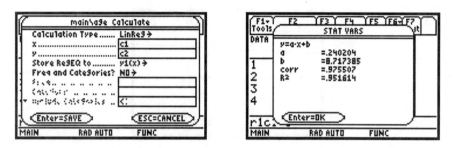

Note that values for "corr" (the correlation coefficient) and r^2 (the coefficient of determination) will also be displayed. These numbers indicate how well the regression line fits the data. While it is possible to suppress these numbers on some graphers, this cannot be done on the TI-89.

(b) To predict the number of apartment households in 2003, evaluate the regression equation for $x = 33$. (2003 is 33 years after 1970.) Use any of the methods for evaluating a function presented earlier in this chapter. (See pages 243 and 244 of this manual.) We will use function notation on the home screen.

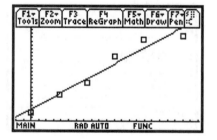

When $x = 33, y \approx 16.6$, so we predict that there will be about 16.6 million apartment households in the United States in 2003.

We can also plot the data points along with the graph of the regression equation. To do this we first define a plot as described on page 231 of this manual. Now select a viewing window. Press $\diamond$ WINDOW to go to the WINDOW screen and then press F2 9 to activate the ZoomData operation which automatically defines a viewing window that displays all of the points and also displays the graph.

Turn off the plot as described on page 242 of this manual before graphing other functions.

THE MAXIMUM AND MINIMUM FEATURES

Section 1.4, Example 2 Use a grapher to determine any relative maxima or minima of the function $f(x) = 0.1x^3 - 0.6x^2 - 0.1x + 2$.

First graph $y_1 = 0.1x^3 - 0.6x^2 - 0.1x + 2$ in a window that displays the relative extrema of the function. Trial and error reveals that one good choice is $[-4, 6, -3, 3]$. Observe that a relative maximum occurs near $x = 0$ and a relative minimum occurs near $x = 4$.

To find the relative maximum, first press $\boxed{\text{F5}}$ 4 or $\boxed{\text{F5}}$ $\boxed{\triangledown}$ $\boxed{\triangledown}$ $\boxed{\triangledown}$ $\boxed{\text{ENTER}}$ to select the Maximum feature from the Math menu on the Graph screen. We are prompted to select a lower bound for the relative maximum. This means that we must choose an x-value that is to the left of the x-value of the point where the relative maximum occurs. This can be done by using the left- and right-arrow keys to move the cursor to a point to the left of the relative maximum or by keying in an appropriate value.

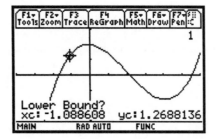

Once this is done, press $\boxed{\text{ENTER}}$. Now we are prompted to select an upper bound. We move the cursor to a point to the right of the relative maximum or we key in an appropriate value.

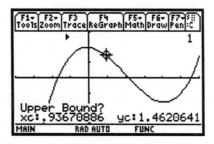

Press $\boxed{\text{ENTER}}$ again. We see that a relative maximum function value of approximately 2.004 occurs when $x \approx -0.082$.

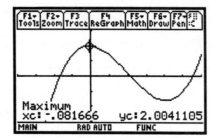

To find the relative minimum, select the Minimum feature from the Math menu by pressing $\boxed{\text{F5}}$ 3 or $\boxed{\text{F5}}$ $\boxed{\triangledown}$ $\boxed{\triangledown}$

ENTER . Select lower and upper bounds for the relative minimum as described above. We see that a relative minimum function value of approximately -1.604 occurs when $x \approx 4.082$.

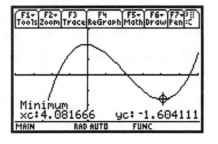

GRAPHING FUNCTIONS DEFINED PIECEWISE

Section 1.4, Example 5 Graph

$$f(x) = \begin{cases} 4, & \text{for } x \leq 0, \\ 4 - x^2, & \text{for } 0 < x \leq 2, \\ 2x - 6, & \text{for } x > 2. \end{cases}$$

We will create a multi-statement, user-defined function to graph this function. It is presented here first in block form.

> Func
>
> > If x<=0 Then
> >
> > Return 4
> >
> ElseIf x>0 and x<2 Then
> >
> > Return 4-x^2
> >
> Else
> >
> > Return 2x-6
> >
> EndIf
> >
> EndFunc

When this function is entered on the equation-editor screen, the entire function must be entered on a single line with a colon used to separate statements. That is, we enter Func:If x<=0 Then:Return 4: . . . :EndIf:EndFunc.

Letters must be capitalized and spaces used exactly as shown above. To type a capital letter press ↑ followed by the letter key. To type a single lower case letter, press alpha and then the letter key. To turn on the lower case alpha-lock press 2nd a-lock . (a-lock is the second operation associated with the alpha key.) Press alpha to turn off the alpha-lock. The : is the second operation associated with the 4 numeric key. Enter a space by pressing alpha and then the (−) key.

After the function has been entered, the equation-editor screen will display "y1 = Func."

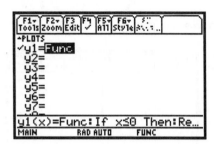

Now select the Dot graph style. If this is not done, a vertical line that is not part of the graph will appear. Dot style can be selected from the Style menu by highlighting Func on the equation-editor screen and pressing $\boxed{\text{2nd}}$ $\boxed{\text{F6}}$ 2 or $\boxed{\text{2nd}}$ $\boxed{\text{F6}}$ $\boxed{\triangledown}$ $\boxed{\text{ENTER}}$. Choose and enter window dimensions and then press $\boxed{\diamond}$ $\boxed{\text{GRAPH}}$ to see the graph of the function. It is shown here in the window $[-5, 5, -3, 6]$.

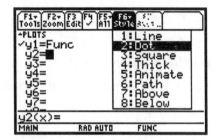

THE GREATEST INTEGER FUNCTION

The greatest integer function is found in the Catalog and is denoted "int." To find int(1.9) first press $\boxed{\text{CATALOG}}$ $\boxed{\text{I}}$ to go to the first item in the Catalog that begins with I. (I is the purple alphabetic operation associated with the 9 numeric key.) Note that it is not necessary to press $\boxed{\text{alpha}}$ before $\boxed{\text{I}}$ when the Catalog is displayed. Now move the triangular selection cursor beside "int(" and press $\boxed{\text{ENTER}}$ to copy "int(" to the entry line of the home screen. Then press 1 $\boxed{.}$ 9 $\boxed{)}$ $\boxed{\text{ENTER}}$. We can also type "int" directly on the entry line of the home screen. Press $\boxed{\text{2nd}}$ $\boxed{\text{a-lock}}$ $\boxed{\text{I}}$ $\boxed{\text{N}}$ $\boxed{\text{T}}$ $\boxed{\text{alpha}}$ to do this. Then finish entering int(1.9) by pressing $\boxed{(}$ 1 $\boxed{.}$ 9 $\boxed{)}$ $\boxed{\text{ENTER}}$.

We can also graph the greatest integer function.

Section 1.4, Example 7 Graph $f(x) = \text{int}(x)$.

Press $\boxed{\diamond}$ $\boxed{\text{Y} =}$ and clear any previously entered functions. Position the cursor beside "$y_1 =$" and select "int(" from the Catalog or type "int" as described above. Finish entering the expression "int(x)". Select the Dot graph style as described on page 239 of this manual. Choose a window and press $\boxed{\diamond}$ $\boxed{\text{GRAPH}}$. The window $[-6, 6, -6, 6]$ is shown here.

THE ALGEBRA OF FUNCTIONS

The grapher can be used to evaluate and graph combinations of functions.

Section 1.4, Example 8 (b) Given that $f(x) = x + 1$ and $g(x) = \sqrt{x + 3}$, find $(f + g)(6)$.

Press $\boxed{\diamond}$ $\boxed{\text{Y} =}$ and enter $y_1 = x + 1$, $y_2 = \sqrt{x + 3}$, and $y_3 = y_1 + y_2$. To enter $y_3 = y_1 + y_2$, position the cursor beside $y_3 =$ and press $\boxed{\text{Y}}$ 1 $\boxed{(}$ $\boxed{\text{X}}$ $\boxed{)}$ $\boxed{+}$ $\boxed{\text{Y}}$ 2 $\boxed{(}$ $\boxed{\text{X}}$ $\boxed{)}$. Note that $y_3 = f(x) + g(x)$, or $(f + g)(x)$. Use y_3 to find $(f + g)(6)$ employing one of the methods for finding function values described on pages 243 and 244 of this manual. We find that $(f + g)(6) = 10$.

To view the graphs of $f(x)$, $g(x)$, and $(f + g)(x)$ enter y_1, y_2, and y_3 as above, select a window, and press $\boxed{\diamond}$ $\boxed{\text{GRAPH}}$. These graphs appear on page 115 of the text. It is possible to deselect one or two of these functions and display the graph(s) of the remaining function(s). For example, to display only the graph of y_3 without deleting the equations of y_1 and y_2, press $\boxed{\diamond}$ $\boxed{\text{Y} =}$. Then highlight the expression beside y_1 and press $\boxed{\text{F4}}$. This deselects or turns off y_1. Do the same for y_2. Note that there are no longer check marks to the left of y_1 and y_2. This indicates that y_1 and y_2 have been deselected and, thus, their graphs will not appear with the graph of y_3 which continues to be selected. Now press $\boxed{\diamond}$ $\boxed{\text{GRAPH}}$ and see only the graph of y_3.

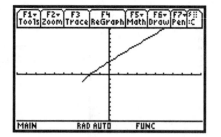

To select or turn on a function again, repeat this process. Note that a check mark appears to the left of a selected function on the equation-editor screen.

SQUARING THE VIEWING WINDOW

In the standard window, the distance between tick marks on the y-axis is about 1/2 the distance between tick marks on the x-axis. It is often desirable to choose window dimensions for which these distances are the same, creating a "square" window. Any window in which the ratio of the length of the y-axis to the length of the x-axis is $1/2$ will produce this effect.

This can be accomplished by selecting dimensions for which ymax $-$ ymin $= \dfrac{1}{2}$(xmax $-$ xmin). For example, the windows $[-12, 12, -6, 6]$ and $[-6, 6, -3, 3]$ are square. To illustrate this, we graph the circle $x^2 + y^2 = 9$ in the standard window. Note that the graph does not appear to be a circle. (We will explain how to graph a circle later in this chapter.)

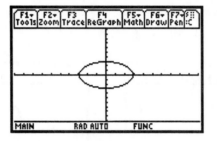

Now change the window dimensions to $[-8, 8, -4, 4]$, xscl $= 1$, yscl $= 1$, and press $\boxed{\diamond}$ $\boxed{\text{GRAPH}}$. Observe that the distance between tick marks appears to be the same on both axes and that the graph appears to be a circle.

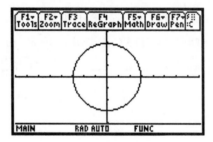

The window can also be squared using the grapher's ZoomSqr feature. From the equation-editor, Window, or Graph screen, press $\boxed{\text{F2}}$ 5 to select the ZoomSqr window. The resulting window dimensions and graph are shown below. Here the window was squared from the standard window. Note that the graph also appears to be a circle in this window.

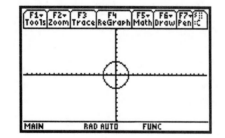

GRAPHING CIRCLES

If the center and radius of a circle are known, the circle can be graphed using the Circle feature from the Catalog.

Section 1.7, Exercise 37 Graph $(x - 1)^2 + (y - 5)^2 = 36$.

The center of this circle is (1,5) and its radius is 6. To graph it first press $\boxed{\diamond}$ $\boxed{\text{Y}=}$ and clear or deselect all previously entered equations on the equation-editor screen. Then select a square window. The dimensions $[-16, 16, -4, 12]$, Xscl $= 2$, yscl $= 2$, are a good choice for this circle. Now, to select Circle from the Catalog, first press $\boxed{\text{HOME}}$ or $\boxed{\text{2nd}}$ $\boxed{\text{QUIT}}$

to go to the home screen. Then press $\boxed{\text{CATALOG}}$ $\boxed{\text{C}}$ to go to the beginning of the items in the Catalog that start with C. (Note that it is not necessary to press $\boxed{\text{alpha}}$ before a letter key when the Catalog is displayed.) Now use $\boxed{\triangledown}$ to go to "Circle" and press $\boxed{\text{ENTER}}$. The Circle command appears on the entry line of the home screen. "Circle" can also be typed directly on the entry line of the home screen by pressing $\boxed{\text{2nd}}$ $\boxed{\text{a-lock}}$ $\boxed{\text{C}}$ $\boxed{\text{I}}$ $\boxed{\text{R}}$ $\boxed{\text{C}}$ $\boxed{\text{L}}$ $\boxed{\text{E}}$ $\boxed{\text{alpha}}$. Enter the x-coordinate of the center, the y-coordinate of the center, and the length of the radius, all separated by commas. To do this press 1 $\boxed{,}$ 5 $\boxed{,}$ 6. Press $\boxed{\text{ENTER}}$ to see the graph.

This graph can be cleared from the Graph screen by pressing $\boxed{\text{F4}}$ (ReGraph) or by pressing $\boxed{\text{2nd}}$ $\boxed{\text{F6}}$ to display the Draw menu and then pressing 1 to select ClrDraw. The ClrDraw command can also be accessed from the Catalog. From the home screen, press $\boxed{\text{CATALOG}}$ $\boxed{\text{C}}$, scroll to ClrDraw, and press $\boxed{\text{ENTER}}$ $\boxed{\text{ENTER}}$.

Chapter 2
Functions and Equations: Zeros and Solutions

THE ZERO FEATURE

When an equation is expressed in the form $f(x) = 0$, it can be solved using the Zero feature from the Math menu on the Graph screen.

Section 2.1, Example 1 Find the zero of $f(x) = 5x - 9$.

On the equation-editor screen, clear any existing entries and then enter $y_1 = 5x - 9$. Now graph the function in a viewing window that shows the x-intercept clearly. The standard window is a good choice.

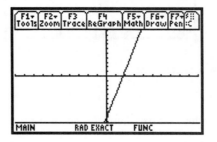

Press F5 2 to select the Zero feature from the Math menu. We are prompted to select a lower bound. This means that we must choose an x-value that is to the left of the x-intercept. This can be done by using the left- and right-arrow keys to move to a point on the curve to the left of the x-intercept or by keying in a value less than the x-coordinate of the intercept.

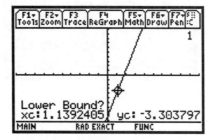

Once this is done press ENTER . Now we are prompted to select an upper bound that is to the right of the x-intercept. Again, this can be done by using the arrow keys to move to a point on the curve to the right of the x-intercept or by keying in a value greater than the x-coordinate of the intercept.

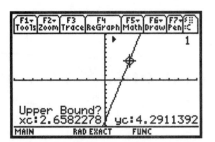

Press $\boxed{\text{ENTER}}$ again. We see that $y = 0$ when $x = 1.8$, so 1.8 is the zero of the function f.

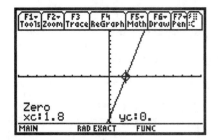

OPERATIONS WITH COMPLEX NUMBERS

Operations with complex numbers can be performed on the TI-89. First set the grapher in the rectangular mode by pressing $\boxed{\text{MODE}}$, highlighting the entry for Complex Format, and then pressing $\boxed{\triangleright}$ 2 $\boxed{\text{ENTER}}$ or $\boxed{\triangleright}$ $\boxed{\triangledown}$ $\boxed{\text{ENTER}}$ $\boxed{\text{ENTER}}$.

Section 2.1, Example 4

(a) Add: $(8 + 6i) + (3 + 2i)$.

To find this sum go to the home screen and press 8 $\boxed{+}$ 6 $\boxed{\text{2nd}}$ $\boxed{i}$ $\boxed{+}$ 3 $\boxed{+}$ 2 $\boxed{\text{2nd}}$ $\boxed{i}$ $\boxed{\text{ENTER}}$. (The number i is the second operation associated with the $\boxed{\text{CATALOG}}$ key.) Note that it is not necessary to include parentheses when we are adding.

(b) Subtract: $(4 + 5i) - (6 - 3i)$.

Press 4 $\boxed{+}$ 5 $\boxed{\text{2nd}}$ $\boxed{i}$ $\boxed{-}$ $\boxed{(}$ 6 $\boxed{-}$ 3 $\boxed{\text{2nd}}$ $\boxed{i}$ $\boxed{)}$ $\boxed{\text{ENTER}}$. Note that the parentheses must be included as shown so that the entire number $6 - 3i$ is subtracted.

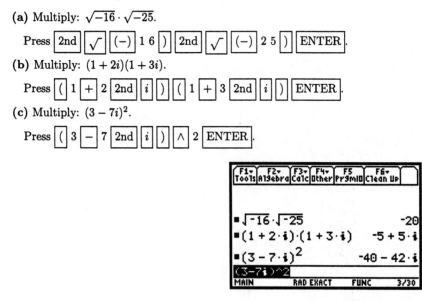

Section 2.1, Example 5

(a) Multiply: $\sqrt{-16} \cdot \sqrt{-25}$.

Press [2nd] [√] [(−)] 1 6 [)] [2nd] [√] [(−)] 2 5 [)] [ENTER].

(b) Multiply: $(1 + 2i)(1 + 3i)$.

Press [(] 1 [+] 2 [2nd] [i] [)] [(] 1 [+] 3 [2nd] [i] [)] [ENTER].

(c) Multiply: $(3 - 7i)^2$.

Press [(] 3 [−] 7 [2nd] [i] [)] [∧] 2 [ENTER].

QUADRATIC REGRESSION

Quadratic functions can be fit to data using the quadratic regression operation. The operations of entering data, making scatterplots, and graphing and evaluating quadratic regression functions are the same as for linear regression functions.

Section 2.5, Example 1 *Leisure Time* The following table shows the median number of hours of leisure time that Americans had each week in various years.

Year	Median Number of Leisure Hours per Week
0, 1973	26.2
7, 1980	19.2
14, 1987	16.6
20, 1993	18.8
24, 1997	19.5

(a) Make a scatterplot of the data, letting x represent the number of years since 1973, and determine whether a linear function, a quadratic function, or neither seems to fit the data.

(b) Use a grapher to fit the type of function determined in part (a) to the data.

(c) Graph the equation with the scatterplot.

(d) Use the function found in part (c) to estimate the number of leisure hours per week in 1978; in 1990; in 2005.

(a) Clear any existing entries on the equation-editor screen. Then enter the data in the Data/Matrix editor and make a scatterplot as described on pages 231 and 232 of this manual. We have used a ZoomData window here. It appears that a quadratic function fits the data.

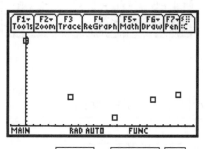

(b) To fit a quadratic function to the data, press $\boxed{\text{APPS}}$ 6 $\boxed{\text{ENTER}}$ $\boxed{\text{F5}}$ to view the Calculate menu. Then select QuadReg by pressing $\boxed{\triangleright}$ 9. Then press $\boxed{\triangledown}$ $\boxed{\text{alpha}}$ $\boxed{\text{C}}$ 1 $\boxed{\triangledown}$ $\boxed{\text{alpha}}$ $\boxed{\text{C}}$ 2 to indicate that the data in c1 and c2 will be used for x and y, respectively. Press $\boxed{\triangledown}$ $\boxed{\triangleright}$ $\boxed{\triangledown}$ $\boxed{\text{ENTER}}$ to indicate that the regression equation should be copied to the equation-editor screen as y_1. Finally press $\boxed{\text{ENTER}}$ again to see the STAT VARS screen which displays the coefficients $a, b,$ and c of the regression equation $y = ax^2 + bx + c$. Note that at least three data points are required for quadratic regression.

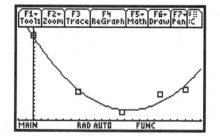

(c) The regression equation was copied to the "Y =" screen, so it can be graphed with the scatterplot. Press $\boxed{\diamond}$ $\boxed{\text{GRAPH}}$ to do this.

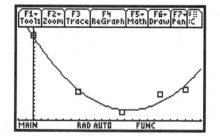

Be sure to turn off the STAT PLOT as described on page 248 of this manual before graphing future equations.

(d) To estimate the number of leisure hours per week in 1978, 1990, and 2005, we evaluate the regression function for 5, 17, and 32, respectively. We can use any of the methods for evaluating a function found on pages 243 and 244 of this manual. Here we show a table set in Ask mode.

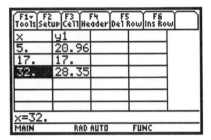

CHECKING SOLUTIONS OF INEQUALITIES

We can perform a partial check of the solution of an inequality with a user-defined function.

Section 2.7, Example 2 Solve: $-3 < 2x + 5 \le 7$.

The solution set is found algebraically in the text. It is $\{x| -4 < x \le 1\}$, or $(-4, 1]$. We can perform a partial check of this solution by creating a multi-statment, user-defined function as we did when we graphed a piecewise-defined function. (See page 248 of this manual.) Enter Func:If $-3 < (2x + 5)$ and $(2x + 5 <= 7$Then:Return 1:Else:Return 0:EndIf:EndFunc.

Now select a window and press $\boxed{\diamond}$ $\boxed{\text{GRAPH}}$. We use the window $[-10, 10, -1, 2]$.

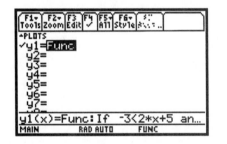

We see that $y = 1$ for x-values from -4 to 1, confirming that all x-values from -4 to 1 are in the solution set. The algebraic solution indicates that the endpoint 1 is also in the solution set.

Chapter 3
Polynomial and Rational Functions

POWER MODELS

A power model $y = ax^b$ can be fit to data using the power regression feature.

Section 3.1, Example 4 (a) *Cholesterol Level and the Risk of Heart Attack.* The data in the following table show the relationship of cholesterol level in men to the risk of a heart attack. Use a grapher to fit a power function to the data.

Cholesterol Level, x	Men Per 10,000 Who Suffer a Heart Attack
100	30
200	65
250	100
275	130
300	180

Enter the data in the Data/Matrix editor as described on page 230 of this manual. Then select power regression from the Calculate menu by pressing $\boxed{\text{F5}}$ $\boxed{\triangleright}$ 8. Indicate that the data in c1 and c2 will be used for x and y, respectively, and that the equation should be copied to the equation-editor screen as y_1 as described on page 245 of this manual. The grapher displays the coefficient a and the exponent b for the power function $y = ax^b$.

The function has been copied to the Y = screen, so it can be graphed. It can also be evaluated using one of the methods on pages 243 and 244.

CUBIC AND QUARTIC REGRESSION

We can fit third-degree, or cubic, functions and fourth-degree, or quartic, functions to data on a grapher.

Section 3.1, Example 5 (a) The table below shows the number of farms, in millions, for years after 1900. Model the data with both cubic and quartic functions. Let the first coordinate of each data point be the number of years after 1900.

Years after 1900	Number of Farms, in millions
10, 1910	6.4
20, 1920	6.5
30, 1930	6.3
40, 1940	6.1
50, 1950	5.4
59, 1959	3.7
69, 1969	2.7
78, 1978	2.3
87, 1987	2.1
97, 1997	1.9

Enter the data in the Data/Matrix editor as described on page 230 of this manual. To select cubic regression from the Calculate menu press $\boxed{\text{F5}}$ $\boxed{\triangleright}$ $\boxed{3}$ $\boxed{\text{ENTER}}$. Indicate that the data in c1 and c2 will be used for x and y, respectively, and that the equation should be copied to the equation-editor screen as y_1 as described on page 245 of this manual. The grapher displays the coefficients of a cubic function $y = ax^3 + bx^2 + cx + d$.

To model the data with a quartic function select quartic regression from the Calculate menu after the data are entered. Press $\boxed{\text{F5}}$ $\boxed{\triangleright}$ $\boxed{\text{alpha}}$ $\boxed{\text{A}}$ $\boxed{\text{ENTER}}$. Indicate that the data in c1 and c2 will be used for x and y, respectively, and that the equation should be copied to the equation-editor screen as y_1 as described on page 245 of this manual. The grapher displays the coefficients of a quartic function $y = ax^4 + bx^3 + cx^2 + dx + e$.

A scatterplot of the data can be graphed as described on pages 231 and 232 of this manual. The function has been copied to the Y = screen, so it can be graphed along with the scatterplot. It can also be evaluated using one of the methods on pages 243 and 244.

Chapter 4
Exponential and Logarithmic Functions

THE COMPOSITION OF FUNCTIONS

We can evaluate composite functions on a grapher.

Section 4.1, Example 1 (a) Given that $f(x) = 2x - 5$ and $g(x) = x^2 - 3x + 8$, find $(f \circ g)(7)$ and $(g \circ f)(7)$.

On the equation-editor screen enter $y_1 = 2x - 5$ and $y_2 = x^2 - 3x + 8$. Then $(f \circ g)(7) = (y_1 \circ y_2)(7)$, or $y_1(y_2(7))$ and $(g \circ f)(7) = (y_2 \circ y_1)(7)$, or $y_2(y_1(7))$. To find these function values press $\boxed{\text{HOME}}$ or $\boxed{\text{2nd}}$ $\boxed{\text{QUIT}}$ to go to the home screen. Then enter $y_1(y_2(7))$ by pressing $\boxed{\text{Y}}$ 1 $\boxed{(}$ $\boxed{\text{Y}}$ 2 $\boxed{(}$ 7 $\boxed{)}$ $\boxed{)}$ $\boxed{\text{ENTER}}$. Now enter $y_2(y_1(7))$ by pressing $\boxed{\text{Y}}$ 2 $\boxed{(}$ $\boxed{\text{Y}}$ 1 $\boxed{(}$ 7 $\boxed{)}$ $\boxed{)}$ $\boxed{\text{ENTER}}$.

```
┌─────────────────────────────────────┐
│ F1▾  F2▾  F3▾ F4▾  F5    F6▾         │
│Tools Algebra Calc Other PrgmIO Clean Up│
│                                     │
│                                     │
│                                     │
│ ■ y1(y2(7))                      67 │
│ ■ y2(y1(7))                      62 │
│ y2(y1(7))                           │
│ MAIN      RAD AUTO   FUNC    2/30   │
└─────────────────────────────────────┘
```

GRAPHING AN INVERSE FUNCTION

The DrawInv operation can be used to graph a function and its inverse on the same screen. A formula for the inverse function need not be found in order to do this. The grapher must be set in Func mode when this operation is used.

Section 4.1, Example 7 Graph $f(x) = 2x - 3$ and $f^{-1}(x)$ using the same set of axes.

Enter $y_1 = 2x - 3$, either clear or deselect all other functions on the Y = screen, and choose a viewing window. Press $\boxed{\text{HOME}}$ to go to the home screen. Then press $\boxed{\text{CATALOG}}$ $\boxed{\text{D}}$ to go to the first item in the Catalog that begins with D. Use the $\boxed{\triangledown}$ key to scroll down to DrawInv and then press $\boxed{\text{ENTER}}$ to copy DrawInv to the entry line of the home screen. Follow these keystrokes with $\boxed{\text{Y}}$ 1 $\boxed{(}$ $\boxed{\text{X}}$ $\boxed{)}$ to select function y_1. Press $\boxed{\text{ENTER}}$ to see the graph of the function and its inverse. The graphs are shown here in the standard window.

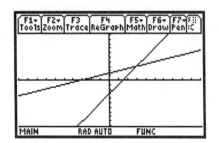

EVALUATING e^x, Log x, and Ln x

Use the grapher's scientific keys to evaluate e^x, $\log x$, and $\ln x$ for specific values of x.

Section 4.2, Example 6 (a), (b) Find the value of e^3 and $e^{-0.23}$. Round to four decimal places.

First select Approximate mode by pressing [MODE] [F2] [▽] [▽] [▷] 3 [ENTER]. Then to find e^3 press [◇] [e^x] 3 [)] [ENTER]. (e^x is the green ◇ operation associated with the [X] key.) The grapher returns 20.0855369232. Thus, $e^3 \approx$ 20.0855. To find $e^{-0.23}$ press [◇] [e^x] [(−)] [·] 2 3 [)] [ENTER]. The grapher returns .794533602503, so $e^{-0.23} \approx 0.7945$.

Section 4.3, Example 4 Find the values of log 645,778, log 0.0000239, and log (−3). Round to four decimal places.

The grapher must be in Approximate mode as described in Example 6 above. To find log 645,778 press [2nd] [a-lock] [L] [O] [G] [alpha] [(] 6 4 5 7 7 8 [)] [ENTER] and read 5.81008324563. Thus, log $645,778 \approx 5.8101$. The operation "log(" can also be selected from the Catalog. To find log 0.0000239 press [2nd] [a-lock] [L] [O] [G] [alpha] [(] [·] 0 0 0 0 2 3 9 [)] [ENTER]. The grapher returns −4.62160209905, so log $0.0000239 \approx -4.6216$. The previous entry, log 645,778, can also be edited to find log 0.0000239. When the TI-89 has Real selected for the Complex Format mode the keystrokes [2nd] [a-lock] [L] [O] [G] [alpha] [(] [(−)] 3 [)] [ENTER] produce the error message "Non-real result" indicating that the result of this calculation is not a real number. We could also have entered log(−3) by editing the previous entry.

Section 4.3, Example 5 (a), (b), (c) Find the values of ln 645,778, ln 0.0000239, and ln (−5). Round to four decimal places.

The grapher must be in Approximate mode as described in Example 6 above. To find ln 645,778 and ln 0.0000239 repeat the keystrokes used above to find log 645,778 and log 0.0000239 but press [2nd] [LN] rather than [2nd] [a-lock] [L] [O] [G] [alpha] [(]. (LN is the second operation associated with the [X] key.) We find that ln $645,778 \approx 13.3782$ and ln $0.0000239 \approx -10.6416$. When the TI-89 has Real selected for the Complex Format mode the keystrokes [2nd] [LN] [(−)] 5 [)] [ENTER] produce the error message "Non-real result" indicating that the result of this calculation is not a real number.

USING THE CHANGE OF BASE FORMULA

To find a logarithm with a base other than 10 or e we use the change-of-base formula, $\log_b M = \dfrac{\log_a M}{\log_a b}$, where a and b are any logarithmic bases and M is any positive number.

Section 4.3, Example 6 Find $\log_5 8$ using common logarithms.

The grapher must be in Approximate mode as described in Example 6 above. We let $a = 10$, $b = 5$, and $M = 8$ and substitute in the change-of-base formula. Press [2nd] [a-lock] [L] [O] [G] [alpha] [(] 8 [)] [÷] [2nd] [a-lock] [L] [O] [G] [alpha] [(] 5 [)] [ENTER]. The result is about 1.2920. We could have let $a = e$ and used natural logarithms to find $\log_5 8$ as well.

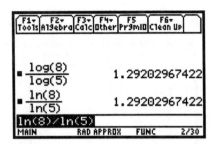

Section 4.3, Example 9 Graph $y = \log_5 x$.

To use a grapher we must first change the base to e or 10. Here we use e. Let $a = e$, $b = 5$, and $M = x$ and substitute in the change-of-base formula. Enter $y_1 = \dfrac{\ln x}{\ln 5}$ on the Y = screen, select a window, and press $\boxed{\diamond}$ $\boxed{\text{GRAPH}}$.

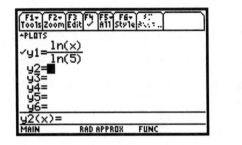 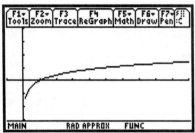

EXPONENTIAL AND LOGARITHMIC REGRESSION

In addition to the types of polynomial regression discussed earlier, exponential and logarithmic functions can be fit to data. The operations of entering data, making scatterplots, and graphing and evaluating these functions are the same as for linear regression functions. So are the procedures for copying a regression equation to the Y = screen, graphing it, and using it to find function values.

Section 4.6, Example 6 (a) *Credit Card Volume.* The total credit card volume for Visa, MasterCard, American Express, and Discover has increased dramatically in recent years. Use a grapher to fit an exponential function to the data.

Year, x	Credit Card Volume (in billions)
1988, 0	$261.0
1989, 1	296.3
1990, 2	338.4
1991, 3	361.0
1992, 4	403.1
1993, 5	476.7
1994, 6	584.8
1995, 7	701.2
1996, 8	798.3
1997, 9	885.2

Enter the data in the Data/Matrix editor as described on page 230 of this manual. Then select exponential regression from the Calculate menu by pressing $\boxed{\text{F5}}$ $\boxed{\triangleright}$ $\boxed{4}$ $\boxed{\text{ENTER}}$. Indicate that the data in c1 and c2 will be used for x and y, respectively, and that the equation should be copied to the equation-editor screen as y_1 as described on page 245 of this manual. The grapher displays the coefficient a and the base b for the exponential function $y = a \cdot b^x$.

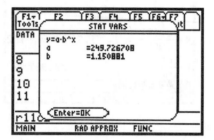

A scatterplot of the data can be graphed as described on pages 231 and 232 of this manual. The function has been copied to the Y = screen, so it can be graphed along with the scatterplot. It can also be evaluated using one of the methods on pages 243 and 244.

Section 4.6, Exercise 26 (a) *Forgetting.* In an art class, students were tested at the end of the course on a final exam. Then they were retested with an equivalent test at subsequent time intervals. Their scores after time t, in months, are given in the following table. Use a grapher to fit a logarithmic function $y = a + b \ln(x)$ to the data.

Time, t (in months)	Score, y
1	84.9%
2	84.6%
3	84.4%
4	84.2%
5	84.1%
6	83.9%

After entering the data in the Data/Matrix editor as described on page 230 of this manual, press F5 ▷ 6 ENTER to go to the Calculate menu and select LnReg. Indicate that the data in c1 and c2 will be used for x and y, respectively, and that the equation should be copied to the equation-editor screen as y_1 as described on page 245 of this manual. The values of a and b for the logarithmic function $y = a + b \ln(x)$ are displayed.

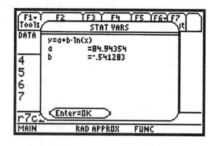

LOGISTIC REGRESSION

A logistic function can be fit to data using the TI-89.

Section 4.6, Exercise 28 (a) *Effect of Advertising.* A company introduces a new software product on a trial run in a city. They advertised the product on television and found the following data relating the percent P of people who bought the product after x ads were run. Use a grapher to fit a logistic function to the data.

Number of Ads, x	Percent Who Bought, P
0	0.2
10	0.7
20	2.7
30	9.2
40	27
50	57.6
60	83.3
70	94.8
80	98.5
90	99.6

After entering the data in the Data/Matrix editor as described on page 230 of this manual, press ⌈F5⌉ ⌈▷⌉ ⌈alpha⌉ ⌈C⌉ to go to the Calculate menu and select Logistic. Indicate that the data in c1 and c2 will be used for x and y, respectively, and that the equation should be copied to the equation-editor screen as y_1 as described on page 245 of this manual. The values of a, b, and c for the logistic function $y = a/(1 + be^{cx}) + d$ are displayed.

Chapter 5
The Trigonometric Functions

FINDING TRIGONOMETRIC FUNCTION VALUES OF REAL NUMBERS

The grapher's SIN, COS, and TAN operations can be used to find trigonometric function values of any real number. The grapher must be set in Radian mode when this is done. We must also select Approximate for the Exact/Approx mode setting.

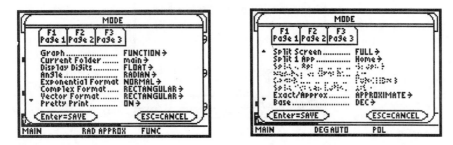

Section 5.2, Example 5 Find each of the following function values using a grapher. Round the answers to four decimal places.

a) $\cos \dfrac{2\pi}{5}$ b) $\tan(-3)$ c) $\sin 24.9$ d) $\sin \dfrac{\pi}{7}$

a) With the grapher set in Radian and Approx modes, press $\boxed{\text{2nd}}$ $\boxed{\text{COS}}$ 2 $\boxed{\text{2nd}}$ $\boxed{\pi}$ $\boxed{\div}$ 5 $\boxed{)}$ $\boxed{\text{ENTER}}$. (COS is the second operation associated with the $\boxed{\text{Z}}$ key. π is the second operation associated with the $\boxed{\wedge}$ key.) We find that $\cos \dfrac{2\pi}{5} \approx 0.3090$.

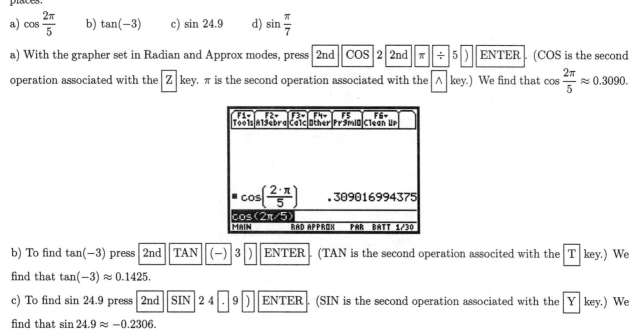

b) To find $\tan(-3)$ press $\boxed{\text{2nd}}$ $\boxed{\text{TAN}}$ $\boxed{(-)}$ 3 $\boxed{)}$ $\boxed{\text{ENTER}}$. (TAN is the second operation associted with the $\boxed{\text{T}}$ key.) We find that $\tan(-3) \approx 0.1425$.

c) To find $\sin 24.9$ press $\boxed{\text{2nd}}$ $\boxed{\text{SIN}}$ $2\,4$ $\boxed{.}$ 9 $\boxed{)}$ $\boxed{\text{ENTER}}$. (SIN is the second operation associated with the $\boxed{\text{Y}}$ key.) We find that $\sin 24.9 \approx -0.2306$.

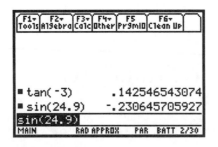

d) The secant, cosecant, and cotangent functions can be found by taking the reciprocals of the cosine, sine, and tangent functions, respectively. To find $\sec \frac{\pi}{7}$ press 1 $\boxed{\div}$ $\boxed{\text{2nd}}$ $\boxed{\text{COS}}$ $\boxed{\text{2nd}}$ $\boxed{\pi}$ $\boxed{\div}$ 7 $\boxed{)}$ $\boxed{\text{ENTER}}$. The result is $\sec \frac{\pi}{7} \approx 1.1099$.

```
  ┌F1┬─┐┌F2┬┐┌F3┬┐┌F4┬┐┌F5──┐┌F6┬──┐
  │Tools│Algebra│Calc│Other│PrgmIO│Clean Up│
  ├─────────────────────────────────┤
  │                                 │
  │                                 │
  │                                 │
  │    ┌──1──                        │
  │ ■  ────────        1.10991626417 │
  │    cos(π/7)                      │
  ├─────────────────────────────────┤
  │1/cos(π/7)                       │
  │MAIN        RAD APPROX    PAR BATT 1/30│
  └─────────────────────────────────┘
```

CONVERTING BETWEEN D°M′S″ AND DECIMAL DEGREE MEASURE

We can convert decimal notation to D°M′S″ notation and vice versa on the TI-89.

Section 5.3, Example 2 Convert $5°42'30''$ to decimal degree notation.

Select Degree for the Angle mode setting and Approximate for the Exact/Approx setting, Then press 5 $\boxed{\text{2nd}}$ $\boxed{°}$ 4 2 $\boxed{\text{2nd}}$ $\boxed{'}$ 3 0 $\boxed{\text{2nd}}$ $\boxed{''}$ $\boxed{\text{ENTER}}$. (°, ′, and ″ are the second operations associated with the $\boxed{\;|\;}$, $\boxed{=}$, and 1 keys, respectively.) The grapher returns 5.70833333333, so $5°42'30'' \approx 5.71°$.

```
  ┌F1┬─┐┌F2┬┐┌F3┬┐┌F4┬┐┌F5──┐┌F6┬──┐
  │Tools│Algebra│Calc│Other│PrgmIO│Clean Up│
  ├─────────────────────────────────┤
  │                                 │
  │                                 │
  │                                 │
  │                                 │
  │ ■ 5°42'30"      5.70833333333   │
  ├─────────────────────────────────┤
  │5°42'30"                         │
  │MAIN        DEG APPROX    POL  1/30│
  └─────────────────────────────────┘
```

Section 5.3, Example 3 Convert $72.18°$ to D°M′S″ notation.

Select Degree for the Angle mode setting. Then press 7 2 $\boxed{\cdot}$ 1 8 $\boxed{\text{2nd}}$ $\boxed{\text{MATH}}$ $\boxed{\triangledown}$ $\boxed{\triangleright}$ to enter the angle and display the MATH Angle menu. (MATH is the second operation associated with the 5 numeric key.) Press 8 to select ▷DMS and then press $\boxed{\text{ENTER}}$ to see D°M′S″ notation for the angle. The grapher returns $72°10'48''$.

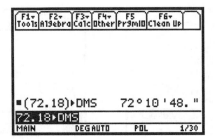

CONVERTING BETWEEN DEGREE AND RADIAN MEASURE

We can use the grapher to convert from degree to radian measure and vice versa. Radian should be selected for the Angle mode when converting from degree to radian measure and Degree should be selected when converting from radian to degree measure.

Section 5.3, Example 5 Convert each of the following to radians.

a) 120°   b) −297.25°

a) Select Radian for the Angle mode. Press 1 2 0 $\boxed{\text{2nd}}$ $\boxed{°}$ $\boxed{\text{ENTER}}$ to enter 120°. When the grapher is set in Auto or Exact mode, it returns $2\pi/3$ radians.

b) With Radian selected for the Angle mode press $\boxed{(-)}$ 2 9 7 $\boxed{\cdot}$ 2 5 $\boxed{\text{2nd}}$ $\boxed{°}$ $\boxed{\text{ENTER}}$. We see that $-297.25° \approx -5.19$ radians.

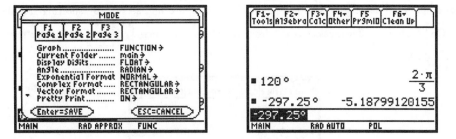

Section 5.3, Example 6 Convert each of the following to degrees.

a) $\dfrac{3\pi}{4}$ radians   b) 8.5 radians

a) Select Degree for the Angle mode and Approximate for the Exact/Approx mode. Then press $\boxed{(}$ 3 $\boxed{\text{2nd}}$ $\boxed{\pi}$ $\boxed{\div}$ 4 $\boxed{)}$ $\boxed{\text{2nd}}$ $\boxed{\text{MATH}}$ $\boxed{\triangledown}$ $\boxed{\triangleright}$ 2 $\boxed{\text{ENTER}}$ to enter $\dfrac{3\pi}{4}$ radians. (π is the second operation associated with the $\boxed{\wedge}$ key). The grapher returns 135, so $3\pi/4$ radians $= 135°$. Note that the parentheses are necessary in order to enter the entire expression in radian measure. Without the parentheses, the grapher reads only the denominator, 4, in radian measure and an incorrect result occurs.

b) With the grapher set in Degree mode press 8 $\boxed{\cdot}$ 5 $\boxed{\text{2nd}}$ $\boxed{\text{MATH}}$ $\boxed{\triangledown}$ $\boxed{\triangleright}$ 2 $\boxed{\text{ENTER}}$. The grapher returns 487.0141259, so 8.5 radians $\approx 487.01°$.

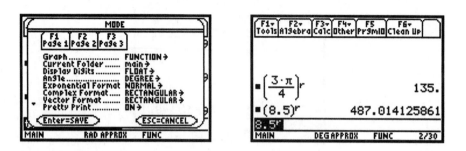

FINDING TRIGONOMETRIC FUNCTION VALUES OF ANGLES

The grapher's SIN, COS, and TAN operations can be used to find the values of trigonometric functions of angles measured in degrees. Degree must be selected for the Angle mode when this is done. We must also select Approximate for the Exact/Approx mode setting.

Section 5.5, Example 5 Find the trigonometric function value, rounded to four decimal places, of each of the following.

a) tan 29.7°   b) sec 48°   c) sin 84°10′39″

a) Press $\boxed{2nd}$ $\boxed{TAN}$ 2 9 $\boxed{\cdot}$ 7 $\boxed{)}$ $\boxed{ENTER}$. (TAN is the second operation associated with the $\boxed{T}$ key.) We find that tan 29.7° ≈ 0.5704.

b) The secant, cosecant, and cotangent functions can be found by taking the reciprocals of the cosine, sine, and tangent functions, respectively. To find sec 48° we enter the reciprocal of cos 48° by pressing 1 $\boxed{\div}$ $\boxed{2nd}$ $\boxed{COS}$ 4 8 $\boxed{)}$ $\boxed{ENTER}$. (COS is the second operation associated with the $\boxed{Z}$ key.) We can also find sec 48° by entering $(\cos(48))^{-1}$. To do this press $\boxed{(}$ $\boxed{2nd}$ $\boxed{COS}$ 4 8 $\boxed{)}$ $\boxed{)}$. Then select $\wedge - 1$ from the Catalog or press $\boxed{\wedge}$ $\boxed{(-)}$ 1. Finally press $\boxed{ENTER}$. The result is sec 48° ≈ 1.4945.

c) Press $\boxed{2nd}$ $\boxed{SIN}$ 8 4 $\boxed{2nd}$ $\boxed{°}$ 1 0 $\boxed{2nd}$ $\boxed{′}$ 3 9 $\boxed{2nd}$ $\boxed{″}$ $\boxed{)}$ $\boxed{ENTER}$. We find that sin 84°10′39″ ≈ 0.9948.

FINDING ANGLES

The inverse trigonometric function keys provide a quick way to find an angle given a trigonometric function value for that angle.

Section 5.5, Example 6 Find the acute angle, to the nearest tenth of a degree, whose sine value is approximately 0.20113.

Although the TABLE feature can be used to approximate this angle, it is faster to use the inverse sine key. With the grapher set in Degree and Approximate modes, press $\boxed{\diamond}$ $\boxed{\text{SIN}^{-1}}$ $\boxed{\cdot}$ 2 0 1 1 3 $\boxed{)}$ $\boxed{\text{ENTER}}$. (SIN^{-1} is the green $\diamond$ operation associated with the $\boxed{\text{Y}}$ key.) We find that the desired acute angle is approximately 11.6°.

```
┌F1┬──┬F2┬──┬F3┬─┬F4┬──┬─F5──┬─F6┬───┐
│Tools│Algebra│Calc│Other│PrgmIO│Clean Up│
├──────────────────────────────────┤
│                                    │
│                                    │
│                                    │
│ ■ sin⁻¹(.20113)                    │
│                     11.6030461313  │
│ sin⁻¹(.20113)                      │
│ MAIN      DEG APPROX    POL    1/30 │
└──────────────────────────────────┘
```

Section 5.5, Exercise 39 Find the acute angle, to the nearest tenth of a degree, whose cotangent value is 2.127.

Angles whose secant, cosecant, or cotangent values are known can be found using the reciprocals of the cosine, sine, and tangent functions, respectively. Since $\cot\theta = \dfrac{1}{\tan\theta} = 2.127$, we have $\tan\theta = \dfrac{1}{2.127}$, or $(2.127)^{-1}$. To find θ press $\boxed{\diamond}$ $\boxed{\text{TAN}^{-1}}$ 1 $\boxed{\div}$ 2 $\boxed{\cdot}$ 1 2 7 $\boxed{)}$ $\boxed{\text{ENTER}}$ or $\boxed{\diamond}$ $\boxed{\text{TAN}^{-1}}$ 2 $\boxed{\cdot}$ 1 2 7 $\wedge$ -1 $\boxed{)}$ $\boxed{\text{ENTER}}$. (TAN^{-1} is the green $\diamond$ operation associated with the $\boxed{\text{T}}$ key. $\wedge$$-1$ is entered by pressing $\boxed{\wedge}$ $\boxed{(-)}$ 1 or can be selected from the Catalog.) We find that $\theta \approx 25.2°$.

```
┌F1┬──┬F2┬──┬F3┬─┬F4┬──┬─F5──┬─F6┬───┐
│Tools│Algebra│Calc│Other│PrgmIO│Clean Up│
├──────────────────────────────────┤
│      ⎛  1  ⎞                        │
│ ■ tan⁻¹⎜─────⎟                      │
│      ⎝2.127⎠                        │
│                    25.1803638359    │
│ ■ tan⁻¹((2.127)⁻¹)                  │
│                    25.1803638359    │
│ tan⁻¹(2.127^-1)                     │
│ MAIN      DEG APPROX    POL    2/30 │
└──────────────────────────────────┘
```

Chapter 6
Trigonometric Identities, Inverse Functions, and Equations

FINDING INVERSE FUNCTION VALUES

We can use a grapher to find inverse function values in both radians and degrees.

Section 6.4, Example 2 (a), (e) Approximate $\cos^{-1}(-0.2689)$ and $\csc^{-1} 8.205$ in both radians and degrees.

To find inverse function values in radians, first select Radian for the Angle mode. Then, to approximate $\cos^{-1}(-0.2689)$ press $\boxed{\diamond}$ $\boxed{\text{COS}^{-1}}$ $\boxed{(-)}$ $\boxed{\cdot}$ 2 6 8 9 $\boxed{)}$ $\boxed{\text{ENTER}}$. (COS^{-1} is the green $\diamond$ operation associated with the $\boxed{\text{Z}}$ key.) The grapher returns 1.84304711, so $\cos^{-1}(-0.2689) \approx 1.8430$ radians.

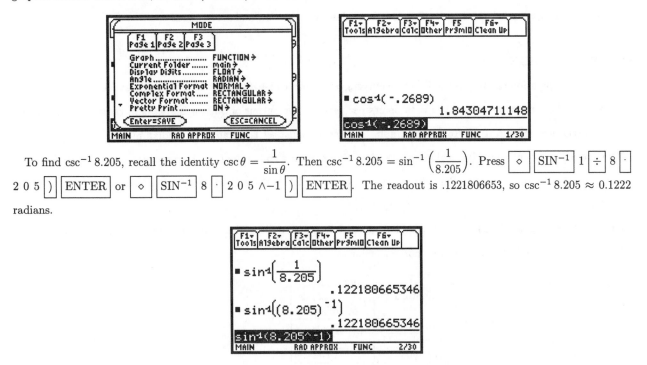

To find $\csc^{-1} 8.205$, recall the identity $\csc \theta = \dfrac{1}{\sin \theta}$. Then $\csc^{-1} 8.205 = \sin^{-1}\left(\dfrac{1}{8.205}\right)$. Press $\boxed{\diamond}$ $\boxed{\text{SIN}^{-1}}$ 1 $\boxed{\div}$ 8 $\boxed{\cdot}$ 2 0 5 $\boxed{)}$ $\boxed{\text{ENTER}}$ or $\boxed{\diamond}$ $\boxed{\text{SIN}^{-1}}$ 8 $\boxed{\cdot}$ 2 0 5 $\wedge -1$ $\boxed{)}$ $\boxed{\text{ENTER}}$. The readout is .1221806653, so $\csc^{-1} 8.205 \approx 0.1222$ radians.

To find inverse function values in degrees, set the grapher in degree mode. Then use the keystrokes above to find that $\cos^{-1}(-0.2689) \approx 105.6°$ and $\csc^{-1} 8.205 \approx 7.0°$.

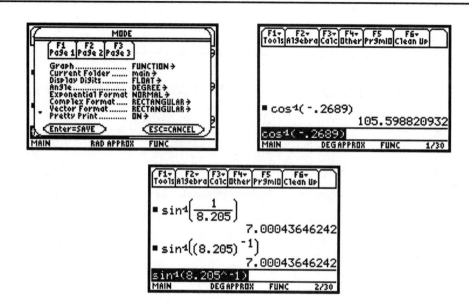

We also use reciprocal relationships to find function values for arcsecant and arccotangent.

SINE REGRESSION

The SinReg operation can be used to fit a sine curve $y = a\sin(bx + c) + d$ to a set of data. At least four data points are required and there must be at least two data points per period. The output of SinReg is always in radians, regardless of the Radian/Degree mode setting. To see the graph, however, we must set the grapher in Radian mode.

The operations of entering data, making scatterplots, and graphing and evaluating the regression function are the same as for linear regression functions. Reread the material on pages 230 - 232 and 243 - 246 of this manual to review these procedures.

Section 6.5, Exercise 57 (a) Sales of certain products fluctuate in cycles. The data in the following table show the total sales of skis per month for a business in a northern climate.

Month, x	Total Sales, y (in thousands of dollars)
August, 8	0
November, 11	7
February, 2	14
May, 5	7
August, 8	0

Using the sine regression feature on a grapher, fit a sine function of the form $y = A\sin(Bx - C) + D$ to this set of data.

Enter the data in the Data/Matrix editor as described in the Introduction to Graphs and the Graphing Calculator chapter of this manual. Then press F5 to display the Calculate menu. Select SinReg by pressing ▷ alpha B . Then press ▽ alpha C 1 ▽ alpha C 2 to indicate that the data in c1 and c2 will be used for x and y, respectively. Press ▽ ▷ ▽ ENTER to indicate that the regression equation should be copied to the equation-editor screen as y_1. Finally press

ENTER again to see the STAT VARS screen which displays the coefficients a, b, c, and d of the sine regression function $y = a\sin(bx + c) + d$

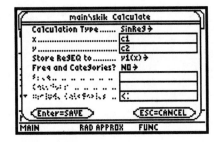 

Chapter 7
Applications of Trigonometry

FINDING TRIGONOMETRIC NOTATION FOR COMPLEX NUMBERS

The TI-89 can be used to find trigonometric notation for a complex number.

Section 7.4, Example 3 (a) Find trigonometric notation for $1 + i$.

Trigonometric notation for a complex number has the form $r(\cos \theta + i \sin \theta)$. We can find r using the abs feature from the MATH Number menu. Press $\boxed{\text{2nd}}$ $\boxed{\text{MATH}}$ $\boxed{\triangleright}$ to display this menu. Then press 2 to copy "abs" to the home screen. (We could also use $\boxed{\triangledown}$ to highlight 2 and then press $\boxed{\text{ENTER}}$.) Then press 1 $\boxed{+}$ $\boxed{\text{2nd}}$ $\boxed{i}$ $\boxed{)}$ $\boxed{\text{ENTER}}$. The grapher returns $|1 + i|$, the value of r. When Auto or Exact is selected for the Exact/Approx mode setting the grapher returns the exact value of r, $\sqrt{2}$. When Approximate is selected the grapher returns a decimal approximation for $\sqrt{2}$, 1.414213562.

Now use the MATH Complex menu again to find θ. We will do this first with Degree selected for the Angle mode. Press $\boxed{\text{2nd}}$ $\boxed{\text{MATH}}$ 5 to display the MATH Complex menu. Select item 4, "angle," by pressing 4 or by using $\boxed{\triangledown}$ to highlight 4 and then pressing $\boxed{\text{ENTER}}$. Then press 1 $\boxed{+}$ $\boxed{\text{2nd}}$ $\boxed{i}$ $\boxed{)}$ $\boxed{\text{ENTER}}$. The grapher returns 45, so the angle θ is 45°. When Radian and Auto or Exact modes are selected the grapher returns $\pi/4$.

Chapter 8
Systems of Equations and Matrices

MATRICES AND ROW-EQUIVALENT OPERATIONS

Matrices with up to 999 rows and 99 columns can be entered on the grapher. Row-equivalent operations can be performed on matrices on the grapher.

Section 8.3, Example 1 Solve the following system:

$$2x - y + 4z = -3,$$
$$x - 2y - 10z = -6,$$
$$3x \qquad + 4z = 7.$$

First we enter the augmented matrix

$$\begin{bmatrix} 2 & -1 & 4 & -3 \\ 1 & -2 & -10 & -6 \\ 3 & 0 & 4 & 7 \end{bmatrix}$$

in the Data/Matrix editor. We will call the Matrix A. Press $\boxed{\text{APPS}}$ 6 3 $\boxed{\triangleright}$ 2 $\boxed{\triangledown}$ $\boxed{\triangledown}$ $\boxed{\text{alpha}}$ $\boxed{\text{A}}$ $\boxed{\triangledown}$ 3 $\boxed{\triangledown}$ 4 $\boxed{\text{ENTER}}$ $\boxed{\text{ENTER}}$ to go to the Data/Matrix editor and set up a matrix named A with 3 rows and 4 columns. If a matrix named A has previously been saved in your grapher, an error message will be displayed. If this happens, you can select a different name for the matrix we are about to enter or you can delete the current matrix A and then enter the new matrix as A. To delete a matrix press $\boxed{\text{2nd}}$ $\boxed{\text{VAR-LINK}}$, use $\boxed{\triangledown}$ to highlight the name of the matrix being deleted, and then press $\boxed{\text{F1}}$ 1 $\boxed{\text{ENTER}}$ or $\boxed{\text{F1}}$ $\boxed{\text{ENTER}}$ $\boxed{\text{ENTER}}$. (VAR-LINK is the second operation associated with the $\boxed{-}$ key.)

```
┌──F4──┬──F5──┬──F6──┬──F7──┬──F8──┬──F9──┐
│               NEW                        │
│  Type:       Matrix→                     │
│  Folder:     main→                       │
│  Variable:   [a        ]                 │
│  Row dimension: [3 ]                     │
│  Col dimension: [4 ]                     │
│                                          │
│  <Enter=OK>            <ESC=CANCEL>      │
├──────────────────────────────────────────┤
│ MAIN        RAD APPROX    FUNC           │
└──────────────────────────────────────────┘
```

Enter the elements of the first row of the matrix by pressing 2 $\boxed{\text{ENTER}}$ $\boxed{(-)}$ 1 $\boxed{\text{ENTER}}$ 4 $\boxed{\text{ENTER}}$ $\boxed{(-)}$ 3 $\boxed{\text{ENTER}}$. The cursor moves to the element in the second row and first column of the matrix. Enter the elements of the second and third rows of the augmented matrix by typing each in turn followed by $\boxed{\text{ENTER}}$ as above. Note that the screen only displays three columns of the matrix. The arrow keys can be used to move the cursor to any element at any time.

Matrix operations are performed on the home screen and are found on the Math Matrix menu. Press $\boxed{\text{HOME}}$ or $\boxed{\text{2nd}}$ $\boxed{\text{QUIT}}$ to leave the matrix editor and go to this screen. Access the Math Matrix menu by pressing $\boxed{\text{2nd}}$ $\boxed{\text{MATH}}$ 4. (MATH is the second operation associated with the 5 numeric key.)

Press $\boxed{\text{alpha}}$ $\boxed{\text{J}}$ to see the four row-equivalent operations: rowSwap, rowAdd, nRow, and nRowAdd. These operations interchange two rows of a matrix, add two rows, multiply a row by a number, and multiply a row by a number and add it to a second row, respectively.

We will use the grapher to perform the row-equivalent operations that were done algebraically in the text. First, to interchange row 1 and row 2 of matrix **A**, with the MATH Matrix menu displayed, press 1 to select rowSwap. Then press $\boxed{\text{alpha}}$ $\boxed{\text{A}}$ to select **A**. Follow this with a comma and the rows to be interchanged, $\boxed{,}$ 1 $\boxed{,}$ 2 $\boxed{)}$ $\boxed{\text{ENTER}}$.

The grapher will not store the matrix produced using a row-equivalent operation, so when several operations are to be performed in succession it is helpful to store the result of each operation as it is produced. For example, to store the matrix resulting from interchanging the first and second rows of **A** as matrix **B** press $\boxed{\text{STO▷}}$ $\boxed{\text{alpha}}$ $\boxed{\text{B}}$ $\boxed{\text{ENTER}}$ immediately after interchanging the rows. This can also be done before $\boxed{\text{ENTER}}$ is pressed at the end of the rowSwap.

Next we multiply the first row of **B** by -2, add it to the second row and store the result as **B** again by pressing $\boxed{\text{2nd}}$ $\boxed{\text{MATH}}$ 4 $\boxed{\text{alpha}}$ $\boxed{\text{J}}$ 4 $\boxed{(-)}$ 2 $\boxed{,}$ $\boxed{\text{alpha}}$ $\boxed{\text{B}}$ $\boxed{,}$ 1 $\boxed{,}$ 2 $\boxed{)}$ $\boxed{\text{STO▷}}$ $\boxed{\text{alpha}}$ $\boxed{\text{B}}$ $\boxed{\text{ENTER}}$. These keystrokes select mRowAdd(from the MATH Matrix menu; then they specify that the value of the multiplier is -2, the matrix being operated on is **B**, and that a multiple of row 1 is being added to row 2; finally they store the result as **B**.

To multiply row 1 by -3, add it to row 3, and store the result as **B** press $\boxed{\text{2nd}}$ $\boxed{\text{MATH}}$ 4 $\boxed{\text{alpha}}$ $\boxed{\text{J}}$ 4 $\boxed{(-)}$ 3 $\boxed{,}$ $\boxed{\text{alpha}}$ $\boxed{\text{B}}$ $\boxed{,}$ 1 $\boxed{,}$ 3 $\boxed{)}$ $\boxed{\text{STO▷}}$ $\boxed{\text{alpha}}$ $\boxed{\text{B}}$ $\boxed{\text{ENTER}}$.

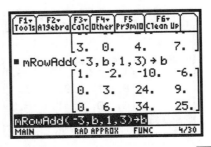

Now multiply the second row by 1/3 and store the result as **B** again. Press [2nd] [MATH] 4 [alpha] [J] 3 1 [(÷)] 3 [ˌ] [alpha] [B] [ˌ] 2 [)] [STO▷] [alpha] [B] [ENTER]. These keystrokes select mRow(from the MATH Matrix menu; then they specify that the value of the multiplier is 1/3, the matrix being operated on is **B**, and row 2 is being multiplied; finally they store the result as **B**.

Multiply the second row by −6 and add it to the third row using mRowAdd(. Press [2nd] [MATH] 4 [ALPHA] [J] 4 [(−)] 6 [ˌ] [alpha] [B] [ˌ] 2 [ˌ] 3 [)] [STO▷] [alpha] [B] [ENTER]. The entry in the third row, second column is 1E−13. This is an approximation of 0 that occurs because of the manner in which the grapher performs calculations and should be treated as 0. In fact, it would be a good idea to return to the Data/Matrix editor at this point to replace this entry of **B** with 0. Press [APPS] 6 2 [▷] 2 [▽] [▽] [▷]. Then highlight **B** and press [ENTER] [ENTER]. Now highlight the entry in the third, row, second column and press 0 [ENTER]. Press [HOME] [alpha] [B] [ENTER] to see the edited version of **B**.

Finally, multiply the third row by −1/14 by pressing [2nd] [MATH] 4 [ALPHA] [J] 3 [(−)] 1 [(÷)] 1 4 [ˌ] [alpha] [B] [ˌ] 3 [)] [ENTER].

```
  F1▾   F2▾   F3▾  F4▾   F5     F6▾
Tools A19ebra Calc Other Pr9mIO Clean Up
```

■ mRow(-1/14,b,3)

$$\begin{bmatrix} 1. & -2. & -10. & -6. \\ 0. & 1. & 8. & 3. \\ 0. & 0. & -1. & -.5 \end{bmatrix}$$

mRow(-1/14,b,3)
MAIN   RAD APPROX   FUNC   1/30

Write the system of equations that corresponds to the final matrix. Then use back-substitution to solve for x, y, and z as illustrated in the text.

Instead of stopping with row-echelon form as we did above, we can continue to apply row-equivalent operations until the matrix is in reduced row-echelon form as in Example 3 in Section 8.3 of the text. Reduced row-echelon form of a matrix can be found directly by using the rref(operation from the MATH Matrix menu. For example, to find reduced row-echelon form for matrix $\mathbf{A}$ in Example 1 above, after entering $\mathbf{A}$ and leaving the Data/Matrix screen $\boxed{\text{2nd}}$ $\boxed{\text{MATH}}$ 4 4 $\boxed{\text{alpha}}$ $\boxed{\text{A}}$ $\boxed{)}$ $\boxed{\text{ENTER}}$. We can read the solution of the system of equations, $(3, 7, -0.5)$ directly from the resulting matrix.

```
  F1▾   F2▾   F3▾  F4▾   F5     F6▾
Tools A19ebra Calc Other Pr9mIO Clean Up
```

■ rref(a)

$$\begin{bmatrix} 1. & 0. & 0. & 3. \\ 0. & 1. & 0. & 7. \\ 0. & 0. & 1. & -.5 \end{bmatrix}$$

rref(a)
MAIN   RAD APPROX   FUNC   1/30

MATRIX OPERATIONS

We can use the grapher to add and subtract matrices, to multiply a matrix by a scalar, and to multiply matrices.

Section 8.4, Example 1 (a) Find $\mathbf{A} + \mathbf{B}$ for

a) $\mathbf{A} = \begin{bmatrix} -5 & 0 \\ 4 & \frac{1}{2} \end{bmatrix}$, $\mathbf{B} = \begin{bmatrix} 6 & -3 \\ 2 & 3 \end{bmatrix}$.

Enter $\mathbf{A}$ and $\mathbf{B}$ in the Data/Matrix editor as described earlier in this chapter of the Graphing Calculator Manual. If you used the matrix names $\mathbf{A}$ and $\mathbf{B}$ above in Example 1 from Section 8.3, it will be necessary to delete those matrices before matrices $\mathbf{A}$ and $\mathbf{B}$ from this example can be entered. See page 279 of this manual for the procedure. Press $\boxed{\text{HOME}}$ or $\boxed{\text{2nd}}$ $\boxed{\text{QUIT}}$ to leave the Data/Matrix screen. Then press $\boxed{\text{alpha}}$ $\boxed{\text{A}}$ $\boxed{+}$ $\boxed{\text{alpha}}$ $\boxed{\text{B}}$ $\boxed{\text{ENTER}}$ to display the sum.

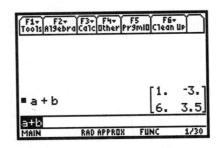

Section 8.4, Example 2 Find **C** − **D** for each of the following.

a) $\mathbf{C} = \begin{bmatrix} 1 & 2 \\ -2 & 0 \\ -3 & -1 \end{bmatrix}$, $\mathbf{D} = \begin{bmatrix} 1 & -1 \\ 1 & 3 \\ 2 & 3 \end{bmatrix}$ b) $\mathbf{C} = \begin{bmatrix} 5 & -6 \\ -3 & 4 \end{bmatrix}$, $\mathbf{D} = \begin{bmatrix} -4 \\ 1 \end{bmatrix}$

a) Enter **C** and **D** in the Data/Matrix editor. Press $\boxed{\text{HOME}}$ or $\boxed{\text{2nd}}$ $\boxed{\text{QUIT}}$ to leave this screen. Then press $\boxed{\text{alpha}}$ $\boxed{\text{C}}$ $\boxed{-}$ $\boxed{\text{alpha}}$ $\boxed{\text{D}}$ $\boxed{\text{ENTER}}$ to display the difference.

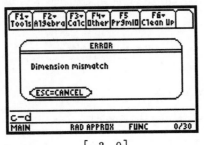

b) Enter **C** and **D** in the Data/Matrix editor after deleting **C** and **D** from part(a) above if necessary. (See page 279 of this manual for the procedure.) Press $\boxed{\text{HOME}}$ or $\boxed{\text{2nd}}$ $\boxed{\text{QUIT}}$ to leave the Data/Matrix screen. Then press $\boxed{\text{alpha}}$ $\boxed{\text{C}}$ $\boxed{-}$ $\boxed{\text{alpha}}$ $\boxed{\text{D}}$ $\boxed{\text{ENTER}}$. The grapher returns the error message "Dimension mismatch," indicating that this subtraction is not possible. This is the case because the matrices have different orders.

```
┌F1▾─┬F2▾───┬F3▾─┬F4▾──┬F5────┬F6▾──────┐
│Tools│Algebra│Calc│Other│PrgmIO│Clean Up│
├─────┴───────┴────┴─────┴──────┴─────────┤
│        ┌──────────────────┐             │
│        │      ERROR        │            │
│        │                   │            │
│        │ Dimension mismatch│            │
│        │                   │            │
│        │   ◁ESC=CANCEL▷     │           │
│        └──────────────────┘             │
├─────────────────────────────────────────┤
│c-d                                       │
│MAIN       RAD APPROX    FUNC       0/30  │
└─────────────────────────────────────────┘
```

Section 8.4, Example 4 Find 3**A** and (−1)**A**, for $\mathbf{A} = \begin{bmatrix} -3 & 0 \\ 4 & 5 \end{bmatrix}$

Enter **A** in the Data/Matrix editor after deleting the matrix that was previously entered as **A** if necessary. (See page 279 of this manual for the procedure.) Press $\boxed{\text{HOME}}$ or $\boxed{\text{2nd}}$ $\boxed{\text{QUIT}}$ to leave the Data/Matrix screen. Then to find 3**A** press 3 $\boxed{\text{alpha}}$ $\boxed{\text{A}}$ $\boxed{\text{ENTER}}$ and to find (−1)**A** press $\boxed{(-)}$ 1 $\boxed{\text{alpha}}$ $\boxed{\text{A}}$ $\boxed{\text{ENTER}}$. Note that (−1)**A** is the opposite, or additive inverse, of **A** and can also be found by pressing $\boxed{(-)}$ $\boxed{\text{alpha}}$ $\boxed{\text{A}}$ $\boxed{\text{ENTER}}$.

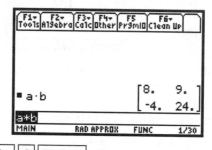

Section 8.4, Example 6 (a), (d) For

$$\mathbf{A} = \begin{bmatrix} 3 & 1 & -1 \\ 2 & 0 & 3 \end{bmatrix}, \mathbf{B} = \begin{bmatrix} 1 & 6 \\ 3 & -5 \\ -2 & 4 \end{bmatrix}, \text{ and } \mathbf{C} = \begin{bmatrix} 4 & -6 \\ 1 & 2 \end{bmatrix}$$

find each of the following.

a) **AB**   d) **AC**

First enter **A**, **B**, and **C** in the Data/Matrix editor after first deleting any matrices that were previously entered with those names. (See page 279 of this manual for the procedure.) Then press HOME or 2nd QUIT to leave this screen.

a) To find **AB** press alpha A × alpha B ENTER. Note that the multiplication symbol must be used so that the grapher can differentiate this multiplication from a variable named *ab*.

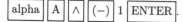

d) To find **AC** press alpha A × alpha C ENTER. The grapher returns the error message "Dimension," indicating that this multiplication is not possible. This is the case because the number of columns in **A** is not the same as the number of rows in **C**. Thus, the matrices cannot be multiplied in this order.

FINDING THE INVERSE OF A MATRIX

The inverse of a matrix can be found quickly on the grapher.

Section 8.5, Example 3 Find $\mathbf{A}^{-1}$, where

$$\mathbf{A} = \begin{bmatrix} -2 & 3 \\ -3 & 4 \end{bmatrix}.$$

Enter **A** in the Data/Matrix editor after first deleting the matrix that was previously entered as **A** if necessary. (See page 279 of this manual for the procedure.) Then press HOME or 2nd QUIT to leave the Data Matrix screen. Now press alpha A ∧ (−) 1 ENTER.

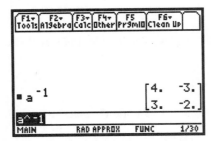

Section 8.5, Exercise 7 Find $\mathbf{A}^{-1}$, where

$$\mathbf{A} = \begin{bmatrix} 6 & 9 \\ 4 & 6 \end{bmatrix}.$$

Enter $\mathbf{A}$ in the Data/Matrix editor after first deleting the matrix that was previously entered as $\mathbf{A}$ if necessary. (See page 279 of this manual for the procedure.) Then press $\boxed{\text{HOME}}$ or $\boxed{\text{2nd}}$ $\boxed{\text{QUIT}}$ to leave the Data Matrix screen. Now press $\boxed{\text{alpha}}$ $\boxed{\text{A}}$ $\boxed{\wedge}$ $\boxed{(-)}$ 1 $\boxed{\text{ENTER}}$. The grapher returns the message "Singular matrix," indicating that $\mathbf{A}^{-1}$ does not exist.

MATRIX SOLUTIONS OF SYSTEMS OF EQUATIONS

We can write a system of n linear equations in n variables as a matrix equation $\mathbf{AX} = \mathbf{B}$. If $\mathbf{A}$ has an inverse the solution of the system of equations is given by $\mathbf{X} = \mathbf{A}^{-1}\mathbf{B}$.

Section 8.5, Example 4 Use an inverse matrix to solve the following system of equations:

$$\begin{aligned} x + 2y - z &= -2, \\ 3x + 5y + 3z &= 3, \\ 2x + 4y + 3z &= 1. \end{aligned}$$

Enter $\mathbf{A} = \begin{bmatrix} 1 & 2 & -1 \\ 3 & 5 & 3 \\ 2 & 4 & 3 \end{bmatrix}$ and $\mathbf{B} = \begin{bmatrix} -2 \\ 3 \\ 1 \end{bmatrix}$ in the Data/Matrix editor after first deleting any matrices that were previously entered with those names. (See page 279 of this manual for the procedure.) Then press $\boxed{\text{HOME}}$ or $\boxed{\text{2nd}}$ $\boxed{\text{QUIT}}$ to leave the Data/Matrix screen. Press $\boxed{\text{alpha}}$ $\boxed{\text{A}}$ $\boxed{\wedge}$ $\boxed{(-)}$ 1 $\boxed{\times}$ $\boxed{\text{alpha}}$ $\boxed{\text{B}}$ $\boxed{\text{ENTER}}$. The result is the 3 x 1 matrix $\begin{bmatrix} 5 \\ -3 \\ 1 \end{bmatrix}$, so the solution is $(5, -3, 1)$.

GRAPHS OF INEQUALITIES

We can graph linear inequalities on the grapher, shading the region of the solution set. The grapher should be set in Func mode at this point.

Section 8.6, Example 1 Graph: $y < x + 3$.

First we graph the related equation $y = x + 3$. We use the standard window $[-10, 10, -10, 10]$. Since the inequality symbol is $<$ we know that the line $y = x + 3$ is not part of the solution set. In a hand-drawn graph we would use a dashed line to indicate this. After determining that the solution set of the inequality consists of all points below the line, we can use the "shade below" graph style to shade this region. After entering the related equation, highlight it and press $\boxed{\text{2nd}}$ $\boxed{\text{F6}}$ 8. Then press $\boxed{\diamond}$ $\boxed{\text{GRAPH}}$ to display the graph of the inequality. Keep in mind the fact that the line $y = x + 3$ is not included in the solution set.

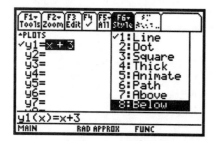 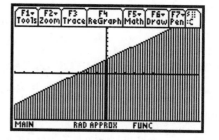

We can also use the Shade feature from the Catalog to graph this inequality. Copy Shade to the entry line of the home screen by pressing $\boxed{\text{HOME}}$ $\boxed{\text{CATALOG}}$ $\boxed{\text{S}}$, scrolling down to Shade, and pressing $\boxed{\text{ENTER}}$. We can also type Shade directly on the entry line by pressing $\boxed{\text{2nd}}$ $\boxed{\text{a-lock}}$ $\boxed{\text{S}}$ $\boxed{\text{H}}$ $\boxed{\text{A}}$ $\boxed{\text{D}}$ $\boxed{\text{E}}$ $\boxed{\text{alpha}}$.

Now enter a lower function and an upper function. The region between them will be shaded. We want to shade the area between the bottom of the window, $y = -10$, and the line $y = x + 3$ so we enter $\boxed{(-)}$ 1 0 $\boxed{\cdot}$ $\boxed{\text{X}}$ $\boxed{+}$ 3 $\boxed{\text{ENTER}}$. We can also enter $x + 3$ as $y_1(x)$. The result is shown below. Keep in mind that the line $y = x + 3$ is not included in the solution set.

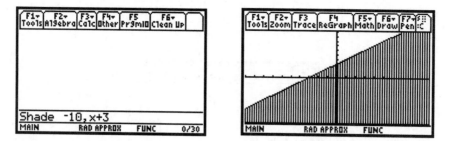

We can also graph a system of inequalities when the solution set lies between the graphs of two functions.

Section 8.6, Exercise 37 Graph:
$$y \leq x,$$
$$y \geq 3 - x.$$

First graph the related equations $y_1 = x$ and $y_2 = 3 - x$ and determine that the solution set consists of all the points on or below the graph of $y_1 = x$ and on or above the graph of $y_2 = 3 - x$. We can graph the system of inequalities by shading the solution set of each inequality in the system with a different pattern. When the "shade above" or "shade below" graph style options are selected the TI-89 rotates through four shading patterns. These patterns repeat if more than four functions are graphed. The region where the shaded areas overlap is the solution set of the inequality. Shade below $y_1 = x$ by highlighting the equation and then pressing $\boxed{\text{2nd}}$ $\boxed{\text{F6}}$ 8. Shade above $y_2 = 3 - x$ by highlighting the equation and pressing $\boxed{\text{2nd}}$ $\boxed{\text{F6}}$ 7. Then press $\boxed{\diamond}$ $\boxed{\text{GRAPH}}$.

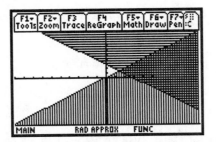

We can also use the Shade feature from the Catalog to graph this system of inequalities. Copy Shade to the entry line of the home screen or type it directly as described in Example 1 above. Then enter $3 - x$ as the lower function and x as the upper function.

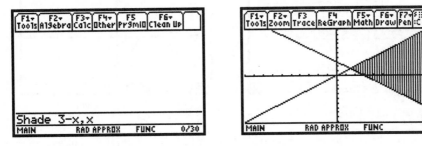

Chapter 9
Analytic Geometry Topics

Many conic sections are represented by equations that are not functions. Consequently, these equations must be entered on the TI-89 as two equations, each of which is a function.

GRAPHING PARABOLAS

To graph a parabola of the form $y^2 = 4px$ or $(y-k)^2 = 4p(x-h)$, we must first solve the equation for y.

Section 9.1, Example 4 Graph the parabola $y^2 - 2y - 8x - 31 = 0$.

In the text we used the quadratic formula to solve the equation for y:

$$y = \frac{2 \pm \sqrt{32x + 128}}{2}.$$

One way to produce the graph of the parabola is to enter $y_1 = \dfrac{2 + \sqrt{32x + 128}}{2}$ and $y_2 = \dfrac{2 - \sqrt{32x + 128}}{2}$, select a window, and press $\boxed{\diamond}$ $\boxed{\text{GRAPH}}$ to see the graph. Here we use $[-16, 16, -8, 8]$. The first equation produces the top half of the parabola and the second equation produces the lower half.

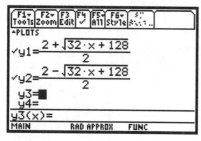
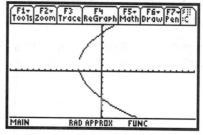

We can also enter $y_1 = \sqrt{32x + 128}$ and then enter $y_2 = \dfrac{2 + y_1(x)}{2}$ and $y_3 = \dfrac{2 - y_1(x)}{2}$. For example, to enter $y_2 = \dfrac{2 + y_1(x)}{2}$ position the cursor beside "$y_2 =$" and press $\boxed{(}$ $\boxed{2}$ $\boxed{+}$ $\boxed{Y}$ 1 $\boxed{(}$ $\boxed{X}$ $\boxed{)}$ $\boxed{)}$ $\boxed{\div}$ 2. Enter $y_3 = \dfrac{2 - y_1}{2}$ in a similar manner. Finally, deselect y_1 by highlighting the expression for y_1 and pressing $\boxed{\text{F4}}$. The top half of the graph is produced by y_2 and the lower half by y_3. The expression for y_1 was entered to avoid entering the square root more than once. By deselecting y_1 we prevent its graph from appearing on the screen with the graph of the parabola.

We could also use the standard equation of the parabola found in the text:

$$(y-1)^2 = 8(x+4).$$

Solve this equation for y.

$$y - 1 = \pm\sqrt{8(x + 4)}$$
$$y = 1 \pm \sqrt{8(x + 4)}$$

Then enter $y_1 = 1 + \sqrt{8(x + 4)}$ and $y_2 = 1 - \sqrt{8(x + 4)}$, or enter $y_1 = \sqrt{8(x + 4)}$, $y_2 = 1 + y_1(x)$, and $y_3 = 1 - y_1(x)$, and deselect y_1 as described above.

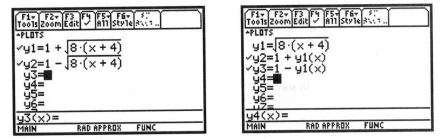

GRAPHING CIRCLES

The equation of an ellipse must be solved for y before it can be entered on the TI-89.

Section 9.2, Example 1 Graph the circle $x^2 + y^2 - 16x + 14y + 32 = 0$.

In the text we found the standard form for the equation of the circle and then solved for y:

$$y = -7 \pm \sqrt{81 - (x - 8)^2}.$$

We could also have solved the original equation using the quadratic formula.

One way to produce the graph is to enter $y_1 = -7 + \sqrt{81 - (x - 8)^2}$ and $y_2 = -7 - \sqrt{81 - (x - 8)^2}$, select a square window, and press $\boxed{\diamond}$ $\boxed{\text{GRAPH}}$. Here we use $[-16, 28, -18, 4]$. The first equation produces the top half of the circle and the second equation produces the lower half.

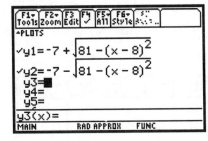
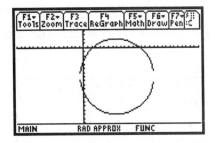

We can also enter $y_1 = \sqrt{81 - (x - 8)^2}$ and then enter $y_2 = -7 + y_1(x)$ and $y_3 = -7 - y_1(x)$. Then deselect y_1, select a square window, and press $\boxed{\diamond}$ $\boxed{\text{GRAPH}}$. We use y_1 to eliminate the need to enter the square root more than once. Deselecting it prevents the graph of y_1 from appearing on the screen with the graph of the circle. The top half of the graph is produced by y_2 and the lower half by y_3.

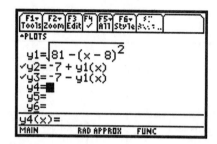

GRAPHING ELLIPSES

The equation of an ellipse must be solved for y before it can be entered on a TI-89. In Example 2 of Section 9.2 of the text the procedure for graphing an ellipse of the form $\dfrac{x^2}{a^2} + \dfrac{y^2}{b^2} = 1$ or $\dfrac{x^2}{b^2} + \dfrac{y^2}{a^2} = 1$ is described. Here we consider ellipses of the form $\dfrac{(x-h)^2}{a^2} + \dfrac{(y-k)^2}{b^2} = 1$ or $\dfrac{(x-h)^2}{b^2} + \dfrac{(y-k)^2}{a^2} = 1$

Section 9.2, Example 4 Graph the ellipse $4x^2 + y^2 + 24x - 2y + 21 = 0$.

Completing the square in the text, we found that the equation can be written as

$$\frac{(x+3)^2}{4} + \frac{(y-1)^2}{16} = 1.$$

Solve this equation for y.

$$\frac{(x+3)^2}{4} + \frac{(y-1)^2}{16} = 1$$

$$\frac{(y-1)^2}{16} = 1 - \frac{(x+3)^2}{4}$$

$$(y-1)^2 = 16 - 4(x+3)^2 \qquad \text{Multiplying by 16}$$

$$y - 1 = \pm\sqrt{16 - 4(x+3)^2}$$

$$y = 1 \pm \sqrt{16 - 4(x+3)^2}$$

Now we can produce the graph in either of two ways. One is to enter $y_1 = 1 + \sqrt{16 - 4(x+3)^2}$ and $y_2 = 1 - \sqrt{16 - 4(x+3)^2}$, select a square window, and press $\boxed{\diamond}\ \boxed{\text{GRAPH}}$. Here we use $[-15, 9, -6, 6]$. The first equation produces the top half of the ellipse and the second equation produces the lower half.

We can also enter $y_1 = \sqrt{16 - 4(x+3)^2}$ and then enter $y_2 = 1 + y_1(x)$ and $y_3 = 1 - y_1(x)$. Deselect y_1, select a square window, and press $\boxed{\diamond}\ \boxed{\text{GRAPH}}$. We use y_1 to eliminate the need to enter the square root more than once. Deselecting it prevents the graph of y_1 from appearing on the screen with the graph of the ellipse. The top half of the graph is produced by y_2 and the lower half by y_3.

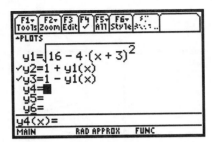

We could also begin by using the quadratic formula to solve the original equation for y.

$$4x^2 + y^2 + 24x - 2y + 21 = 0$$

$$y^2 - 2y + (4x^2 + 24x + 21) = 0$$

$$y = \frac{-(-2) \pm \sqrt{(-2)^2 - 4 \cdot 1 \cdot (4x^2 + 24x + 21)}}{2 \cdot 1}$$

$$y = \frac{2 \pm \sqrt{4 - 16x^2 - 96x - 84}}{2}$$

$$y = \frac{2 \pm \sqrt{-16x^2 - 96x - 80}}{2}$$

Then enter $y_1 = \dfrac{2 + \sqrt{-16x^2 - 96x - 80}}{2}$ and $y_2 = \dfrac{2 - \sqrt{-16x^2 - 96x - 80}}{2}$, or enter $y_1 = \sqrt{-16x^2 - 96x - 80}$, $y_2 = \dfrac{2 + y_1(x)}{2}$, and $y_3 = \dfrac{2 - y_1(x)}{2}$, and deselect y_1.

Select a square window and press $\boxed{\diamond}$ $\boxed{\text{GRAPH}}$ to display the graph.

GRAPHING HYPERBOLAS

As with equations of circles, parabolas, and ellipses, equations of hyperbolas must be solved for y before they can be entered on a TI-89.

Section 9.3, Example 2 Graph the hyperbola $9x^2 - 16y^2 = 144$.

First solve the equation for y.
$$9x^2 - 16y^2 = 144$$

$$-16y^2 = -9x^2 + 144$$

$$y^2 = \frac{-9x^2 + 144}{-16}$$

$$y = \pm\sqrt{\frac{-9x^2 + 144}{-16}}, \text{ or } \pm\sqrt{\frac{9x^2 - 144}{16}}$$

It is not necessary to simplify further.

Now enter $y_1 = \sqrt{\dfrac{9x^2 - 144}{16}}$ and either $y_2 = -\sqrt{\dfrac{9x^2 - 144}{16}}$ or $y_2 = -y_1(x)$, select a square window, and press $\boxed{\diamond}$

GRAPH . Here we use $[-12, 12, -6, 6]$. The top half of the graph is produced by y_1 and the lower half by y_2.

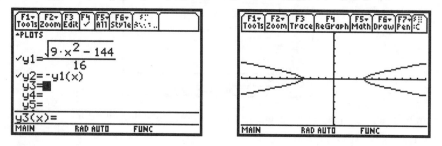

Section 9.3, Example 3 Graph the hyperbola $4y^2 - x^2 + 24y + 4x + 28 = 0$.

In the text we completed the square to get the standard form of the equation. Now solve the equation for y.

$$\frac{(y+3)^2}{1} - \frac{(x-2)^2}{4} = 1$$

$$(y+3)^2 = \frac{(x-2)^2}{4} + 1$$

$$y + 3 = \pm\sqrt{\frac{(x-2)^2}{4} + 1}$$

$$y = -3 \pm \sqrt{\frac{(x-2)^2}{4} + 1}$$

The graph can be produced in either of two ways. One is to enter $y_1 = -3 + \sqrt{\frac{(x-2)^2}{4} + 1}$ and $y_2 = -3 - \sqrt{\frac{(x-2)^2}{4} + 1}$, select a square window, and press $\boxed{\diamond}$ $\boxed{\text{GRAPH}}$. Here we use $[-15, 15, -9, 6]$. The first equation produces the top half of the hyperbola and the second the lower half.

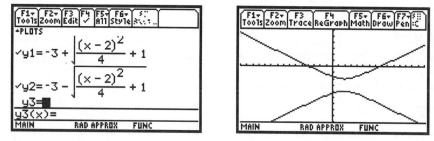

We can also enter $y_1 = \sqrt{\frac{(x-2)^2}{4} + 1}$, $y_2 = -3 + y_1(x)$, and $y_3 = -3 - y_1(x)$. Then deselect y_1, select a square window, and press $\boxed{\diamond}$ $\boxed{\text{GRAPH}}$. Again, y_1 is used to eliminate the need to enter the square root more than once. Deselecting it prevents the graph of y_1 from appearing on the screen with the graph of the hyperbola. The top half of the graph is produced by y_2 and the lower half by y_3.

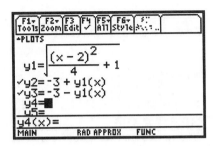

CONVERTING FROM RECTANGULAR TO POLAR COORDINATES

The grapher can be used to convert from rectangular to polar coordinates, expressing the result using either degrees or radians. The grapher will supply a positive value for r and an angle in the interval $(-180°, 180°]$, or $(-\pi, \pi]$.

Section 9.5, Example 2 (a) Convert (3,3) to polar coordinates.

To find r, regardless of the type of angle measure, press $\boxed{\text{2nd}}$ $\boxed{\text{MATH}}$ 2 5 3 $\boxed{\,,\,}$ 3 $\boxed{)}$ $\boxed{\text{ENTER}}$. When the grapher is set in Auto or Exact mode, it returns $3\sqrt{2}$. Now, to find θ in degrees, set the grapher in Degree mode and press $\boxed{\text{2nd}}$ $\boxed{\text{MATH}}$ 2 6 3 $\boxed{\,,\,}$ 3 $\boxed{)}$ $\boxed{\text{ENTER}}$. The readout is 45, so $\theta = 45°$. Thus polar notation for (3,3) is $(3\sqrt{2}, 45°)$.

Set the grapher in Radian mode to find θ in radians. Repeat the keystrokes for finding θ above to find that $\theta = \pi/4$. Thus polar notation for (3,3) is $(3\sqrt{2}, \pi/4)$.

CONVERTING FROM POLAR TO RECTANGULAR COORDINATES

The grapher can also be used to convert from polar to rectangular coordinates.

Section 9.5, Example 3 Convert each of the following to rectangular coordinates.

(a) $(10, \pi/3)$ (b) $(-5, 135°)$

(a) Since the angle is given in radians, set the grapher in Radian mode. To find the x-coordinate of rectangular notation, press $\boxed{\text{2nd}}$ $\boxed{\text{MATH}}$ 2 3 1 0 $\boxed{\,,\,}$ $\boxed{\text{2nd}}$ $\boxed{\pi}$ $\boxed{\div}$ 3 $\boxed{)}$ $\boxed{\text{ENTER}}$. The readout is 5, so $x = 5$. The y-coordinate is found by pressing $\boxed{\text{2nd}}$ $\boxed{\text{MATH}}$ 2 4 1 0 $\boxed{\,,\,}$ $\boxed{\text{2nd}}$ $\boxed{\pi}$ $\boxed{\div}$ 3 $\boxed{)}$ $\boxed{\text{ENTER}}$. When the grapher is set in Auto or Exact mode, it returns $5\sqrt{3}$. Thus, rectangular notation for $(10, \pi/3)$ is $(5, 5\sqrt{3})$.

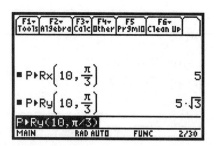

(b) The angle is given in degrees, so we set the grapher in Degree mode. To find the x-coordinate of rectangular notation, press $\boxed{\text{2nd}}$ $\boxed{\text{MATH}}$ 2 3 $\boxed{(-)}$ 5 $\boxed{\text{,}}$ 1 3 5 $\boxed{)}$ $\boxed{\text{ENTER}}$. When the grapher is set in Auto or Exact mode, it returns $\frac{5\sqrt{2}}{2}$. The y-coordinate is found by pressing $\boxed{\text{2nd}}$ $\boxed{\text{MATH}}$ 2 4 $\boxed{(-)}$ 5 $\boxed{\text{,}}$ 1 3 5 $\boxed{)}$ $\boxed{\text{ENTER}}$. The readout is $-\frac{5\sqrt{2}}{2}$. Thus, rectangular notation for $(-5, 135°)$ is $(\frac{5\sqrt{2}}{2}, -\frac{5\sqrt{2}}{2})$.

GRAPHING POLAR EQUATIONS

Polar equations can be graphed in either Radian mode or Degree mode. The equation must be written in the form $r = f(\theta)$ and the grapher must be set in Polar mode. Typically we begin with a range of $[0, 2\pi]$ or $[0°, 360°]$, but it might be necessary to increase the range to ensure that sufficient points are plotted to display the entire graph.

Section 9.5, Example 6 Graph: $r = 1 - \sin\theta$.

First set the grapher in Polar mode by pressing $\boxed{\text{MODE}}$ $\boxed{\triangleright}$ 3 $\boxed{\text{ENTER}}$ or $\boxed{\text{MODE}}$ $\boxed{\triangleright}$ $\boxed{\triangledown}$ $\boxed{\triangledown}$ $\boxed{\text{ENTER}}$ $\boxed{\text{ENTER}}$. We will also select Radian mode.

The equation is given in $r = f(\theta)$ form. Press $\boxed{\diamond}$ $\boxed{\text{Y} =}$ to go to the "Y =" screen. Clear any existing entries and, with the cursor beside "$r_1 =$," press 1 $\boxed{-}$ $\boxed{\text{2nd}}$ $\boxed{\text{SIN}}$ $\boxed{\diamond}$ $\boxed{\theta}$ $\boxed{)}$ $\boxed{\text{ENTER}}$. (θ is the green $\diamond$ operation associated with the $\boxed{\wedge}$ key.) Now press $\boxed{\diamond}$ $\boxed{\text{WINDOW}}$ and enter the following settings:

θmin $= 0$ (Smallest value of θ to be evaluated)
θmax $= 2\pi$ (Largest value of θ to be evaluated)
θstep $= \pi/24$ (Increment in θ values)
xmin $= -4$
xmax $= 4$
xscl $= 1$
ymin $= -3$
ymax $= 1$
yscl $= 1$

With these settings the grapher evaluates the function from $\theta = 0$ to $\theta = 2\pi$ in increments of $\pi/24$ and displays the graph

in the square window $[-4, 4, -3, 1]$. Values entered in terms of π appear on the screen as decimal approximations. Press

◇ GRAPH to display the graph.

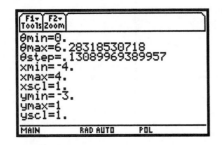   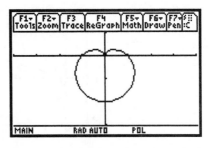

The curve can be traced with either rectangular or polar coordinates being displayed. The value of θ is also displayed

when rectangular coordinates are selected. The choice of coordinates is made on the GRAPH FORMATS screen. While

the graph is displayed, press F1 9 to display this screen. Then press ▷ and select either RECT or POLAR.

GRAPHING PARAMETRIC EQUATIONS

Plane curves described with parametric equations can be graphed on a grapher.

Section 9.8, Example 1 (a) Using a grapher, graph the plane curve given by the set of parametric equations and the

restriction for the parameter.

$$x = t^2, \ y = t - 1,; \ -1 \le t \le 4$$

First press MODE and select Parametric mode.

Then press ◇ Y = to display the equation-editor screen. Enter xt1 $= t^2$ and yt1 $= t - 1$. Now press ◇ WINDOW

and enter the following settings:

tmin $= -1$ (Smallest value of t to be evaluated)
tmax $= 4$ (Largest value of t to be evaluated)
tstep $= .1$ (Increment in t values)
xmin $= -2$
xmax $= 18$
xscl $= 1$
ymin $= -4$
ymax $= 4$
yscl $= 1$

Since $x = t^2$ and $-1 \leq t \leq 4$, we have $0 \leq x \leq 16$. Thus, we choose xmin and xmax to display this interval. Similarly, since $y = t - 1$, we have $-2 \leq y \leq 3$ and we choose ymin and ymax to show this interval. Press $\boxed{\diamond}$ $\boxed{\text{GRAPH}}$ to display the graph.

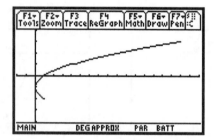

The curve can be traced as described in Example 6 from Section 9.5 above.

Chapter 10
Sequences, Series, and Combinatorics

Both the graphing capabilities and the computational capabilities of the grapher can be used when working with sequences, series, and combinatorics.

FINDING THE TERMS OF A SEQUENCE

Section 10.1, Example 2 Use a grapher to find the first 5 terms of the sequence whose general term is given by $a_n = n/(n + 1)$.

Although we could use a table, we will use the Seq feature from the MATH List menu. Select Auto for the Exact/Approx mode setting so that the terms will be expressed in fractional form. Press $\boxed{\text{2nd}}$ $\boxed{\text{MATH}}$ 3 to display the MATH List menu. Then press 1 or $\boxed{\text{ENTER}}$ to paste "seq(" to the entry line of the home screen. Now enter the general term of the sequence. Follow this with the variable and the numbers of the first and last terms desired. Press $\boxed{\text{X}}$ $\boxed{\div}$ $\boxed{(}$ $\boxed{\text{X}}$ $\boxed{+}$ 1 $\boxed{)}$ $\boxed{,}$ $\boxed{\text{X}}$ $\boxed{,}$ 1 $\boxed{,}$ 5 $\boxed{)}$ $\boxed{\text{ENTER}}$.

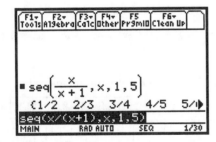 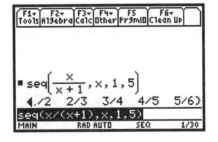

GRAPHING SEQUENCES

The grapher can be used to graph a sequence.

Section 10.1, Example 3 Graph the sequence whose general term is given by $a_n = n/(n + 1)$.

Begin by selecting Sequence for the Graph mode setting. Press $\boxed{\text{MODE}}$ $\boxed{\triangleright}$ 4 $\boxed{\text{ENTER}}$ to do this. Then press $\boxed{\diamond}$ $\boxed{\text{Y} =}$. Note that the function names that appear on the equation-editor screen are u_1, u_2, and so on rather than y_1, y_2, and so on. Enter $u_1 = n/(n + 1)$ by positioning the cursor beside $u_1 =$ and pressing $\boxed{\text{ENTER}}$ $\boxed{\text{alpha}}$ $\boxed{\text{N}}$ $\boxed{\div}$ $\boxed{(}$ $\boxed{\text{alpha}}$ $\boxed{\text{N}}$ $\boxed{+}$ 1 $\boxed{)}$ $\boxed{\text{ENTER}}$. Set the graph-style to "dot" by highlighting the expression for u_1 and pressing $\boxed{\text{2nd}}$ $\boxed{\text{F6}}$ 2.

Next we enter the window dimensions. We will graph the sequence from $n = 1$ through $n = 15$, so we let nmin = 1, nmax = 15, xmin = 1, and xmax = 20. The terms of the sequence will be between 0 and 1, so we let ymin = 0 and ymax = 1. We also set both plotStrt and plotStep to 1. These settings cause the graph to begin with the first term in the sequence and to plot each term of the sequence.

Press ◇ | GRAPH | to see the graph of the sequence.

FINDING PARTIAL SUMS

We can use a grapher to find partial sums of a sequence when a formula for the general term is known.

Section 10.1, Example 6 Use a grapher to find S_1, S_2, S_3, and S_4 for the sequence whose general term is given by $a_n = n^2 - 3$.

We will use the cumSum feature from the MATH List menu. The grapher will write the partial sums as a list. First press | 2nd | MATH | 3 7 to paste "cumSum(" to the home screen. Then press | 2nd | MATH | 3 | ENTER | or | 2nd | MATH | 3 1 to paste "seq(" into the cumSum expression. Finally press | X | ^ | 2 | − | 3 | , | X | , | 1 | , | 4 |) |) | ENTER |. We see that $S_1 = -2, S_3 = -1, S_3 = 5$, and $S_4 = 18$.

Section 10.1, Example 7 (a) Evaluate $\displaystyle\sum_{k=1}^{5} k^3$.

We will use the sum feature from the MATH List menu along with the seq feature. Press | 2nd | MATH | 3 6 | 2nd | MATH | 3 | ENTER | X | ^ | 3 | , | X | , | 1 | , | 5 |) |) | ENTER |.

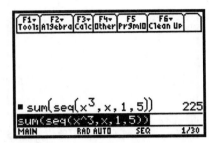

RECURSIVELY DEFINED SEQUENCES

Recursively defined sequences can also be entered on a grapher set in Seq mode.

Section 10.1, Example 7 Find the first 5 terms of the sequence defined by

$$a_1 = 5, \; a_{k+1} = 2a_k - 3, \text{ for } k \geq 1.$$

Press ◇ ⎡Y =⎤ and enter the recursive function by positioning the cursor beside $u_1 =$ and pressing ⎡ENTER⎤ 2 ⎡alpha⎤ ⎡U⎤ 1 ⎡(⎤ ⎡alpha⎤ ⎡N⎤ ⎡−⎤ 1 ⎡)⎤ ⎡−⎤ 3 ⎡ENTER⎤. Then press ⎡2nd⎤ ⎡{⎤ 5 ⎡2nd⎤ ⎡}⎤ ⎡ENTER⎤ to enter the initial value of 5 beside $ui_1 =$. ({ and } are the second operations associated with the ⎡(⎤ and ⎡)⎤ keys, respectively.)

Next press ◇ ⎡TblSet⎤ to display the Table Setup screen. Set Independent to Auto, tblStart = 1, Δtbl = 1. Also press ◇ ⎡WINDOW⎤ and check to be sure that nmin has the same value as tblStart. Then press ◇ ⎡TABLE⎤ to display the table of values for the recursive function. We see that $a_1 = 5$, $a_2 = 7$, $a_3 = 11$, $a_4 = 19$, and $a_5 = 35$.

EVALUATING FACTORIALS, PERMUTATIONS, AND COMBINATIONS

Operations from the MATH Probability menu can be used to evaluate factorials, permutations, and combinations.

Section 10.5, Exercise 6 Evaluate 7!.

On the home screen press 7 ⎡2nd⎤ ⎡MATH⎤ 7 1 ⎡ENTER⎤ or 7 ⎡2nd⎤ ⎡MATH⎤ 7 ⎡ENTER⎤ ⎡ENTER⎤. These keystrokes enter 7, display the MATH Probability menu, select item 1, !, from that menu, and then cause 7! to be evaluated. The result is 5040.

Section 10.5, Exercise 9 Evaluate $\dfrac{9!}{5!}$.

Press 9 ⎡2nd⎤ ⎡MATH⎤ 7 1 ⎡÷⎤ 5 ⎡2nd⎤ ⎡MATH⎤ 7 1 ⎡ENTER⎤. Both 1's can be replaced by ⎡ENTER⎤ if desired. The result is 3024.

Section 10.5, Example 3 (a) Compute $_4P_4$.

Press $\boxed{\text{2nd}}$ $\boxed{\text{MATH}}$ 7 2 4 $\boxed{,}$ 4 $\boxed{)}$ $\boxed{\text{ENTER}}$. These keystrokes display the MATH Probability menu, select item 2, $_nP_r$, from that menu, enter 4 for 4 objects and 4 for 4 objects taken at a time, and then cause the calculation to be performed. The result is 24.

Section 10.5, Example 6 Compute $_8P_4$.

Press $\boxed{\text{2nd}}$ $\boxed{\text{MATH}}$ 7 2 8 $\boxed{,}$ 4 $\boxed{)}$ $\boxed{\text{ENTER}}$. These keystrokes display the MATH Probability menu, select item 2, $_nP_r$, from that menu, enter 8 for 8 objects and 4 for 4 objects taken at a time, and then cause the calculation to be performed. The result is 1680. The previous entry could also be edited to obtain this result.

Section 10.5, Example 3 Evaluate $\begin{pmatrix} 7 \\ 5 \end{pmatrix}$.

Press $\boxed{\text{2nd}}$ $\boxed{\text{MATH}}$ 7 3 7 $\boxed{,}$ 5 $\boxed{)}$ $\boxed{\text{ENTER}}$. These keystrokes display the MATH Probability menu, select item 3, $_nC_r$, from that menu, enter 7 for 7 objects and 5 for 5 objects taken at a time, and then cause the calculation to be performed. The result is 21.